The Empire of Oil

The
EMPIRE
of
OIL

HARVEY O'CONNOR

MONTHLY REVIEW PRESS
New York 1955

Library of Congress catalog card number: 55-12156

To Henry Demarest Lloyd
Pioneer in Exploring the Public Interest
in a Basic Natural Resource

There is no country in the world which has the body of technical doctrine regarding petroleum in all its aspects which is possessed in the United States. There is no country which is so thoroughly geared to the power supplied by petroleum. Yet, thanks to the mixture of unsupported argument, official reticence and sheer hypocrisy which befog the subject, there can be few peoples so poorly informed of the global implications of oil production and distribution as the Americans.

—*New York Herald Tribune,*
January 9, 1948

PUBLISHER'S FOREWORD

ACCORDING to a recent tabulation of the First National City Bank of New York, published in its *Monthly Letter* for August 1955, there are no fewer than thirty nonfinancial corporations in the United States with assets of more than a billion dollars. Here is a breakdown of the list:

Field of operation	No. of companies	Assets (billion $)
Oil	10	21.1
Public utilities	5	18.4
Railroads	6	11.8
Motors	2	6.1
Steel	2	4.9
Chemicals	2	3.2
Electrical equipment	2	3.0
Trade	1	1.5
Total	30	70.0

One out of three billion-dollar corporations in the United States is an oil company. The oil companies have 30 percent of the assets of all billion-dollar corporations. If we omit the utilities and rails, and center attention on what are usually called the industrials, the predominance of oil is overwhelming: there are ten billion-dollar oil companies with assets of $21.1 billion compared to nine billion-dollar companies with assets of $18.7 billion *in all other fields of industry combined.*

It has been said, with complete justification, that anyone who wants to understand the United States must understand Big Business. It is no less true that to understand Big Business one must understand oil. Oil is Big Business incarnate.

The oil industry is aware of its importance, and it spends millions of dollars every year to put before the public its own portrait of itself and of the Big Business system of which it forms so massive a part. Whether the result is understanding is another matter. We quote here, because we think it will bear repetition again and again, the passage which Mr. O'Connor has chosen as an epigraph for this book:

> There is no country in the world which has the body of technical doctrine regarding petroleum in all its aspects which is possessed in the United States. There is no country which is so thoroughly geared to the power supplied by petroleum. Yet, thanks to the mixture of unsupported argument, official reticence and sheer hypocrisy which befog the subject, there can be few peoples so poorly informed of the global implications of oil production and distribution as the Americans.

This is not the ranting of a wild-eyed radical; it is the sober voice of the conservative *New York Herald Tribune*.

Who must be held responsible for the "unsupported argument . . . and sheer hypocrisy which befog the subject" of oil? Who, indeed, if not the oil industry itself which has ready access through all the expensive media of mass communication to the public ear and the public mind?

Not that there have been no attempts in this country to present the facts about oil from the point of view of consumers and workers—that is to say, from the point of view of the public interest. There have been, and some of them have attained a justified fame in the annals of the nation's history. Such were Henry Demarest Lloyd's *Wealth Against Commonwealth* (1894) and Ida Tarbell's *History of the Standard Oil Company* which followed exactly a decade later. The twenties brought George W. Stocking's *The Oil Industry and the Competitive System: A Study in Waste* (1925), and the thirties Myron W. Watkins' *Oil: Stabilization or Conservation?* (1937) and William J. Kemnitzer's *Rebirth of Monopoly: A Critical Analysis of Economic Conduct in the Petroleum Industry of the United States* (1938). The closing days of the New Deal saw the publication, through the instrumentality of the Temporary National Economic Committee, of a vast mass of descriptive and analytical material bearing on the operations of the oil industry.

But in recent years there have been but few additions to this distinguished body of critical literature. Spokesmen for the oil companies have had their say, virtually unchallenged. In the meantime, the industry has grown in size and riches as never before. For the public, the result has been that abysmal ignorance of which the *Herald Tribune* so feelingly speaks.

It seems crystal clear that the time has come for a fresh review of oil in the spirit of the great critics and reformers of the past. And we believe that this is just what Harvey O'Connor has provided in *The Empire of Oil*.

Between us, the undersigned have had a good deal of experience writing and teaching in the fields of history and economics, and we think we know a first-rate piece of work when we see it. *The Empire of Oil* is all of that. Based on extensive first-hand knowledge and intensive research, it is a masterpiece of condensation and exposition. If only enough Americans will read and study it, we shall change from being one of the most poorly informed to being one of the best informed peoples on "the global implications of oil production and distribution."

LEO HUBERMAN
PAUL M. SWEEZY

New York City
October 1955

CONTENTS

xi

PART V - *The Industry and Government*

PART VI - *The Industry Abroad*

PART VII - *The Future of Oil*

Part I

Scope of the Industry

1

The Controls of Power

THE oil industry of the United States is dominated by ten billion-dollar corporations. Standard Oil of New Jersey rises in majestic eminence among them, both in size and power. It is the all-seeing, the all-knowing, the perfect corporation, answerable to no one but itself. Even its owners, the stockholders, gaze with awe upon this golden Jersey, for to them it is untouchable. It responds, not to their direction, but to its own; theirs only to ratify decisions made by "The Corporation," to trust to the wisdom of its self-renewing directorate, to know that their dividends are almost as certain as death and taxes.

In a past generation one man, John D. Rockefeller, the founder, personified this power. His successors, the directors of Jersey, seem almost anonymous, lost in the vastness of the empire he founded.

Jersey's annual revenue of nearly $6 billion is greater than that of the Canadian government, and six times that of its affluent Latin American dependency, Venezuela. Its annual profit of half a billion is greater than the tax revenues of all but a handful of states.

And yet Jersey is but one of the Standard Oil companies that sprang, hydralike, from the parent when its head was severed by the United States Supreme Court in 1911. Jersey's Midwestern brother, Indiana, half as large, counts its assets at more than two billion; its New York associate, Socony-Vacuum, and the West Coast company, Standard of California, both rank high among the billion-dollar corporations.

Flanking these mammoths are six non-Standard companies— Texas, Gulf, Cities Service, Sinclair, Phillips, and Shell—all members of the exclusive club of billion-dollar corporations. There are others, too. Of the 100 largest manufacturing firms, 20 are oil; of the total assets of these 100 firms, oil holds a third, or some $23 billion. Of the 17 billion-dollar manufacturing corporations, ten are oil, and Jersey is the largest of them all.

Most of these companies are congeries of subsidiaries—Jersey has more than 300—doing business around the world, producing in out-of-the-way places and selling to all who need their wares. In these foreign ventures, the titans intertwine. Texas Company, Standard of California, Standard of New Jersey, and Socony-Vacuum own together the Arabian American Oil Company (Aramco), with exclusive rights to the petroleum under the sands of Araby. These four, with Gulf, are the United States members of the consortium which took over 40 percent of Anglo-Iranian's interests in Iran.* Standard of California and the Texas Company own Bahrein Petroleum, controlling the resources of that island in the Persian Gulf; they also run Caltex, with production in the East Indies and markets everywhere. Standard of New Jersey and Socony-Vacuum own Standard-Vacuum, producing and marketing throughout the Eastern Hemisphere. Gulf has taken a foreign partner, Anglo-Iranian, in joint command of Kuwait, that fantastic sheikdom straight out of the Arabian Nights, perhaps the richest concentrated oil field in all the world. Standard of New Jersey and Socony-Vacuum join hands with Royal Dutch/Shell and Compagnie Française des Pétroles to control the output of Iraq. Standard of New Jersey, all by itself, controls Creole and Lago which between them produce and refine almost half the golden flow of Venezuela; it is the dominating partner, with Gulf and Shell, in 99 percent of Venezuela's production. And the state of Texas ranks as but another colony, with Jersey's Humble lording it as viceroy.

The preeminent position of these companies in the nation's foreign affairs follows from their investment of some $5.1 billion abroad—20 percent of all foreign holdings by U. S. nationals.[1]

---

* Since the reorganization of its properties in Iran by the international consortium, Anglo-Iranian has changed its name to British Petroleum. Originally it was known as Anglo-Persian. The company is referred to in this book as Anglo-Iranian.

[1] Numbered footnotes are in References, pages 343-364.

The rise has been meteoric in recent years, from $1.4 billion in 1943. Nearly all the expansion has been around the Persian Gulf, in Venezuela, and in Canada.

These intermingled companies among themselves control the major oil resources of the world outside the Soviet sector. To say that they do not act in unison and with an understanding harmony would be to contradict their open affiliations in their joint enterprises. The harsh word "cartel" has been applied to their entente; this they deny, but production and prices throughout their world move together in majestic concord. The unseen hands which harmonize their efforts are above the controls of such sovereigns as the United States and British governments.

Within their home country, too, the United States oil companies deny that they constitute a monopoly. Prices may be the same at every major service station in each region, but that, they contend, is only in response to laws of the higher competition. Production is kept under control so that prices may be stable but that, they say, is not their fiat, but that of various regulatory agencies, such as the Texas Railroad Commission.

Not even the major integrated corporations would deny that they dominate the market, for it is incontestable that they control the sales of 85 percent of the oil products sold in this country. But they do not meet periodically to set prices or production. What with the controls they have thoughtfully sponsored, they don't need to.

The "international" companies number but five—masters of the Caribbean and the Persian Gulf, the chief sources of oil in the non-Soviet world outside the United States. A score or so of "major" companies, including the Big Five, dominate the domestic market from well to service station. Under the majors, and behind them, is the legion of those who stand to profit from the private exploitation of the greatest natural resource. This legion is topped by the millionaire wildcatters of Texas, the plungers in the feverish hunt for new sources of crude, the men who can hardly lose, thanks to the peculiar federal tax structure known as "depletion allowance." These, the Haroldson Hunts, the H. R. Cullens, the Clint Murchisons, the Sid Richardsons, constitute the elite of the nouveaux riches of the mid-twentieth century. Flushed with millions they have done nothing to earn, these speculators reach out for financial and political domination of the country. They are the "independent" producers, together with thousands of smaller fry, who clash with the "international" companies on the disturbing issue of imported oil. Were there no imports, the price of domestic crude oil could be pushed even higher; and it taxes the ingenuity of companies like Jersey to balance their stake in Venezuela and Arabia against their stake in Humble and other domestic affiliates, and to pacify their impatient independent suppliers of crude. Yet inasmuch as the international companies base the price of the cheaper oil abroad on the price of high-cost Texas crude, they see no point in unduly depressing the domestic price.

Political control of the important producing states of Texas, Oklahoma, Louisiana, and California is a simple matter for the great corporations. They retire conveniently to give the stage to the independent producers.* Due to individual ownership of subsoil resources, every landowner in oil territory has a stake in corporate control. The producers scatter a largesse of $1.5 billion a year in lease, bonus, and royalty payments to hundreds of thousands of landowners; and even those who now receive none of this hope to share in the bonanza later, if and when the geologist locates oil beneath their acres.

On this solid local political base, the dominant companies feel secure. Internationally, they find either political party in tune with their own needs; domestically, they prefer the Republican brand of politics and keep a restraining hand on distasteful policies within the Democratic party by control of ruling cliques in Southern states. To shape public opinion closer to their heart's desire, they spend freely, through the Oil Industry Information Committee, through their own "institutional" advertising, through subsidies given to schools, colleges, molders of public opinion, and organizations in touch with farmers and other crucial elements of the population.

Thus, in hard times and good, the dominant corporations

* The Oil Industry Information Committee reported in 1952 that there were 12,000 "producers" of petroleum.

preserve their profitability. All petty risks have been erased. There remains only one overshadowing risk which they cannot exorcise—the rise of peoples, nations, and ideas. This risk they meet resolutely out of the public treasury of their government, heaping arms upon arms until the earth groans under the burden.

2

The Four Ages of Oil

IN THE early nineteenth century, candles struggled against the gloom. More prosperous people could afford whale oil, and New Bedford flourished. Rock oil, scooped up from seepages, was famed for its medicinal properties but was too expensive to be used widely as an illuminant.

Edwin L. Drake, a colonel by courtesy but a man blessed with a simple, workable and original idea, brought more light. He copied the salt well driller's technique and deliberately drilled for the rock oil which had polluted so many brine wells. It bubbled up by the barrel. And the kerosene lamp followed. It still illumines more homes and huts around the world than electricity.

The history of oil can be grouped conveniently around the names of five men, who by design or accident marked off its periods. *Drake* in 1859 found how to get oil out of the earth, but *John D. Rockefeller* found how to get money out of oil. Almost in the beginning of the kerosene era there was Rockefeller, who cared little about drilling or producing but a lot about organizing the market for petroleum. He built a towering fortune on the kerosene lamp and on lubricants. When the kerosene age began to sputter out, in this country, around the end of the nineteenth century, his market position was so massive and impregnable that his fortune continued to mushroom, almost effortlessly, in the era that followed Spindletop in 1901.

This second period, that of fuel oil, was opened by a Dalmatian engineer, *Anthony F. Lucas*—he preferred that form to the original "Luchich." The prospecting for petroleum had spread from Oil Creek, in western Pennsylvania, to West Virginia and Ohio and even as far west as Kansas. Lucas, a mineral prospector, believed that oil might be found in the salt domes along the Gulf Coast. He brought in the mighty Lucas gusher on Spindletop, near Beaumont, Texas, in 1901. Oil gushed from the wells of Spindletop and neighboring fields in such enormous quantity that it not only escaped Rockefeller's marketing apparatus, but demanded new outlets for its sale. Texas oil began to power the British Navy. Thus crude oil, which had been converted mostly into kerosene and lubricants, now found a major use as a fuel; indeed in the earlier years of this period there was little other use for the "sour" Texas product until refiners found out how to extract the lighter "ends," such as kerosene and gasoline.

The fuel oil era eased into the gasoline era when *Henry Ford* perfected a cheap and useful automobile. A convenient arbitrary date to select is the year 1911, when the U. S. Supreme Court dissolved the Standard Oil trust. Rockefeller's monopoly had already been dissolved, in effect, by the rise of other big companies based on the oil of Texas and Oklahoma, and the Supreme Court's ruling merely put a legal termination to an illegal combination.

The industry in its present form developed in the gasoline era but the current structure of price and production controls is the product of the Great Depression, compounded by *C. M. ("Dad") Joiner's* amazing discovery of the east Texas field in 1930. This field, the richest ever found in this country, began to pour its treasure upon the market just when the bottom was falling out anyway. Oil threatened to drown the industry. It took a few years for the major companies to find the formula. By 1935 the formula for controlled production, legally sanctioned, was working, and the profitability of the industry was assured for the future as long as there was oil in the ground and the formula could be maintained.

In this era the larger U. S. companies, reaching out around the world, overthrew what had hitherto been a British-Dutch monopoly and themselves became the masters of Venezuela, the Middle East, and the Far Eastern oil reserves. In this era, too, rock oil elbowed rock coal to one side and became the major energy source for railroads and public utilities and even surpassed the coal tars in the rising industry of petrochemicals.

The oil under ground comes out easier than coal, and is handier to use. That it is really in short supply and might become, in the lifetime of those now living, as expensive as rock oil had been before 1859, does not concern those who pile up profit from it. Burn it up—in auto motors, in locomotives, in furnaces for industry and the utilities, in home heating units, no matter where, so long as this precious irreplaceable natural resource can be converted through energy and heat into dollars.

THE KEROSENE ERA

For a half century the history of oil was also the personal history of John D. Rockefeller, who tamed an anarchic industry and brought it under the direct control of Standard Oil. The oft-told tale ran the spectrum of the devices of monopoly. Competitors were bought out or ruined, legislators and public officials were also bought out (and many ruined), laws were flouted with impunity or by stealthy indirection. When it became obvious that this monolithic monopoly could not be controlled by law, the government then cut it into segments, hopeful that at last a cure had been found for overweening power.

Rockefeller had been content to leave the hazards of the tumultuous and unpredictable production of petroleum to free enterprise. He stationed himself along the highways where oil flowed to the market, whether by rail or pipe line. He allied himself with the railroads and then forced them to give him not only rebates on his own product, but rebates on the oil his competitors shipped. After others pioneered pipe lines to escape his exactions, he bought them up to secure complete control of all oil that flowed from western Pennsylvania to tidewater.

His first investment in oil was made in 1862, only three years after Drake's discovery; in 1865 he had organized his first oil company; in 1870 he amalgamated this with the Harkness and Flagler plants and formed Standard Oil. Then he reached out for the New York refineries. From St. Louis to Boston his wagons sold kerosene to grocers and even sold groceries when necessary to control retail trade in order to drive out other kerosene dealers.

Rockefeller was both ruthless, as pictured in the bitter invective of his enemies, and cooperative. He was no lone wolf, but the leader of the wolf pack, as is still testified by the diamond-studded fortunes of the families of Harkness, Flagler, Pratt, Rogers, Whitney, Payne, Archbold, and Bedford. Usually Rockefeller offered a price to a substantial competitor and ruined him only if he would not accept. If the price was Standard Oil stock, and the erstwhile competitor held on to it, he was rich beyond the dreams of avarice, and so are his heirs—for as long as they and Standard Oil will live.

THE FUEL OIL ERA

It was a fatal flaw in the Rockefeller technique that ended his monopoly. The wastes of production were not to his taste and the hazards of exploration out of his line. He was interested in oil only when it was out of the ground and ready for his refineries. As the center of production swung westward to Ohio and Indiana and then across the Mississippi to the new fields of Kansas, Standard Oil gradually veered in its policy on production. But its magnates in New York had never heard of Lucas, the gold prospector and salt dome driller who had picked up an abandoned lease in the desolate marsh country near Beaumont, Texas. They didn't think much of Texas, anyway, for a Standard Oil subsidiary had been kicked out of the state for violation of the antitrust law in marketing kerosene.

During the winter of 1900-1901 Lucas kept his rotary rig drilling on a dome. At 575 feet, having exhausted all the resources he could touch, he appealed to John H. Galey of the Pittsburgh oil firm of Guffey & Galey. Galey took a major interest in the hole. On January 10, 1901, the Lucas gusher crashed through, hurtling a thousand feet of pipe and drilling tools 200 feet into the air and wrecking the derrick. Nearly 100,000 barrels gushed out of Spindletop each day before it could be capped. Despite the efforts of fifty guards to keep the crowds away from the awesome spectacle, fire broke out and consumed the lake of oil.

A more modest well would not have changed the course of history, but this was the mightiest producer yet struck on the American continent. Guffey and Galey could stand the expense of drilling, of putting out the fire and capping the well, but to find outlets for the enormous flow was too much for them. Obviously only Standard Oil was able and ready to absorb and market such wealth, but the Pittsburgh firm had no relish for dealing with the New Yorkers. So the other half of the Guffey & Galey firm, Joseph M. Guffey himself, turned to the richest man in western Pennsylvania—Andrew W. Mellon, the wispy head of Pittsburgh's House of Mellon. As a financier, Mellon understood oil. His family had pioneered the Crescent pipe line across the southern part of the state to tidewater despite Rockefeller. Standard Oil reached out for that, but the legislature had passed a law forbidding the acquisition of competing pipe lines. Another legislature obligingly repealed the law and the Mellons sold out to Standard at a fat profit.

So when Guffey laid his Spindletop problem before Mellon, the banker apparently felt, on the basis of past experience, that he could hold his own with Standard to the point, if need be, of selling out at a good price. He took a flyer on Guffey's black Golconda. Guffey got nearly $750,000 and 70,000 shares in the new J. M. Guffey Petroleum Company, Lucas got $400,000, and the Mellons kept 40 percent of the $15,000,000 stock, after spreading some of the rest among Pennsylvania politicians and friends.

More sweetening seemed required by the Texas politicos, so one of the Guffey leases of acreage at Spindletop was sold to the Swayne-Hogg syndicate. Jim Hogg had been governor, the same who with indefatigable Texas humor had named his daughters Ima, Ura, and Shesa. "Northern men," Guffey recounted later, "were not very well respected in Texas in those days. Governor Hogg was a power there and I wanted him on my side because I was going to spend a lot of money."

From this lease arose the Texas Company. This and Gulf Oil—successor to the Guffey enterprise—became the leading non-Standard firms.

A third great oil company, Shell, also arose from this very same Spindletop. In those days it was known as Shell Transport and Trading Company of London, whose specialty was indicated by its name; it had started by peddling mother-of-pearl made from seashells. It would haul anything anywhere, even Texas oil. So Shell signed a contract with Guffey to take 4.5 million barrels of oil in the next 20 years—mostly for the needs of the British Navy—at a purchase price of 25 cents a barrel. At the time the contract looked good, but when oil went up later to 30 cents and higher, the contract threatened to bankrupt the Guffey company. Andrew Mellon, on one of his London trips, was able to modify it. By then, Shell had acquired tankers and was firmly launched in the oil business. Later it merged with Royal Dutch to become a leading factor in world petroleum.

Spindletop was indeed the Klondike of oil. Men rushed in from all ends of the eastern oil country and from the new mid-continent fields to lease, drill, gamble, and float stock. Beaumont turned overnight from a sleepy Texas rice town to a world oil center.

The Texas oil, heavy, asphaltic, sulphurous, and "sour," defied the eastern refining processes used on "sweet" crude. It seemed impossible to extract a good kerosene and it was not suitable for lubrication. That left no use for it except as fuel oil for boilers in ships and industry, at a price far below the Pennsylvania product. The great gushers, under the primitive methods of that day, soon blew their gas pressure uselessly into the air; after the pumps went to work, production fell quickly from the astonishing 100,000 barrels a day to a trickle. Then came a feverish hunt for more gushers, which in turn quickly exhausted themselves. Under this feast-and-famine flow, the price of oil fluctuated wildly; within a few weeks it could decline from 50 cents to 10 cents, and then shoot up again as another gusher faded out. In 1902 crude was being hawked at a nickel a barrel. Small wonder Rockefeller disdained this end of the business.

It became something of a nightmare for the Mellons, too. They had just floated $4 million in bonds and their own expert, young William Larimer Mellon, had given them a gloomy report on Guffey's management. So Andrew Mellon and his nephew hied themselves to 26 Broadway to talk matters over with Henry H. Rogers and John D. Archbold, the Standard moguls. Perhaps the Texas problem could be unloaded on them.

Rogers seemed amused as he listened to the Mellon woes. Standard preferred to leave such problems to the likes of the Mellons, while it bought the crude, refined it, marketed it, and made millions. In addition, Rogers reminded the Mellons that Standard had just been booted out of Texas (because of its marketing techniques) and Mr. Rockefeller would never put another dime into the state. It happened that "never" was too long a word, but it had to suffice for the Mellons then.

Yet, as it turned out, that was a good day for the Mellons and a very poor one for Standard Oil. It forced Guffey Petroleum to become the first "integrated" oil company, handling the product all the way from exploration to marketing. Mellon thus discarded the old Standard formula and created a new one which became basic to the new era. The Pittsburgh bankers got rid of Guffey ("They throwed me out") and reorganized his company into Gulf Oil. They would have preferred the name "Texas" but the Hogg-Swayne syndicate had preempted that and so the Mellons took the name nearest to Texas.

Gulf expanded into the new Indian Territory fields, where the oil was of better quality and in steadier supply. Soon Oklahoma became the principal producing state, next to California, and interest lagged in the boom-and-bust Texas fields.*

THE GASOLINE ERA

In the early days gasoline was a nuisance. Kerosene brought money but there was no use for gasoline. Honest refineries

* PREMIER OIL STATES[1]

Pennsylvania	1859-1894
Ohio	1895-1903
California	1904-1915
Oklahoma	1916-1918
California	1919-1920
Oklahoma	1921-1928
Texas	1929-

California, an important oil state since the 1880s, was separated geographically and economically from the rest of the United States industry. Because of the distances, California oil was marketed on the Pacific Coast, which was inaccessible economically to oil from east of the Rockies. After the dissolution in 1911, Standard Oil of California inherited the trust's West Coast business. Smaller California companies, such as Union, remained independent, while others were acquired later by Socony (General Petroleum), Tide Water (Associated), and Sinclair-Cities Service (Richfield). But in the past 50 years, the bulk of the oil used east of the Rockies has come from Kansas, Oklahoma, Texas and Louisiana.

floated it downstream to get rid of it; the less conscientious left
as much as they dared in the kerosene despite laws to the contrary; kerosene fires and explosions were more frequent in the
United States than in England where regulation was stricter.
But soon after Henry Ford perfected the Model T, kerosene
became safe again. In 1911, which we have selected arbitrarily
as the beginning of the gasoline era because it coincides with the
dissolution of the Standard Oil monopoly, there were 619,000
automobiles and most gasoline was sold from hand pumps in
front of grocery stores. By 1930, there were 23 million cars on the
road and the industry had built its own gasoline marketing
outlets.[2]

Gasoline meant quick riches to the oil companies, particularly
those in the newer western fields. Selling oil for ships' bunkers
and industrial boilers was at best a marginal business because
oil has to compete with cheap coal. But there was no competitor
to gasoline. The price was what the traffic could bear. The profits
from the great new fields of the Southwest, which had eluded
Standard control while it was a monopoly, now nourished the
rise of a dozen large integrated companies. H. L. Doherty, an
audacious stock promoter who wanted oil and gas for his utilities
companies in the East, put together rickety Cities Service; the
industry's maverick, Harry F. Sinclair, built up his Consolidated
by methods that some considered not "ethical"; the Phillips company based itself on the great gas fields of Kansas, Oklahoma,
and the Texas Panhandle; Skelly and Mid-Continent, smaller
fry, carved themselves a slice of the mid-continent markets.

In the East, two small companies, Sun and Pure, which had
managed to survive the monopoly period, expanded; on the West
Coast, Union Oil gained a toehold in territory dominated by
Standard, and Shell euchred its way in.

But Standard survived. It was still the dominant refiner and
marketer in the rich territory from the Mississippi to the Atlantic.
Its rivals based themselves on the new mid-continent and southwestern fields but they had to fight their way into the prime
market where most of U. S. industry was concentrated in the
North and East.

In the gasoline era from 1911 on, the central company, Standard of New Jersey, maintained its sway over the Atlantic seaboard southward from New York; Standard of New York, which became known as Socony, was dominant in New York and New England. The smaller Atlantic, Tide Water, and Vacuum companies maintained their specialized markets along the seaboard. In the Midwest, Standard of Indiana reigned almost unchallenged except in Ohio, which was the preserve of Standard of Ohio in marketing and Ohio Oil in production. Continental was dominant in the Rockies and Standard of California along the West Coast.

These companies reached out for their own crude oil supplies. Standard of Indiana in particular was spectacular in its expansion into the Southwest and the Rockies. It offered to gobble up the Mellon Gulf properties, but it was too late for that. Instead, it acquired E. L. Doheny's Pan American with its Gulf Coast and Mexican properties and some Sinclair properties. Standard of Jersey, reversing Rockefeller's dictum about "never" wasting another dime in Texas, bought out the Humble interests and became the biggest of Southwestern producers. By picking up Carter in Wyoming, it became important in the Rockies. Socony entered Texas by purchase of the Magnolia company.

By 1930, the U. S. oil empire had been staked out in its present provinces; its structure has continued in the past twenty-five years without significant change. Some twenty companies had attained the status of "major" entities in the empire although the lesser among them were quite provincial in their scope. Indeed only one, the Texas Company, could claim that it marketed in every state; but the Standard companies, taken together, still blanketed the nation, as had the old monopoly. Aside from them, perhaps only five companies could be said to have nearly nationwide distribution facilities—the Texas Company, Gulf, Sinclair, Shell, and Cities Service.

During the 1920s, the twenty "majors" seemed assured a never-ending prosperity. That prospect came to a sudden halt the day that "Dad" Joiner struck oil in east Texas.

THE ERA OF "ALLOWABLE" PRODUCTION

C. M. Joiner was just another wildcatter, chasing the pot of gold under the legs of a derrick. As his drill went down, his money ran out and the rig shut down. Then he sold another lease, borrowed some more money, started his rig working again. On October 9, 1930, at 3000 feet, he struck oil. Nothing like Spindletop, just a steady flow of 300 barrels a day—but it opened up the current era of oil.[3]

Soon it was proved that the east Texas field was two to six miles wide and 40 miles long, a great pool of a good grade of crude. Year by year the estimates on this field have climbed, million by million, until today it is estimated that in its virgin state east Texas contained at least six billion barrels—the greatest field in this country's history.

If it was a lucky day for Dad Joiner, it was a mighty unlucky one for the major companies. Despite their million-dollar geophysical gadgets, they had passed up east Texas. Now when they rushed in to grab acreage, they found the field divided into thousands of parcels held by small farmers and, worse yet, tens of thousands of town lots. It was a "poor boy" field and hundreds of pore ol' country boys rushed in, with the majors, to drill. Lashed on by the rule of capture—get your neighbor's oil before he gets yours—they, poor boys and majors alike, brought in the most wasteful period in the history of oil production. To complicate the catastrophe, the nation had slipped over the precipice into the Great Depression. By a triumph of the most senseless methods of exploitation conceivable, a deluge of oil hit the market exactly when it was least needed.

The flood of cheap oil pouring into a hundred "coffeepot" refineries threatened the price structure which the majors had so laboriously erected. Almost anybody could—and did—drill a well, and it took no great wealth to throw up a refinery to top the gasoline from the residual oil. The cheap gasoline flooded into the cities where depression-hit car owners were glad to save money on gas for their jalopies and without a thought of the brand names.

The problem of the majors now became that of harnessing

the fierce individual ruggedness of east Texas and bringing the market back under control. The legislatures passed laws, the militia closed the fields at bayonet point, the National Industrial Recovery Administration imposed code rules, the Connally "hot oil" act sealed off "illegal" east Texas production. When the field was finally throttled, the state prorationing laws took over and law and order ruled.*

Hardly had the majors "capped" the field and reduced the flow to a fraction of its potential than World War II came along, adding to demand and profitability. The law and order imposed on the east Texas field became a nationwide pattern that weathered successfully wars major and minor, hot and cold, recessions, Congressional inquisitiveness and the plaintive cries of the little fellows in the marketing end of the industry. By 1955 the industry had never had it so good.

* See Chapter 6, "Conservation," for a detailed account of the development of production limitation.

3

The Majors and the Minors

CORPORATIONS in the oil industry range from Standard of New Jersey down to provincial firms, some in production with a few rigs for drilling, others in marketing with a bulk station for wholesaling oil products and perhaps a small string of retail stations. From this nether end of the industry the American Petroleum Institute derives proofs of the virility of competition as it counts some 200,000 private enterprises hustling for their share of the consumer's dollar.

One useful distinction in the industry is between those firms with heavy overseas investments and those which are more or less dependent on domestic wells. Another distinction segregates those firms which are "integrated" to produce, refine, and market oil from those interested only in one division of the industry. At either end of the industry are sizable firms engaged only in production or marketing. The producers usually enjoy a high ratio of net income to gross because they do not engage in marketing, where margins are close. On the other hand, some companies such as Standard of Kentucky market only; many a producing company doing a tenth the business makes as much as or more than Standard of Kentucky.

At the top of the industry, in assets and profits, are the "international" companies—Standard of New Jersey, Standard of California, Socony-Vacuum, Gulf, and Texas Company. Rounding out the ranks of the majors are the other integrated companies such as Standard of Indiana, Sinclair, Phillips, Cities Service, and others that are dependent mainly on domestic production and on purchases of foreign crude.*

Toward the bottom of the list of majors, the struggle for existence is intense; there, mergers are the order of the day as they fight for survival. In Oklahoma the tendency is most notable. Sunray has absorbed Barnsdall and now has merged with Mid-Continent; Kerr-McGee has taken over Deep Rock; Derby has consolidated with Colorado Oil & Gas; Chicago Corporation has bought Champlin. Other minor majors are falling into the maws of the major majors: Sinclair has recently absorbed American Republics; Continental has taken over Kirby. Month by month, the majors absorb little producers and little marketers, keeping all the while a wary eye on the Department of Justice and on Congress.

STANDARD OF NEW JERSEY

Standard Oil Company (New Jersey), as it styles itself formally, is the main heir of the older Standard company dissolved in 1911. This marvel of the Western world, this colossus bestriding the flow of petroleum from the richest fields of both the East and West, whose outstretched fingers collect the biggest revenue of any corporation under the sun, neither produces, refines, transports, nor markets a single drop of oil. It is too big to be concerned with such workaday affairs.

Jersey (as it calls itself cozily) just holds, thinks, and plans. Holding the control of 322 companies (at last count[1]) is indeed a chore. When some of these subsidiaries such as Humble and Creole themselves rank among the top corporations of the world, thinking and planning become even more important than holding.

To write of such a company in a few words is in itself *lèse majesté*. A crew of scholars is now at work, backed by half a million dollars, doing the history of Jersey, which is expected to fill four fat volumes, plus an extra one for Humble.[2] Professor N. S. B. Gras of the Harvard Business School and his nineteen

* A list of the majors is given below, page 40, together with figures on assets and on gross and net income.

assistants have been at work seven years, reminding one of Lewis Carroll's

> If seven maids with seven mops
> Swept it for half a year,
> Do you suppose, the Walrus said,
> That they could get it clear?
> I doubt it, said the Carpenter,
> And shed a bitter tear.

Certainly the fruit of their efforts will be more monumental than that of Henry Demarest Lloyd, Ida Tarbell, and others who, singlehanded, dared to hope to describe Standard and its ways.

Through its subsidiaries Jersey does about a fifth of the world's oil business and does it all around the globe with the help of 155,000 people on the payroll. Modestly enough Jersey itself employs but 1300 and is able to house them comfortably on several floors of 30 Rockefeller Plaza, New York City. Jersey's top men hold, think, and plan for:

Humble Oil & Refining, 87 percent owned, the largest crude producer in the country, operator of the biggest U. S. refinery, at Baytown, near Houston.

Creole Petroleum, 95 percent owned, operating enormously lucrative fields in Venezuela.

Esso Standard, 100 percent owned, which refines and markets on the Atlantic seaboard.

Carter, 100 percent owned, principally a producer and refiner in the Rockies.

Imperial, 70 percent owned, the biggest oil concern in Canada.

Lago, 100 percent owned, operating the biggest refinery in the Americas on the Dutch island of Aruba off the Venezuelan coast.

Ethyl Corporation, 50 percent owned (General Motors has the other half), which makes the anti-knock compound.

Arabian American (Aramco), 30 percent owned, sole operator of the great Saudi Arabian fields.

Standard-Vacuum, 50 percent owned (with Socony-Vacuum), producing in the Far East and marketing in the Eastern Hemisphere.

Who owns Standard of New Jersey? The answer, 297,000 holders of 65 million shares of common stock, tells all and reveals nothing. When the old Standard company was dissolved, it was said that the Rockefellers owned 25 percent; in 1939, the last time the public had a look at the figures, they owned 14.52 percent. Edward S. Harkness held a cool million shares in 1939; John D. Rockefeller, Jr., 1,715,722; the Rockefeller Foundation, 1,037,505.[3] While Jersey is proud that 71 percent of its shareholders hold less than 100 shares each, the Temporary National Economic Committee's figures in 1939 showed that 47 percent of the shares were held by the 100 largest shareholders, and that most of these were the descendants of the original Rockefeller and his associates.

Who controls Jersey? Not the Rockefellers, it appears. The thousand and one heirs of the old buccaneers are concerned not with management but with dividends. As these are satisfactory, why bother about management?

The answer is that no one person controls Jersey. It is too big, so big that it is no longer useful to think of single individuals able or even willing to run it. Jersey is run by a collective of managers, perhaps the most powerful collective this side of the Soviet politburo. This collective chooses its own members, entirely from the ranks of top company executives. No outsider—no banker, no representative of suppliers or customers, not even a representative of the shareholders—is permitted on this Olympian board. Nor does it have a Jove. Its chairman and president are merely the first among equals, and most people don't even know their names. In a poll taken by *Forbes* magazine in the business community, only a sixth of those queried could name a Jersey top man.[4]

Jersey's is one of the few all-management boards among leading corporations. A determined fight has been made in recent years to get at least one stockholders' representative on the board, just for an independent look-see at what goes on. No luck. "In our opinion," reported Lewis D. Gilbert and John J. Gilbert in their 1952 report on corporation meetings, "no matter how good the management, there are now too many issues foreign to the actual running of the business to allow all-management director boards to continue to exist. A despotism may be benevolent, but it is still a despotism, unless the owners have the right to have their own directors on these boards to pass on matters such as options, compensations, pensions and similar matters."[5]

If the only purpose in the owners being represented on Jersey's board is to pass on executive salaries, there is little reason for complaint. The chairman gets only $213,000—miserly when ranged against the $581,000 paid Charles E. Wilson in 1952 by General Motors or the $503,000 paid the president of DuPont.

Philosophically, the men of Jersey might answer that their corporation approaches a mystical entity in which mere personal pelf and notoriety are alien. Let the Charles E. Wilsons of General Motors and General Electric get the big salaries, go to Washington on vainglorious governmental missions, attend on pomp and glory. The men of Jersey are too busy to waste their time on the second most important things. Let the Trumans and the Eisenhowers, the Wilsons, the Hoffmans and the Fords carry out the errands; Jersey will content itself with outlining the conditions and the situations for which the errands must be carried out.

The 14 Olympians of the Jersey board elect five of their number to the executive committee, which meets daily. But any one of the 14 is a member of the executive if he chooses to sit in. The full board meets weekly, but rarely are the 14 all present. Many are scattered with the four winds to the Far East, Arabia, Venezuela, Texas, each specializing on the tasks which the board has entrusted to him.

Flanking the board is the coordination committee, composed of the top brains of the various departments—production, pipe lines, marine transport, refining, marketing, and economics. This committee sifts the facts and prepares the programs for the board, and from its ranks may come future directors.

Chairman of the board until 1954 was Frank W. Abrams, a university-trained man, solicitous in public relations, eager to see that the nation understands Jersey and thinks right about it. Now the chairman is former President Eugene Holman, the muscular type of Texan who knows operations intimately from his previous work with Humble.

The results of the board's work are summarized in the 1954
figures on the source of Jersey's profits:

Creole (Venezuela)	$226,858,000
Humble (Texas, etc.)	107,219,000
Imperial (Canada)	42,993,000
Esso Standard	31,274,000
International Petroleum (Latin America)	21,044,000
Other affiliates	95,450,000

The big money nowadays is in production, and preferably in
production abroad. In 1950, for example, three-fourths of Jersey's
profit came from crude, and of the profit in crude, two-thirds
from foreign subsidiaries such as Creole. In 1954 on a gross of
$719 million Creole made $240 million net, a 33 percent profit
margin. Humble made 15 percent while Esso Standard, which
only refines and markets, made but 3½ percent. The extra profitability of foreign production was underscored by the fact that
nearly half of Jersey's profits are made from Latin America,
principally Venezuela.

Such considerations explain the deep concern of Jersey with
foreign policy. Who administers that policy, whether an Acheson
or a Dulles, whether Elihu Root, Charles Evans Hughes, Henry
L. Stimson, James F. Byrnes or George C. Marshall, matters
little. Republicans and Democrats alike are grist for Jersey's mill,
for U. S. foreign policy is at the service of the corporations in
command of the most sensitive, most vital, most essential commodity in the world—petroleum. Without it, navies are beached
and planes are sitting ducks. With apologies to Charles E.
Wilson and General Motors, what is good for Jersey is the *sine
qua non* of U. S. foreign policy. When one considers that Jersey's
board is continuous and that it concentrates much of its attention on foreign policy, Secretaries of State seem mere fleeting
birds of passage and the rise and fall of Presidents are incidents
in the prosecution of Jersey's destinies.

Perhaps for that reason Jersey's top men do not deign to serve
in political positions, no matter how exalted. If a U. S. President
forwards Point Four as a prime objective of foreign policy, a

Jersey chairman (Eugene Holman) can say condescendingly that his company's private Point Four "does more to raise living standards, wherever permitted to operate, than any public program." As the leading importing firm, Jersey would swing wide the doors to foreign goods through "trade, not aid." The Soviet threat to the great Middle Eastern oil fields does not disturb Jersey's equanimity. In 1952 Chairman Abrams soothed stockholders by reminding them that "the greater the risks, the greater the returns." Asked whether it wouldn't be better to come to an accord with the Soviets on Middle Eastern oil, he replied diplomatically that the corporation "follows American policy."[6]

Whether a group of 14 men, sitting at 30 Rockefeller Plaza, should be allowed to formulate the conditions under which U. S. foreign policy must operate is questionable. But to shift control from Jersey's politburo to the nondescript assortment of Secretaries of State and chairmen of the Senate Foreign Relations Committee might be a dubious venture. Whether a Tom Connally, an Alexander Wiley, a Dean Acheson or a John Foster Dulles represents an improvement on The Fourteen Men of Jersey is a highly debatable point.

In retrospect, however, some of the judgments of The Fourteen seem less than desirable from the point of view of the country's interest. There was the matter of Jersey's relations to I. G. Farben in the 1930s. The argument has now degenerated into a squabble as to who rooked whom. Jersey claims it did the rooking. It claims to have cheated I. G. on the famous deal by which both companies would exchange secrets of petrochemical processes and says that it delivered no vital secrets to the Nazi war machine. This contention disturbed the I. G. Farben chiefs no end. According to documents seized by the Army in 1945, I. G. Farben protested to Hitler that they had gained from Jersey information without which "the present method of warfare would be unthinkable." The Wehrmacht claimed that it was able to stockpile aviation gasoline and lubricants, thanks to Jersey. Generously, I. G. Farben also announced its indebtedness to Royal Dutch/Shell.[7]

Whatever the truth of the relations between Jersey and the

Nazi chemical combine, it seems safe to assume that there will be no confidences betrayed to the Soviet chemical trust by Jersey.

STANDARD OF INDIANA

Standard of Indiana and Standard of New Jersey, brothers under the skin, make a study in contrast. Not for Indiana are the far-flung imperial interests of Jersey, its concern over what may happen in Sumatra, Arabia, or Venezuela, its influence on global policies.

As befits a company based in Chicago, the good old United States is good enough for Indiana. In 1932 it sold out its foreign interests in Venezuela and elsewhere to its big brother. Its concern over foreign affairs is limited to dividends paid on the Jersey stock in Indiana's treasury. The State Department may be Jersey's concern; Indiana is more interested in the Department of the Interior. The company emphasizes that "all the officers and directors reside in Chicago or its vicinity"—an obvious poke at Wall Street. Its chairman, Dr. Robert E. Wilson, in business circles the most widely known oil man, is more versed in petroleum research than high finance.

Jersey's "trade, not aid" leaves Indiana cold. It is critical of mounting imports of oil and stands shoulder to shoulder with smaller U. S. producers in crying for limitations. Indiana's statistical department can produce figures to show that the United States needs not a drop of foreign oil in the next fifteen years, if ever. The "if ever" is based on Indiana's own elaborate research department which experiments ceaselessly with sources for petroleum from shale, coal, and lignite.

Assets of $2 billion rank Indiana third to Jersey in oil, and fifth among all U. S. manufacturing companies. Self-denied the extra profits of foreign oil, it ranks 14th among the nation's most profitable corporations but figures perhaps that in the long run this country may prove more lucrative than a dozen Arabias.

Indiana markets nearly everywhere except the West Coast. In the Midwest it's Red Crown and White Crown; in Utah and Idaho, it's Utoco of Utah Oil; in the deep South, Pan-Am for Pan-Am Southern and Pan American Petroleum & Transport;

along the Atlantic seaboard it's Amoco for American Oil. Stanolind buys and produces for Indiana.

Indiana's Whiting refinery, near Chicago, is the biggest in the North and the company has other big refineries near St. Louis and Kansas City, at Texas City, Salt Lake City, and Casper, Wyoming.

Back in 1939 the Rockefellers held 13.5 percent of the company's stock, and the 100 largest stockholders held a third of its shares. As befits a Midwestern company, it resents being tied in with the Rockefeller name but back in the 1930s John D., Jr., was able to oust its chairman, Robert W. Stewart, for his connivance with Harry F. Sinclair and E. L. Doheny in the shenanigans surrounding the Teapot Dome affair.[8]

While no great shakes as oil companies go in making money, Indiana netted $117 million in 1954 on a gross of $1.7 billion and had by 1950 earned a tidy total of $2,056 million since 1889.

SOCONY-VACUUM (SOCONY MOBIL OIL)

The Flying Red Horse gets all around the world. "We have direct or indirect interests in practically every important oil area in the Free World," boasts Socony (a contraction for Standard Oil Company of New York). In obvious allusion to Anglo-Iranian's tough luck for carrying its eggs in one basket, Socony says its interests "are so distributed geographically that no more than one-fifth of the Company's total crude production originates in any single foreign country."

Production, refining, and marketing range over every continent and five Socony refineries operate in western Europe alone, drawing on Middle Eastern crude. In alliance with Jersey, Socony operates Standard-Vacuum (Stanvac) in all phases of the business in southeastern Asia, Australia, Indonesia, Japan, the Indian subcontinent, and eastern and southern Africa. Socony neatly balances domestic against foreign production—95 million barrels a year in this country to 101 million abroad. Part of its crude comes from Arabian American Oil, in which it is a junior partner.

Socony comes closer to being a Rockefeller company than any other Standard firm. At last report the Rockefellers held 17 percent of its shares. Its offices are still at 26 Broadway, aerie of the old Rockefeller monopoly. Second largest firm in oil, it ranks fourth among all U. S. manufacturing concerns.

On the Pacific Coast it's known as General Petroleum; in the Southwest as Magnolia. Some years ago Socony got a special dispensation from the U. S. Supreme Court to merge with another Standard company, Vacuum Oil, which specialized in lubricants.*

President B. Brewster Jennings of Socony is a mighty man in oil; his board is illumined by the presence of Grayson L. Kirk, who is also the president of Columbia University.

TEXAS COMPANY

The Texas Company has taken its green "T" on a red star atop the lofty pillar to the far corners of the earth as well as into every state of the Union.

Texas Company rose from Spindletop soon after the Lucas gusher of 1901 had changed the entire course of the industry. Joseph S. Cullinan, a Pennsylvania oil man who had pioneered in the little Corsicana, Texas, field, teamed up with former Governor Hogg for a slice of Spindletop. They interested John W. Gates, the Chicago plunger. A crew of hardfisted, hard-hitting developers, in league with speculators willing to take a chance, had pushed Texas Company by 1954 up to second in profits and fifth in assets among all oil firms and fifth in profits among all U. S. manufacturing companies.

Texaco had to find markets around the world in view of Standard's hold on the industrial North and East, so its products streamed everywhere out of Port Arthur. It has pierced deeply into Colombia and Venezuela and has penetrated every country of the Americas except Argentina and Paraguay. It has moved in along the African west coast. Through affiliated companies, it operates in the rest of Africa, along the Indian Ocean, in Australasia, and in western Europe. Texaco's marketing position led to an offer of partnership from Standard of California, which had the vast Arabian and Bahrein fields on its hands while Texaco had a marketing apparatus blanketing the world east of

* In 1955, Socony-Vacuum changed its name to Socony Mobil Oil, presumably to escape from the Vacuum, whose significance as the old Standard trust's lubricating oil subsidiary had become lessened with the years.

Suez, and so Caltex was formed. Texaco's McColl-Frontenac is a leading Canadian firm.[9]

Among the colorful characters who guided Texaco into foreign lands was Captain Torkild Rieber, chairman of the board, whose pronounced Nazi sympathies led to his retirement in 1940.

GULF

Gulf, earliest of the big non-Standard majors, ranking fourth in assets and fifth in profits in the industry, is another member of the billion-dollar group of U. S. corporations.[10]

More than half its shares are held by the top 100 stockholders, and among these the scions of the Mellon family and their friends predominate. At last report, four Mellons each held a million shares or more, and the family held nearly 45 percent of the common stock. Appropriately, head offices are in Pittsburgh.

The Mellon company has ventured far and wide and sits now over the richest field ever discovered, that in the tiny sheikdom of Kuwait, a bit of desert squeezed in between Saudi Arabia and Iraq. This it shares with Anglo-Iranian. As it turned out, Anglo's bad luck in Iran was its partner's good fortune, for they had to turn the valves wide open in Kuwait to make up for the Iranian deficiency. In Venezuela, Gulf is Mene Grande, third largest producer. Two-thirds of Gulf production is outside the United States.

Gulf's orange disc swings over stations east of a line drawn from Texas to Michigan—the cream of the market—and in Canada and in many a foreign land. Because sulphur deposits are often found under domes where oil is sought, the company in 1934 bought a controlling interest in the Texas Gulf Sulphur Company.

J. F. Drake, chairman of the executive committee, and Board Chairman Sidney A. Swensrud are among the highest paid oil executives. Drake, who was Andrew Mellon's right-hand man in Washington while he was Secretary of the Treasury, got $347,000 in 1953. Unlike Jersey, there is not the slightest doubt about the owners' controlling the Gulf board. The Mellons are well satisfied with the progress of their oil company—another gem in their

crown, along with Koppers, Pittsburgh Coal, and Aluminum
Company of America.

SHELL

Shell is the only foreign oil company operating extensively in
the United States. Shell Caribbean owns 65.44 percent of the
U. S. company's stock. Shell Caribbean in turn is owned 60
percent by the Royal Dutch Petroleum Company, and 40 percent
by the Shell Transport and Trading Company of London. Thus
Dutch ownership of the U. S. Shell subsidiary is about 40 percent
and British about 26 percent. U. S. money was permitted to
finance most of Shell's early expansion in this country through
the sale of minority stock, amounting to about a third of the
shares.

The history of the Dutch company revolves about the Napo-
leonic Sir Henri Deterding, a Dutch clerk who became a British
subject after he merged the Dutch and British interests the better
to conduct a worldwide war against Standard Oil.[11]

Shell has large production interests in this country, its largest
refineries being in California, at Houston, and at Wood River,
Illinois (near St. Louis). British, Dutch, German, and Swiss
officials and technicians have been prominent in the management
and conduct of the U. S. company. The Royal Dutch/Shell Company was important in Mexico in the heyday of private exploitation and in Venezuela is second only to Standard of New Jersey.

Shell's early U. S. history before World War I brought out
anti-British reactions when it seemed to some Americans that the
then world-predominant British-Dutch company was trying to
conquer the American market. At one time it aimed to absorb
Union Oil, the most important California company next to
Standard. Its Roxana subsidiary was the original Shell producer
in the mid-continent fields.

While U. S. Shell has its own board of directors, Sir Francis
Hopwood of Royal Dutch/Shell is chairman, and H. Bloemgarten
of the Royal Dutch company also has a seat. F. A. C. Guépin of
Royal Dutch is chairman of the board of Shell Chemical, a
subsidiary of the U. S. Shell company.

STANDARD OF CALIFORNIA

Standard Oil of California is the petroleum giant of the West Coast. Although sixth ranking company in assets, California is third in earnings in the industry, thanks to enormously profitable foreign investments and to its position as the second largest producer in this country.

Its markets include the entire Pacific Coast and intermountain area; its invasion of the north Atlantic seaboard in 1945 was the first disturbance of marketing relations there in twenty years.[12]

"Socal" pioneered in opening up the rich Arabian fields and admitted Texaco into partnership to gain markets in Asia and Africa. Later, its big brothers, Jersey and Socony, demanded "in" and were given 30 percent and 10 percent respectively. But Socal and Texaco run Bahrein without assistance, and the Caltex combine produces in the Far East as well. Their markets now range over the entire non-Soviet world.

With these foreign riches and its preeminent position on the West Coast, the San Francisco company realizes 17 cents profit on each dollar of sales.

The phenomenal rise of this company after its Arabian acquisition is reflected in net income—$36 million in 1943 and $212 million in 1954. While its production in California was constant in that period, the company's output in the Eastern Hemisphere soared from 5.7 million barrels to 326 million. Its share of the net income from the Eastern Hemisphere (mostly Arabia) was $117 million in 1954, based on an investment carried on the books at $25.6 million. However, Standard of California estimates the *value* of these holdings at nearly $400 million, without adding a penny for the oil underground.[13]

SINCLAIR

Sinclair built itself up to seventh position among the majors largely because its founder, Harry F. Sinclair, had pushing ways which may have been at times considered somewhat dubious. Sinclair's rise in the past thirty years has been hailed as proof that competition still rules; some of the competitive methods used brought the name "Teapot Dome" into national notoriety and got Sinclair himself six months in jail.

Bold wildcatting in Oklahoma, audacious financing, and picking up remnants of the old Standard Prairie Oil & Gas firm put the company, known in the 1930s as Consolidated Oil, among the blue-chippers. After his trying experiences with the Republicans over a Wyoming deal that somehow never panned out very well for anybody, Sinclair was inclined to look with an approving eye on the Roosevelt New Deal. In this, as in many other instances, he broke step with the industry. He was the first—and only—oil magnate ever to sign a national agreement with the Oil Workers International Union. Repeatedly, he delighted in breaking the Standard of New Jersey wage program by giving more advantageous terms to the union.[14]

Sinclair is mainly a domestic firm, strong in production in the mid-continent and the Rockies and with far-flung markets. On the Pacific Coast it teams up with the other maverick of the industry—Cities Service—in control of Richfield.[15]

The company is wildcatting in Ethiopia and Italian Somaliland and enjoys some production in Venezuela. Its domestic marketing (together with Richfield) covers every state in the Union except Montana.

Sinclair, having arrived near the top, is through with its maverick role. It is now a champion of big business and a foe of big government, in the words of its president, P. C. Spencer, a one-time Wyoming cowhand, in 1954 president also of the American Petroleum Institute. "The times cry for what might be termed business statesmanship. And this kind of statesmanship certainly should be led by business management. Sinclair is ready and willing to do its part in this vital crusade."

CITIES SERVICE

The other maverick of oil, Cities Service, today ranks ninth in the industry, a monument to the unorthodox financing methods of Henry L. Doherty, who started out as a utilities promoter, got into natural gas, and wound up in oil.

Frenzied finance was the keynote of Cities Service and in the

1930s it was touch and go whether the company would survive. Old-time employees take a lot of the credit for its survival, for they bought shares and then watched their value sink to almost nothing in the Great Depression. Dealers and big customers, too, were led into the Doherty scheme of bootstrap financing.

In 1944, the company was given a choice by the government of being a public utilities firm or an oil company. Knowing where the money is, it plumped for oil.

Cities Service is mainly a domestic company. It looks askance at the flood of foreign oil, amounting early in 1953, Chairman W. Alton Jones said, to a sixth of domestic production and 13 percent over the 1952 average. It was through suspicious eyes, then, that members of the world oil cartel saw Chairman Jones ambling about Teheran at the height of Anglo-Iranian's difficulties. The British suspected U. S. treachery; the U. S. cartel members recalled Cities Service's part in breaking the Standard-Shell boycott on Mexico.

The company markets mainly in the eastern part of the country but is represented on the West Coast through joint control with Sinclair of Richfield. At Lake Charles, Louisiana, it teams up with Continental Oil in operating a big refinery.

PHILLIPS

Phillips is preeminent among oil companies in its huge holdings of natural gas in the great fields that stretch down from western Kansas into the Texas Panhandle. This is mainly responsible for its position as eighth in the industry. It is a new member in the billion-dollar corporation club, and fast climbing higher.

Phillips sells two billion cubic feet of natural gas each day in the year, a 50 percent rise within five years. It is also the leading producer of natural gasoline squeezed from natural gas, of liquefied petroleum gases (bottled gas), of carbon black (used for tires) extracted from gas, and is eminent in the petrochemical industry.[16]

Phillips markets its "66" products in the Rockies, the Mississippi River basin, and in Florida. It is proud of its "country boy" origin and keeps head office down in Bartlesville, Oklahoma. This does not prevent the DuPonts, as well as big New York and Boston interests, from being represented on the board.

SUN

Sun Oil is no great shakes as oil companies go (it would take thirteen Suns to make a Jersey), but it is distinctive. While some firms are anonymous like Jersey, and others, such as Gulf and Texas, arose after the Standard monopoly days, Sun is a tight little family outfit that didn't mind tangling with Rockefeller at the height of his power. But it wasn't much of a company then and perhaps John D. liked to have a few independents around just to prove that after all he only ran 85 percent of the industry —not 100.

Joseph N. Pew, Sr., was the founder of Sun, and control has remained in the family ever since, with seven Pews now on the directorate and Junior serving as chairman. With 85 percent of the stock in the hands of the 100 largest shareholders, Sun is outranked only by Shell as a tightly held concern. The Pew family holds the firm almost as a feudal possession, along with the subsidiary shipbuilding firm on the Delaware.

The Pews are famous as ultraconservative Philadelphia Republicans, prime fat-cats not only for the right wing of the party but for lunatic fringe groups. This conservatism spills over into some of their industrial outlook. When all the majors thought tetraethyl lead was *de rigueur* for their gasoline, Sunoco stubbornly held out, worked on its octanes through the Houdry process, and bragged that motorists could get just as good a gasoline for 2 cents a gallon less, without paying tribute to Standard of New Jersey and General Motors. But after the ethyl patent lapsed, Sunoco tardily joined the crowd.

Paternalism in employee relations has paid off for Sun. It has never had to bargain with the oil workers union, and it never will, as long as benevolent paternalism outbids industrial democracy.

Sun markets throughout the northeastern industrial belt from Indiana to the Atlantic, and in Florida. It is a heavy producer in the Southwest.

ATLANTIC

An oil company can be somewhat obscure and yet count its assets at more than half a billion, like Atlantic. Despite its name it is a chip off the original Standard block though now overshadowed by its bigger Standard brothers, Jersey, Socony, Indiana, and California.

This Philadelphia company refined and marketed in the old days from the Delaware southward along the coast. Now it produces in the Southwest and Venezuela and imports from the Middle East, while its markets have spread northward into New England.

Rockefeller interest is not heavy now in Atlantic, which is headed by a former Philadelphia milkman, Henderson Supplee, Jr.

TIDE WATER ASSOCIATED

Tide Water was one of the early firms which chose to fight Standard but later piped down when the monopoly bought a controlling interest. Rockefeller control has been largely washed out with the years. Now the Mission Corporation and the Getty interests, both of Los Angeles, with investments in many oil companies, are the largest stockholders, followed by an Amsterdam firm.

Tide Water markets its Veedol-Tydol lubricants over the entire country and most of the non-Soviet world, and gasoline in the middle Atlantic and New England states. The Associated firm, strong on the Pacific Coast, also markets in Hawaii and the Philippines. The merged firm ranks sixteenth in the industry in assets and even higher in sales.

CONTINENTAL

Continental is another of the old Standard firms in which Rockefeller interest has waned. Here, too, a Dutch investment firm is in an important position, as the second largest stockholder.

Continental was important in the Rockies as the Standard agent; after dissolution, J. P. Morgan merged the Marland interests at Ponca City, Oklahoma, with Continental and it

became an important factor in the mid-continent as well. Headquarters are now divided between Ponca City and Houston. The
company markets in the Rockies, the Mississippi River Basin, and
the Southwest.

Conoco's president, L. F. McCollum, a former Jersey man, is a
member of the board of J. P. Morgan & Co.

STANDARD OF OHIO

If Standard of New Jersey is the big brother of the Standard
firms, "the Standard Oil Company (an Ohio Corporation)," now
84 years old, is the daddy. Like most of the old Standard units,
Sohio ignored production and concerned itself with what were
then considered the key positions—refining and marketing. It
was one of the few of the old firms so limited in its area, and
after dissolution of the trust it slipped downhill.

W. T. Holliday, one of the few personalities in the industry
who ever seemed to germinate an idea outside of oil, became
its president in 1928. He has written articles in favor of world
federal government. He went to Harvard and brought in some
"longhairs" and "eggheads" to help him. One of them is now
Chairman S. A. Swensrud of Gulf. On their advice Sohio went
into production in the Southwest, far from its own stamping
grounds, and now seems to be a reasonably effective minor
among the majors.[17]

PURE

Pure Oil gets its name from a little company that managed to
weather the Standard Oil trust period and picked up after 1914
when it merged with Columbus Production.

Pure is one of the smaller majors, ranking fifteenth on the list,
and marketing mostly in the Middle West from the Mississippi
to the Alleghenies. Its production comes from the older fields in
the East and from Texas and the mid-continent.

It has long been known as a Dawes family corporation, with
Henry M. Dawes serving for many years as chairman of the
board, along with Sewell L. Avery of Montgomery Ward as a
director. Old-fashioned Chicagoland Republicanism dictated a

tough line during the New Deal. Its employees reacted by turning the company's slogan into "BE POOR WITH PURE."

Pure is a domestic operation with no foreign affiliates, suspicious
of the world cartel and of the government's "globaloney" concerns—à la *Chicago Tribune.*

UNION OIL

Union Oil illustrates the plight of a domestic company in direct
competition with a member of the world oil cartel. On the West
Coast, Union is an important producer and marketer, a rival of
Standard of California. But although its assets are a third of
California's, its profits are but 17 percent as large. Not for Union
is the cream to be skimmed from Arabian crude.

Union has been presumptuous enough to invade eastern
markets with a reputedly marvelous Triton motor oil, purple in
color, which outlasts any other oil produced, so it says. Such
advertising, implying that car owners need not change oil each
thousand miles, is regarded as "unethical" by the industry at large.

Union is based at Los Angeles, against Standard of California's
preference for San Francisco, a preference underscored by the
name of Standard's big refinery in the Los Angeles basin, El
Segundo. El Primero is at Richmond, on San Francisco Bay.

Dillon Reed and Bankers Trust of New York are represented
on Union's board, on which also sat Herbert Hoover, Jr., sent by
the government as a trouble shooter to Iran after Mossadegh's fall
and then named Undersecretary of State. Reese H. Taylor,
president of Union, is a power in the industry.

OHIO OIL

Ohio Oil, originally a producing company, still has its headquarters at Findlay, center of the Ohio fields when they were
important in the early 1900s. All the principal shareholders are
listed under the Rockefeller name, and the family is credited
with 13 percent ownership in this most profitable of the lesser
majors.

The company markets in the Midwest east of the Mississippi
and is an important producer wherever oil is found in the United
States and Canada.

THE MINORS

Ensconced in various niches of the industry exist scores of companies, many substantial in assets and profits. Some are completely integrated from production to marketing in a limited territory, others specialize in production, in lubricants or other fields.

One group of companies, mostly integrated, is encamped in the Oklahoma-mid-continent areas; another group, mostly producers, along the Gulf Coast. Others range from the western Pennsylvania fields, specializing in lubricants, through the Ohio Valley and out into the Rockies and the West Coast.

OIL AND THE BANKS

Armed with tremendous profits and fortified by a policy of plowing back a half or more of earnings into plant, the major companies are mostly independent of outside financial control. The old days, when indigent companies camped on J. P. Morgan's doorstep for handouts, are gone so far as most of the oil companies are concerned. For the Rockefeller companies, of course, that plight never existed. Gulf early became a province in the Mellon empire and Continental was dependent on Morgan. But nowadays it is the banks and investment companies which tip the hat to the petroleum companies.

Chase National, recently become through merger Chase Manhattan, often known as the Rockefeller bank, is still the nation's leading petroleum bank. At least sixteen of the better known companies use its services. These include not only Standard companies such as Socony, Indiana, California, and Sohio, but non-Rockefeller companies such as Sun, Skelly, Mid-Continent, Lion, and Continental.

Guaranty Trust caters to more than a dozen of the leading companies, both Standard and non-Standard. Bankers Trust and Hanover are also leading oil banks. In Chicago, Continental-Illinois and First National specialize in petroleum affairs.

The oil bank par excellence remains Chase Manhattan; its special petroleum department publishes an annual financial analysis of 30 oil companies (since 1953, 35), a standard handbook, and furnishes special services both to companies and investors.

MINOR OIL COMPANIES, 1954

Name	Headquarters	Type	Assets (000 omitted)	Gross Income (000 omitted)	Net Income (000 omitted)
Deep Rock	Cushing, Okla.	Integrated	$ 34,300	$ 38,685	$ 2,481
Warren Petroleum	Tulsa, Okla.	Natural Gas	141,525	112,406	8,930
Colorado Oil & Gas	Denver, Colo.	Integrated	32,855	3,693	302
Anderson-Pritchard	Oklahoma City, Okla.	Integrated	55,413	54,723	3,254
Crown Central	Baltimore, Md.	Integrated	33,594	52,432	1,401
Houston Oil	Houston, Texas	Production	87,581	32,706	6,488
Texas Gulf	Houston, Texas	Production	33,805	13,327	5,246
Louisiana Land & Exploration	New Orleans, La.	Lease-Royalty	25,729	23,863	12,929
Texas Pacific	Fort Worth, Tex.	Production	49,796	21,876	7,856
Chicago Corp.	Fort Worth, Tex.	Integrated	100,689	48,654	5,321
Bay Petroleum	Denver, Colo.	Integrated	29,599	46,099	1,794
Shamrock	Amarillo, Texas	Integrated	58,231	38,175	7,408
Lion	El Dorado, Ark.	Integrated	147,648	98,585	11,071
South Penn Oil	Bradford, Pa.	Lubricants	61,259	52,616	5,057
Quaker State	Oil City, Pa.	Lubricants	31,274	45,744	2,113
Ashland	Ashland, Ky.	Integrated	151,923	227,948	6,628
Hancock	Long Beach, Calif.	Integrated	46,285	15,351	6,881
Richfield	Los Angeles, Calif.	Integrated	289,904	223,311	25,571
Honolulu	San Francisco, Calif.	Production	66,341	30,550	10,236
Signal	Los Angeles, Calif.	Production	97,206	50,220	9,313
Pacific Western	Los Angeles, Calif.	Production	147,739	14,621	12,518
Superior	Los Angeles, Calif.	Production	142,435	76,137	10,360
Amerada	New York, N. Y.	Production	112,518	84,996	19,778
Barber	New York, N. Y.	Production	38,260	8,004	914
Plymouth	Pittsburgh, Pa.	Integrated	81,375	90,920	6,759
Standard of Kentucky	Louisville, Ky.	Marketing	103,537	254,469	12,385
Seaboard	New York, N. Y.	Production	56,346	39,399	7,470

(From annual reports)

1954 FINANCIAL STATEMENT
(In Millions)

Company	Assets	Gross Operating Income	Net Income
Standard of New Jersey	$6,615	$5,661	$585
Socony-Vacuum	2,257	1,689	184
Standard of Indiana	2,187	1,660	117
Gulf	1,969	1,705	183
Texas Company	1,946	1,574	226
Standard of California	1,678	1,113	212
Sinclair	1,187	1,021	75
Phillips	1,093	795	76
Cities Service	1,054	813	44
Shell	1,042	1,312	121
Atlantic	612	596	41
Union	511	350	36
Sun	495	660	40
Continental	480	500	42
Pure	411	388	31
Tide Water Associated	396	459	35
Ohio	325	248	38
Sunray	300	125	23
Standard of Ohio	295	304	19
Skelly	292	211	29
Mid-Continent	186	164	13

(From annual reports; figures rounded to nearest million.)

It also publishes an annual financial analysis of the industry. For 1953, the industry's gross assets were totaled at $43.2 billion, ranking it as the biggest manufacturing industry of all and exceeded in the economy as a whole only by agriculture, railroads, and public utilities—all of them, incidentally, dependent on petroleum for motive power.

The development of the industry between 1934 and 1953 is dramatically shown in the figures for Chase's 30 companies:

	1953	1934
Total income	$20,900,000,000	$3,527,000,000
Net income	2,258,000,000	157,000,000
Net as percent of total	10.8	4.5
Dividends	961,000,000	128,000,000
Dividends as percent of net	42.6	81.7
Return on capital	12.3	2.9

In the span from 1934 to 1950, more than $121 billion passed through the hands of Chase's 30 companies and their net income was $12 billion. Income taxes, thought by many to be confiscatory, took in seventeen years only a little more than $4 billion from the tills of these concerns. So little were they indebted to outside sources for capital that only two-thirds of a billion was diverted to interest. The $12 billion allowed for depreciation, depletion, amortization and retirements neatly matched the net profits. In addition nearly $7 billion of the profit was reinvested in the business, leaving something like $5 billion for cash dividends.

Part II

From Field to Refinery

4

The Law of the Jungle

THERE was no doubt in the minds of the enterprising gentlemen of the Pennsylvania Rock Oil Company who financed the drilling of the world's first oil well that the greenish-black stuff that bubbled to the surface was theirs. They owned the land (near Titusville, Pennsylvania, on Oil Creek) and therefore the oil. That was according to the old English custom that land ownership went down into the earth, as far as man could reach.

But what was so clear to Edwin L. Drake, who promoted the drilling of that first oil well, and to his employers, was soon clouded as hundreds of eager drillers began puncturing the earth's skin all around the Drake well. It became evident that the petroleum lay in a pool (or a stream that flowed from western Pennsylvania into West Virginia, as some then thought). Whoever could first get it sucked up to the surface through his hole possessed it. For oil is a wandering mineral, ignoring the lay of lots, plats, and surveys on the surface above.

The question of ownership became urgent. Lawyers searched their books for an answer. They found that the common law gave minerals to the owners of the surface, but this was little help, for minerals, as known in previous centuries, kept still. Little good it did a man to claim ownership of the petroleum under his property if his neighbors were busy getting it out through their wells. To whom did *that* oil belong?

Finding no more pertinent precedent to guide them, bar and bench turned to the law governing the ownership of wild animals: *res ferae naturae*. He who captures the wild beast owns it. As one authority claimed, citing a quite different kind of oil, he who lodges his harpoon first in the whale may claim it.[1] And so the law of the chase and the jungle was enforced with a vengeance. Get your neighbor's oil before he gets yours. Naturally it roused high enthusiasm among these later pioneers prying open the subsoil of a continent. The fur-bearing animals, the forests, even the soil, had fallen victim to predators eager for the quick kill. Oil was next.[2]

The rule caused astonishment in non-Anglo-Saxon lands. There the sovereign—first the king and later the nation—owned the underground minerals. If the sovereign allowed exploitation of the subsoil, his share was termed the "royalty"—a term persisting to this day even in lands of the Anglo-Saxon law.[3]

Some with a squeamish sense of moral values questioned whether it was right or wise to permit the private and casual appropriation of a resource that evaded staid property rules. Their questionings carried no weight in court or legislature, yet they have never downed. Obscure farmer-labor parties and a handful of Jeremiahs, fearful of the sack of nature's heritage, have called for national ownership of the subsoil, but nature's oil has been too readily converted into private gold to permit common sense to interfere with greed.

The law of capture, appropriate to the jungle, the desert, and the high seas, has ruled petroleum ever since. The hunters of oil have roamed the hills of western Pennsylvania, the plains of Kansas and Oklahoma, the salt marshes and offshore lands of the Gulf Coast, the lakes and deserts of Venezuela and Arabia. Everywhere it has been hunted as a wild animal, and the law of the jungle has entered into the heart and sinew of the industry. The sordid and bloody story has been told in local and world wars, in revolutions and corruption, in continuing world turmoil.

Sardonically, it should be noted that in this hapless slaughter of the wild animal, petroleum, as much was hopelessly gutted and lost in the earth as ever was pulled to the surface. As much money has been sunk into wells and in efforts, military and otherwise, to corner their wealth, as ever was realized from them.

Oil has been described as fossilized sunlight that fell on the seas. That means that primitive animal and plant life, such as plankton, buried along ancient beaches in Paleozoic and Mesozoic times, 10 to 400 million years ago, decomposed after convulsions of the planet buried and then lifted these ancient strands. So today oil is found in Wyoming, as well as off the shores of Louisiana. Great pressures compacted the oil-bearing sands into present shales and limestones, and pressures of rock have squeezed the liquids into pools. And it is also presumed that biochemical processes may have taken a hand.

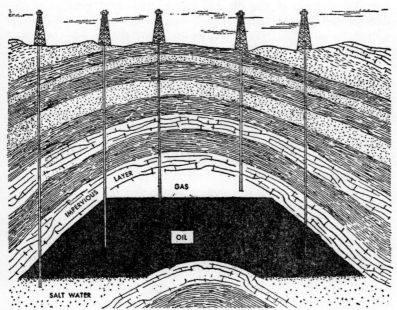

(From *Oil For Today . . . And For Tomorrow,* published by Interstate Oil Compact Commission, Oklahoma City, 1953, p. 18.)

Figure 1: A typical gas, oil and salt water structure. The well at the left will tap only salt water; the fourth well will bring only gas to the surface.

The "pools" are by no means merely oil and gas in spaces between the rocks. Rather, "oil sands," the softer porous sandstones and limestones, sponge up the liquid. If there is a caprock above and a layer of impervious rock below, then the oil and gas are caught in a natural reservoir, along with the old ocean water. Most of the richest deposits seem to border the seas: the

Gulf of Mexico, Lake Maracaibo and the Caribbean, the Persian Gulf, the Caspian.

The accompanying illustration shows a rather common type of reservoir with the characteristics of a "dome." Sometimes gas is at the top of the "oil sand"; more usually, the oil and gas are mixed, with the salt water lying at lower levels. A hole sunk at the right or the left in this field will strike only water; a well near the margin of the oil will bring up only a portion of the deposit and then go "salt." A well sunk to the top of the oil sands will fetch only gas. These are the hazards the geophysicist and driller face.

Oil, gas, and water all lie under great pressure from the surrounding rock structures. Once a hole is punctured from the surface, the gas rushes out, carrying with it oil, sand, and rock— the typical "gusher" of a generation ago. In the old days—and not so long ago, either—pools were allowed to vent their pressure at full force (flush production). Within a short time the gas was expended, the pressure was gone, and the pumps began to work. At the outset, the gas keeps the viscosity of the oil to a kerosene-like consistency; once the gas is gone, the oil becomes much stickier, so sticky that soon even the pumps are unable to coax it to the bottom of the hole. Then as much as two-thirds to three-quarters of the oil is left in the ground, each grain of sand or minute cavity in rock holding on to globules of petroleum. The best engineering techniques today regulate the flow of gas to maintain pressure in the reservoir; sometimes the gas ascending to the surface is forced down again to maintain the pressure; and the pressure of the underlying water can be used to force the oil and gas upward.

If a single operator controls the acreage above this pool or "field," engineering techniques can provide for "maximum efficient recovery" (MER). But it is also likely that several, or hundreds of, farms may cut up the ownership among them; or, for a petroleum engineer's nightmare, the field may underlie a town or city (Oklahoma City, Kilgore, Long Beach).

At this point, the rule of capture enters. Each owner must see that wells are drilled upon his property to capture as much of the pool as possible before his neighbors beat him to it. Actually he will drill the wells along the margins of his property to make sure that he will get as much of his neighbor's oil as possible; his neighbors will reciprocate with "offset" wells along their margins. This is the picture of country drilling, but in the towns the situation becomes more incredible. There, the owner of every lot will drill at least one well; possibly several along the margins of his plot of ground. After his neighbors get through offsetting, the very legs of the derricks may intertwine in wild abandon. Signal Hill in Long Beach is perhaps the worst specimen of "town lot drilling."

WASTE

Most of the gold the Spanish kings claimed from the mines of the New World still exists—in coins, bars, and ornaments. Even the base metal, iron, returns again and again to the furnace as scrap. But oil is fleeting. Once above the earth it is doomed to burn in motors and furnaces, and is gone, not to be replaced short of a geologic age.

This indispensable fuel for airplanes and lubricant for all wheels is condemned by its very usefulness. As a fuel, it can flow in pipes; it leaves no ash; it frees bunker space in ships for cargo and makes possible longer nonstop runs for locomotives. More than half of all U. S. energy comes from the rock oils and gases, the equivalent, it is said, of the muscle power of 22 billion human beings. Coal—bulky, wasting in transport and storage, burdened with ash, hard to mine, hard to handle—can do most everything petroleum can except lubricate, but sluggish research has yet to liquefy or gasify it cheaply enough to permit competition with oil. So while the reserves of coal and lignite suffice for generations and the definitely known future of oil can be measured in a span of years, it is oil, not coal, which is offered as a sacrifice on the altars of industry and commerce.

This sacrifice, involving human energy and material wealth, begins before a drop of the liquid has been taken from the underground. In our own land, the wastes of the gamble and the hunt attend the search for oil; once found, it is then the hapless victim of greedy hands that skim the subsurface and doom the rest to remain locked in the earth. Across the earth, the gamble and the hunt have stirred not merely the greed of individuals but the hatred of nations.

It would seem that the more precious and irreplaceable the resource, the more wastefully it must be exploited. Long before the drill spuds the well, the waste has started. Before the Securities Act of 1933 was passed, swindlers flooded the country with flamboyant prospectuses; "investors" ruefully plastered their walls with gaudy certificates of oil promotions. Many a prospective well scratched deeper into the pockets of the gullible than it ever did into the earth. In 1918-1922, new oil companies with a capitalization of $2 billion were organized each year; most of the money thus raised was pilfered. In these more discreet days, the Wall Street investment houses have lists of oil stocks recommended, in their jargon, "essentially for appreciation," there often being little to discuss in the way of earnings. Right now, Canadian oil stocks are the will o' the wisp for promoters. The money sunk into oil promotions in the past ninety years runs easily into the billions.

Alongside the swindlers marched the army of earnest adventurers who hoped by one lucky strike, following the example of the Forty-niners, to win a life of leisure. Playing hunches, they drilled on a shoestring in ten thousand "poor boy" locations with secondhand tools, a rusty boiler and promises to pay, when and if. They were the legion of the wildcatters, gambling for the unseen. Just often enough someone hit oil to rekindle the flame of hope in the breasts of all.

Up to 1929, according to Kemnitzer and Arnold, petroleum geologists, 95 percent of all wildcat wells—those drilled in unproved territory—were unproductive "dry holes."[4] E. DeGolyer, among the most eminent of petroleum geologists, estimates that the all-time chances of a strike stand at 1 in 30 or 40. With better techniques the chances have improved, but these bar the "poor boys." Even so, only one of nine wildcats drilled in 1945-1950 was successful; in 1950, some 8000 dry holes were sunk. It is estimated that the odds are 44 to 1 against a wildcat opening a field of a million barrels; 1000 to 1 that a field may develop 50 million barrels.[5]

The wildcatter's cupidity is but a minor factor in the record of waste; the legacy of the Anglo-Saxon law governing the surface owner's claim to the underground resources, complicated by *res ferae*, has been the real taproot of waste. The accompanying illustration maps the wells in a section of the Cushing, Oklahoma,

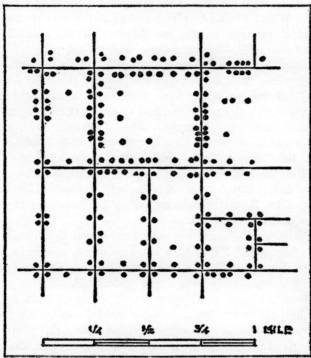

(From *The Oil Industry and the Competitive System*, by George Ward Stocking, Houghton Mifflin, 1925, p. 171.)

Figure 2: Map showing the relation of oil wells to property lines in the Cushing, Oklahoma, oil field. Nearly all the wells are "offset" along property lines to drain as much of the neighbors' oil as possible.

field. The lines show the private property divisions; the dots indicate the wells. There is no well in the center of any property; each owner places them to "offset" the neighbors' wells so as to get as much of their oil as possible before they get his.[6]

This blunderbussing of the earth heaps up needless capital

wastes in unneeded wells; in turn the needless wells quickly exhaust the gas and water pressures of the pool, the pumps soon go to work, the turbid oil robbed of its leavening gas clings to the sands, and perhaps 80 percent is left unclaimed at last.

The Ranger, Texas, field was pillaged, and within a few years its boom towns turned to ghost towns; but it was no exception. Oil was discovered in the Burkburnett, Texas, field in 1918. Within three weeks 56 wells were drilling and practically every lot in town was open sesame to wealth—or so it seemed. Promoters profited themselves and their printers, if no one else. With so much oil coming in, far from markets, in a new field with no storage facilities, the price dropped so low that oil was spilled on the ground, and, marketless, was drained into the Red River. The capital waste in excess wells was estimated at $26 million. After a while the tall grass grew again where once hope had gushed high. The melancholy story could be repeated for each of a hundred fields; names once glittering with promise—Desdemona, Homer, Kern River, Smackover, Orcutt, Tonkawa, Mexia—are now the concern of historians only.

A million wells—more or less—have been drilled in this country, of which some 400,000 are still producing, mostly in driblets of a few barrels a day. In one year, 1938, the cost of drilling 4000-5000 unnecessary wells was estimated at $100 million, equivalent to a gross production tax of nearly 10 cents a barrel.[7] If only half of the million wells were needed—in itself a fantastic exaggeration—the loss in wasted capital across the years would be as high as $5 billion. In the Oklahoma City field, discovered in 1928, an oil company official estimated that $3 million would have drilled all the wells needed, instead of the $70 million actually spent.[8] In 1937-1938, half the 60,000 wells drilled were declared to be unneeded. At $20,000 each, they represented a loss of $300 million.

The average U. S. well produces only 12 barrels a day, or 4500 a year. In the Kirkuk field in Iraq, the average well produced 600,000 barrels in 1935; in the Haft Kell field in Iran the average was 675,000. The great Potrero de Llano field in Mexico yielded 100 million barrels in ten years, mostly from one well.

One must add, to the billions lost in squandered capital to

drill unneeded wells, the billions more wasted because the very proliferation of wells lowered the yield of the fields. All the beer can be emptied from a keg through one bung as well as through a dozen. But if the bung empties through the top of the keg, as with an oil well, about all that will come out is the foam, and if there are twelve bungs the foaming won't last long. In an oil pool the great pressures of gas can be expected to push the oil upward, but if the gas is allowed to vent itself uncontrolled, drilling more holes exhausts the pressure all the more quickly.

In 1915, the U. S. Bureau of Mines estimated that 80 to 90 percent of the oil was left in the ground when the wells were abandoned. Better methods of recovery today bring a third or so to the surface. The National Resources Planning Board estimated that a 50 percent increase in recovery, to bring total recovery to 45 percent of the oil underground, would save 600 million barrels a year, worth in 1938 a dollar a barrel. The board's experts estimated the total waste at one billion dollars a year (capital loss and loss of production). In the Midway field in California in 1910-1911 the waste was so appalling that it was suggested that the unwanted production be burned on the ground.[9]

Another estimate, by a spokesman for the western Pennsylvania oil producers, was that 100 billion barrels would be left in the ground when the wells operating throughout the nation in 1945 are abandoned. Compare that with the total of 28 billion barrels which had been brought to the surface before 1945, and the 20 billion then known to be still recoverable.[10]

Dean Henry M. Bates of the University of Michigan Law School summed it up in 1935:

> The losses thus caused [by the rule of capture] unquestionably mount into the billions of dollars and constitute the most reckless, extravagant waste of natural resources which even the American people have been guilty of. Moreover, this mad and greedy race for wealth has made it impossible in this country to adopt intelligent and effective methods of production, the cost of which has thus been made greatly and unnecessarily high.[11]

The *Tulsa World,* published near the center of the pillage, commented in 1926:

> This western world of ours has never seen a more bewilderingly wasteful business than the oil industry. The wanton waste of it has been a scandal for years. There is no disposition to temper that statement with the slightest qualification.[12]

If most of the oil is doomed to lie uncaptured in the earth, at any rate secondary recovery methods some day may reclaim some of it—at a high cost. There is no such hope for the gas which is gone. Once the earth's skin is punctured, there is no problem in getting the gas; the problem rather is to control its escape. If as late as 1915, as the Bureau of Mines guessed, 80-90 percent of the oil was still left in the earth, it is even more certain that more than 90 percent of all the gas had been flared to the sky. Its main use was to push oil to the surface. After it had done that, it was just a nuisance, usually burned at the end of a pipe but sometimes allowed to pass on in its natural state until immense palls hung over the fields. These could become so dense that automobiles were forbidden entry to the field for fear of explosions.[13]

The Cushing, Oklahoma, field wasted enough gas in 1913 to supply New York City with all its domestic fuel.[14] This gas waste, valued at $75,000 a day, was tolerated since there were no gas pipe lines or storage facilities, in order to produce oil valued at less than $25,000. A Bureau of Mines expert estimated in 1913 the value of wasted gas in Oklahoma exceeded the value of all the oil produced in that state.

From 1922 to 1934, an average of 1¼ billion cubic feet of gas was wasted each day in the oil fields, for a total of six trillion cubic feet, the equivalent of 250 million tons of coal (and this was the kind of fuel that did not need to be mined laboriously by hand). In 1944, more than 600 billion cubic feet of Texas natural gas was wasted out of 900 billion produced; in 1950, nearly 400 billion, of 1.3 trillion produced.

Even this looked small in contrast to the pillage of east Texas, beginning in 1930. Of the first 24,000 wells drilled in that field, at least 21,000 were wholly unnecessary, the National Resources Planning Board estimated.[15] That represented a capital waste of $250 million. DeGolyer said that east Texas had at least eight times too many wells. The Texas Railroad Commission decreed that there should be but one well to every ten acres, and then granted exemptions for no less than 20,000 wells! Between 1932 and 1938, the number of wells went up 300 percent and production 20 percent.[16]

Ralph J. Watkins, economic adviser to the National Resources Planning Board, summed it up:

> The grave waste of capital and of irreplaceable resources that obtains in this industry inhere in the economic organization of the industry, including multiplicity of ownership and operating units and the legal framework—that is, the rule of capture—within which the industry must operate. Consequently, responsibility for this waste must be assessed against us all collectively; that is, against Government, including the courts, since Government must determine this framework.[17]

Such frankness was unremunerative; the National Resources Planning Board, particular object of the industry's hatred, disappeared under attacks from private enterprisers, and the subject of planning became taboo.

Back in 1919, E. Mackay Edgar, a British petroleum engineer, peered into the American future with uncanny insight:

> The size and magnificence of the American inheritance and the rapidity and wantonness with which it has been squandered are an almost incredible commentary on human folly. On no country, perhaps, had "affluent Fortune emptied all her horn" in such varied and bountiful profusion, and no country could have shown itself more utterly ungrateful. The Americans have dealt with their resources, and deal with them today, in the pioneer spirit of sheer unmitigated pillage. . . .
>
> America has recklessly and in sixty years run through a legacy, that, properly conserved, should have lasted her for at least a century and a half. . . . But the effects of fifty years of negligence and inefficiency are now becoming visible.

Just when Americans have become accustomed to use twenty times as much oil per head as is used in Great Britain; just when invention has indefinitely expanded the need for oil in industry; just when it has grown to be as common and as true a saying that "oil is King" as it was twenty years ago that steel was king; just when the point has been reached where oil controls money instead of money controlling oil— the United States finds her chief source of domestic supply beginning to dry up and a time approaching when instead of ruling the oil market of the world she will have to compete with other countries for her share of the crude product.[18]

Edgar wrote before the great discoveries of the 1920s and 1930s, but on balance his words were nevertheless true, for the enormous wastes of that period matched the discoveries, and it took only a decade of hot and cold war to change the United States from an oil-exporting to an oil-importing nation.

5

Lease and Royalty

IF YOU have oil under your land, you are lucky. You may also be rich. If the deposit is lush and you are a west Texas cattle baron, you will quickly advance to front rating among the parvenus. Hollywood will be your oyster and Cannes your resort.

So far as you are concerned, the whole thing is quite accidental. You didn't put the oil there, you didn't discover it there, and neither will you take it out. You will merely sign a document, sometimes a Lease 88, and manna will fall from the heavens.

This kind of manna reaches a cash value of one billion dollars a year, according to Sun Oil statisticians, paid out by the oil and gas industry for leases which give access to your land and for royalties if oil is found.[1] The American Petroleum Institute insists that Sun is too modest; the industry in 1948 paid out $800 million for royalties and $400 million for lease and bonus payments. At that rate it would seem conservative to estimate that in 1952 lease and royalty payments exceeded $1.5 billion.

Ten percent of the entire area of the country is blanketed by such payments. A third of all Texas is covered by oil leases;[2] Florida, California, Kansas, New Mexico, Oklahoma, and Louisiana are other leading lease states, in that order.[3]

Back in 1925, E. W. Marland, the big Ponca City, Oklahoma, oil man, estimated that $4 billion had been paid in royalty, and that the annual rate was $200 million. Accepting the figures of all these authorities, it seems safe to place total payments since 1859 at around $15 billion.

When geologic scouts report that a territory may be promising, the company sends out "lease hounds" to round up "acreage." Assuming that this is wildcat territory, the leases may provide a payment of 10 cents to $2 an acre a year. Lease 88, the standard form, will stipulate, in deference to the law of capture, that if oil is discovered, the lessee must drill if it is apparent that the lessor's oil is being drained off. Lease 88 provides usually that seven-eighths of all oil produced goes to the company; the remaining eighth is "royalty" oil to the landowner's account. In the ground, crude is worth about a dollar a barrel; when it is hoisted to the surface it is paid for at the "posted price" for the field. There is only one posted price and no shopping around for better offers. There aren't any better offers. The posted price takes into consideration the gravity of the crude; the lighter it is, the higher the price.[4]

If oil has been discovered before the lease hound goes to work his job is harder. Then he may have to pay $1 an acre, or much higher, if the acreage is near the discovery well. In addition he may also pay a bonus if the prospect seems hot.

The newer leases often contain no provision that the lessee must drill by a certain date. That is left to the company's discretion and the chances are of course that a drill will never bite through the lessor's land. The newer leases may actually excuse the lessee from drilling even if the lessor's oil is being drained. In lieu thereof he may get a percentage of the oil taken from the field, in accordance with the estimate of geologists as to how much may be coming from under the lessor's land. This is at best an informed guess and the lessor often feels he is being gypped.[5]

Periodically the "lease fever" hits unclaimed territories after a wildcat has been brought in. Within a year after the discovery well of the Williston Basin had opened a new field in 1951, four-fifths of all North Dakota had been placed under lease. Shell held 8.5 million acres, Standard of Indiana 4 million, Amerada and Phillips 1.8 million each, Standard of California 3.7 million. Other companies rushed in to lease what they could.[6]

It was estimated by mid-1951 that $75 million had already been paid for leases in the Williston Basin. Mineral half-rights near wells sold for $75 an acre (a half-right to the minerals under an acre entitles the holder to half of the one-eighth royalty on any oil that may be drawn from it). Leases formerly bid at 10 cents an acre climbed to a dollar, and as high as $25 near proved wells.[7]

In every lessee's and lessor's breast rose high the hope of riches. In the words of E. I. Thompson, executive vice-president of the Texas Independent Producers & Royalty Owners, it's still possible to get rich overnight in the oil business. "It's a matter of percentage. If you keep playing the percentage you're bound to hit sooner or later."[8] It's the same story they tell in Reno, with the slot machines.

While the billion or more paid out yearly in lease and royalty is carried on the oil companies' books as an expense, this expenditure earns political returns of high cash value. Not only every lessor in the land, but the legion of those who hope that oil lies hidden under their properties, are staunch defenders of the rule of capture, and therefore of the companies who do the capturing. Since half the territory of the United States overlies sedimentary basins where there is a possibility of oil, the lightning may strike almost anywhere. This enormously powerful body of property owners, each receiving or hoping for lease and royalty payments, perhaps accounts for the lack of any serious proposal that the rule of capture be abandoned and a less wasteful policy instituted. Public ownership of the subsoil would mean too much private loss.

The private gain resembles more the spin of the lottery wheel than the reward of virtuous labor. It is the biggest gamble in the country, but one which stirs no pious protest from the pulpit or frown from the bench. The $15 billion paid so far to those who did nothing to earn it excites no wonder, much less remonstrance —except in case the land belongs, in the old Indian Territory, to a "blanket" Indian or his tribe. Then the sight of a man used to a pony riding a Cadillac, and living in a showy mansion after a life in a rude sod shack, apparently disturbs the envious, and many a tale is told of *such* unearned wealth and the ease with which white leeches separate the Indians from their inappropriate riches.

In the leasing of federal mineral lands, future generations may marvel that even when we had the chance to discard the rule of capture, we refused. The fact is that anyone may lease federal lands suspected to overlay petroleum and then proceed to hawk his lease to the highest bidder.[9] A news dispatch of November 17, 1951, from Santa Fe is typical. The U. S. Bureau of Land Management was reported to be swamped with 20,000 bids for the leasing of 81 tracts being opened for oil and gas exploration. The figure was only an estimate, since the staff was measuring the stacks of bids rather than counting them.

Most appropriate for this venture in government-sponsored gambling was the use of a lottery system to winnow out the 81 winners from the 20,000 claimants. The luck was not confined to the 81 winners, however, as hundreds had formed share-and-share-alike pools, so that many tracts had multiple lessees. These got their leases for 50 cents an acre. Many turned around and sold their leases to oil companies for $10 to $15 an acre, oil sight unseen. Those who held on hoped to hit the jackpot and get a cut on the value of the oil recovered—or nothing.

"A good share of these people don't know an oil lease from a driver's license," commented J. A. Delany, the government officer in charge of what is known as "land management."[10]

If the federal leasing system has aspects of an outright racket, the outright racketeers have not been slow in seeing the point. From time to time the Department of the Interior finds it necessary to warn would-be lessees that "any qualified citizen" may file applications for leases and that there is no need to hire intermediaries. Nevertheless, a secondary racket rides the back of the primary; advertisers proclaim that for a mere $100 to $200 they can help prospects obtain leases which may unlock untold wealth.

Some 4 million acres of public lands were under lease in 1945 for oil and gas exploration, and production was estimated at 5 percent of the national total. At that time, $125 million had been realized by the federal government in royalties from the leases in 25 years, of which $68 million went into the federal reclamation fund and $48 million was given to the states. It was estimated that there were 1615 million barrels of oil in reserve under public lands in the chief western oil states. In 1944, nearly half the oil recovered from public lands paid a royalty of only 5 percent, compared to the usual 12½ percent paid to private landowners.[11]

In 1952 the federal government received $28.5 million in oil and gas royalties. Crude oil production was 93 million barrels.

Even the low royalties accruing to the government on its own oil were too high to suit the corporations. President A. C. Mattei of Honolulu Oil, industry spokesman at Congressional hearings in 1945, urged that royalties be further reduced. In any event, he argued, such income was chicken feed for a government which counted its tax needs in the tens of billions. He did not believe that "the revenue of the Government, as revenue, was the all-important point in the determination of government royalties." The important point, apparently, was to let the companies at the oil.[12]

While government royalties are on a sliding scale, the usual private royalty is one-eighth. This fraction comes down from the royalty paid in the old western Pennsylvania fields, when it was assumed that the operator would clear about 25 percent and that it was fair to split 50-50 with the landowner.[13] It has been convenient for the companies to continue this figure, although its relevance is outmoded. The western Pennsylvania wells were small producers and costs were high; the wells of Oklahoma, Texas, and California are usually relatively big producers, and profits have usually been far above 25 percent. But the producer, who has the money to venture, necessarily holds the whip hand over the owner, to whom even a small royalty is a windfall.

That the federal oil lands might be kept in reserve as private lands approach exhaustion, or be worked by a federal corporation to pioneer in true conservation practices, and used as a yardstick to measure the efficiency, social and otherwise, of private exploitation, has never been seriously considered. There are too many who covet the trophies of the chase after the fugacious mineral.

6

Conservation

MOST people conserve when there is too little; the oil industry only "conserves" when there is too much. In fact, the very word "conservation" when applied to oil must be understood in a Pickwickian sense.

The problem of "conservation" first became urgent with the opening of the east Texas field after 1930. When this stupendously rich field began dumping its burden on the market during the Great Depression, the industry was faced with stark ruin through abundance. It was then that "conservation" came into its own— not to conserve the oil but to conserve the industry's profitability. Understanding the word in this sense, as the oil industry itself does, we may henceforth dispense with the quotation marks.

The purpose of conservation is to limit production to that level which assures the greatest profit to the biggest corporations. This states the principle roughly, for it is subject to many pressures. A careful definition which took into account the main factors bearing on price and production could well run pages long.[1]

To see the definition of conservation come to life, one would have to attend the monthly meeting of the Texas Railroad Commission when that august body is fixing the "allowable" production for the ensuing month. He would hear bandied about the words "market demand," "imports," "domestic stocks," "over-production," "share of the market," "price stability." And yet he would be attending a meeting which legally has but one purpose: to conserve oil.

Concern with true conservation in the industry hardly antedates the early 1920s. It was then that a pinch was felt, as the stream of automobiles pouring from the factories was unmatched by a comparable increase in domestic production. Calamity howlers predicted an early end to oil, and even President Coolidge, who usually felt that business was capable of taking care of the country's needs, thought it wise in 1924 to create the Federal Oil Conservation Board. Such worries died down with the discovery of the great Seminole field in Oklahoma in 1926, accompanied by big finds in Texas. Then came Oklahoma City and the Kettleman North Dome field in California in 1928.[2]

It was a period of rapid expansion in production and soon the industry was concerned, not with scarcity, but with abundance. In 1930 the cornucopia of east Texas flooded the market; poor boy wells dumped their production into hastily erected coffeepot refineries which in turn dumped their cut-rate gasoline into the metropolitan centers of the Midwest and sold the residual oil for whatever it would bring at the Gulf. There was no way to choke off this rushing torrent of oil, for the law of capture demanded that everybody drill immediately under penalty of losing his oil to his neighbor.

The major corporations now felt obliged to take another look at the word "conservation." In the 1920s they had shied off even from Coolidgean solicitude for their welfare; they feared the ogre of federal control. Now it was seen that perhaps this magic word, so wise, so desirable, so acceptable for the public welfare, might be turned to good use by the industry to conserve its profit margins. Although Coolidge had observed that "the oil industry might be permitted to determine its own future," it was unfortunately impossible for the American Petroleum Institute, created and controlled by the majors, to impose industrial self-government to the extent of setting production quotas. The Department of Justice, interpreting both the antitrust laws and Supreme Court decisions, turned thumbs down on that.

The problem was a neat one providing no simple solution. The industry barred federal interference; the government barred industry control of production. While the sovereign states might enact production control laws, they would have to be concerted, if the forward states were not to penalize themselves. These solutions had been pondered before 1930 but the crisis was not acute enough to require heroic action, and the American Petroleum Institute contented itself with a plan for worldwide limitation of production. Since this required outright cartel action, the Department of Justice frowned again, and the plan was dropped.[3]

By 1931, action could no longer be postponed if joint ruin of all factors in the industry was to be averted. The Secretary of the Interior cried out to the oil states to join together in a compact, and the governors of Texas, Oklahoma, and Kansas—the states with the overwhelming bulk of production east of the Rockies— wheeled into action. An accord was reached late in 1931: production quotas were set, a duty of 21 cents a barrel was slapped on imported oil to quiet independent domestic producers, and the Department of the Interior for a time quit leasing federal oil lands.

The small producers, the poor boys who were about the only factor in the industry profiting at all from the glut on the market, challenged the governors and their compact and continued to produce with wells wide open. In Oklahoma and Texas, the militia were called out to enforce production quotas; General Jacob F. Wolters of the Texas National Guard, also chief counsel for the Texas Company, commanded the guardsmen who patrolled the east Texas fields, the main source of the industry's disaster.[4]

But the hastily drawn production control laws, enacted in the name of conservation, were challenged in the courts by the small independents and cut to ribbons by judges not yet accustomed to the newfangled concepts of those who would interfere with a man's God-given right to produce all the oil he pleased from his own well. Thus spoke the chief justice of the Oklahoma Supreme Court: "In my opinion, prorationing of oil was born of monopoly, sired by arbitrary power, and its progeny [such as these orders] is the deformed child whose playmates are graft, theft, bribery and corruption."[5]

In this period posted price meant little as crude plunged from $1.30 a barrel at the start of 1930 to its lowest level, 24 cents, in July 1931 (although actually crude was sold as low as 5 and 6 cents a barrel), and then began a slow recovery, thanks in part to the compulsory shutdowns enforced at the point of a bayonet.

The price of gasoline fell in the same period from 17 cents to 13 cents a gallon. The contrast between the catastrophic fall in crude and the fractional fall in gasoline pointed up the plight of the producer and the comparatively favored position of the integrated company, commonly called the "refinery price squeeze." While the producer's crude went down to 18 percent of the early 1930 price, the refiner's gasoline was still worth 76 percent. Two gallons of gasoline fetched more than 42 gallons (one barrel) of crude.

Nevertheless the situation was bad for everyone, despite the militia. The big companies were themselves large producers of crude; the nation's purchasing power continued plunging; the production control plan was hopelessly snagged by the courts. It could only be said that the big fellows suffered less than the little fellows.

Shortly after Roosevelt entered office in 1933, his Secretary of the Interior, Harold L. Ickes, announced that "fear of an utter collapse of this essential industry is abroad in the oil fields. The several states have frankly confessed their inability to deal with such a situation. Gentlemen's agreements have proved abortive. . . . Governors of states, throwing up their hands in despair, have urged the federal government to step in and restore order."

Standard of Indiana, for one, agreed. In its annual report for 1933, that company wailed that "competition engendered by the price policies of a small minority of operators brought the oil industry close to disaster." It offered the word "ruin" to describe the plight facing the industry. But Indiana itself, thanks to closing down entire refineries and many field operations, refusing to open new fields and placing its employees on shared work schedules, was nevertheless able to report an $18 million profit, not too bad for those times.

The crux of the problem was the wells of east Texas and Oklahoma City and the "hot oil" products which flowed from them toward St. Louis, Chicago, and other cities to be hawked as cut-rate gasoline. If their output could be throttled so that the coffeepot refineries would be starved out, the major companies could regain control of the price situation. Senator Tom Connally of Texas obliged by inserting a section in the National

Industrial Recovery Act expressly outlawing interstate transportation of "hot oil," that is, oil produced in defiance of state proration control measures which fixed the allowable production for wells and fields. As federal agents swarmed into east Texas and Oklahoma City, all sales of oil there were put under a form of federal license. The "bootleg" production dropped from 150,000 barrels a day to a mere 30,000. Crude thereupon advanced to a dollar a barrel and gasoline "firmed" on the market. After a time the U. S. Supreme Court threw out the Connally amendment as an invalid delegation of Congressional powers to an administrative authority, whereupon Senator Connally had it reenacted as a specific directive of Congress. That stood—the Senator's sure claim to immortality, the Connally hot oil act.[6]

In the meantime, the Oklahoma legislature had devised a court-proof formula which declared that limitation of production to reasonable market demand was a proper method of preventing waste and promoting conservation. Texas promptly followed suit. If such a curb on production thereby stabilized prices, that was merely incidental and couldn't be helped. The U. S. Supreme Court, upholding the Oklahoma law, concurred, the more so as the law very specifically stated that nothing therein was to be construed as a license to fix prices.

It was now needful to coordinate the curbs exercised by the various states, so that one would not gain an advantage over the others. For this purpose, NIRA was quite helpful. First of all, the industry saw to it that oil was exempted from the general control exercised by the National Recovery Administration. Its case was so special, it pleaded, that control must be lodged in an independent agency. So the oil and gas industry emerged, under NIRA, as the only industry with its own special administrator, independent of General Hugh S. Johnson.

The administrator turned out to be Harold L. Ickes, Secretary of the Interior, whose bark proved to be much worse than his bite. Administration of the American Petroleum Institute's code was turned over to a planning and coordination committee composed mostly of representatives of the major companies. Under the code, it was arranged that each month the U. S. Bureau of Mines would estimate the production, by states, that would meet "market demand." These quotas, approved by the administrator, were sent to the state enforcing agencies, such as the Texas Railroad Commission and the Oklahoma Corporation Commission, which in turn broke them down into "allowables" (i.e. the production allowed) for the various fields and wells.

When the Blue Eagle died no tears were shed in oil. The industry was relieved of the threat of federal controls, while its own controls over production were now strong enough to stand alone. Congress on February 16, 1935, had authorized the creation of the Interstate Oil Compact Commission, to coordinate the production controls of the oil states; the U. S. Bureau of Mines continued to send out its "market demand" figures each month; the state authorities were now coordinated and the market was under control. One by one, the hundred refineries in east Texas began closing down as their supplies dried up; what production was permitted flowed, as it should, to the refineries at Port Arthur and Houston which were owned by Standard, Texas Company, Gulf, Shell, and other majors. Within a few years, but three independent refineries remained in operation in the greatest oil field on the continent.[7]

The results were impressive; it might almost be said that the Great Depression was a boon to the majors for it permitted them to erect, legally, a system of control which, for other industries, remains but a hope and a prayer. In no other major sphere of economic activity does government, federal and local, conspire with the owners to see to it that their products will be assured a market at a good price. If the American Petroleum Institute were to send out estimates of next month's probable demand, with the implied suggestion that production be trimmed to suit it, the Department of Justice presumably would charge price-fixing, in line with numerous decisions on this point by the U. S. Supreme Court. But no one is going to indict the U. S. Bureau of Mines for a presumably innocent exercise in statistics, especially when it is specifically authorized by Congressional appropriations. The Bureau also indicates what should be the share of each state in meeting market demand. But this is merely a suggestion, and is not binding on the state authorities and therefore implies no effort at domination by federal bureaucrats.

The states harmonize themselves, voluntarily, through the Interstate Oil Compact Commission.[8] Let it be understood that this Commission, too, is a purely voluntary body without power to force any state to do its bidding. Nearly all the oil states have signed the Compact, and Canadian provinces and Venezuela have been accepted as associates with voice but no vote.[9]

An effort is now being made to install the Canadian provinces and Venezuela as full-fledged members. This move by the major importers looks toward a continental oil compact, enlarging the present interstate setup. If the Middle Eastern countries were to be admitted later, there would be a veritable world oil compact (except for the Soviet sector), administered by the corporations with dominant foreign interests.

The quarterly sessions of the Compact Commission bring together the chief figures of oildom. The governors of Texas, Oklahoma, Kansas, and Louisiana, the members of the state regulatory commissions, federal officials, and the representatives of the major companies and visiting dignitaries often join in the nominal activities of the Commission; but in the lobbies and hotels the real work is done. Here, industrial and political moguls discuss the future, adjust the present, and compliment themselves on the past. Although the Compact itself is based strictly on "conservation," several years passed before the Commission even began to concern itself with true conservation legislation. The reason given was lack of budget! The Commission never got around to drafting a model conservation law for the states and only recently has devoted much attention to engineering aspects of the problem. In 1939, however, the Commission sponsored a meeting to agitate for an increase in the price of crude—a subject presumably outlawed by the statute which created it. It scans closely the "market demand" figures of the Bureau of Mines and debates them carefully, although the law gives it no authority to be concerned with them. Whatever may be the economy moves in Congress to cut the federal budget, the members of the Commission earnestly beg that the appropriation for the Bureau of Mines' statisticians not be touched. Indeed, apart from its function of bringing together the representatives of the major companies and the state commissions which are supposed to regulate their activities, the Compact Commission is mainly a pressure group on Congress, another phase of the "oil lobby" operating under the cloak of official sanction.[10]

The federal law authorizing the Compact comes up for Congressional discussion every four years, upon its expiration. Usually it is Republican Congressmen who are critical and it is left to the Democrats from the oil states to defend the renewal of the statute. In 1951, Congressman John W. Heselton, Republican, of Massachusetts, wondered if the industry were not "bordering on monopoly" with the assistance of the Compact. Congressman Charles A. Wolverton, Republican, of New Jersey, observed that "conservation" seemed to go up and down in accordance with market demand. He backed a bill to require the Compact Commission to submit annual reports to the Antitrust Division of the Department of Justice. As chairman of the House Commerce Committee in 1953, Wolverton urged that the "maximum efficient rate" of production be the sole criterion of prorationing, without regard to the factor of market demand. Congressman Robert Hale, Republican, of Maine, demanded that the Department of Justice express its opinion on the working of the Compact Commission. Congressman Joseph P. O'Hara, Republican, of Minnesota, asked if the oil interests were eager for renewal of the Compact law so as to avoid possible antitrust action. The sole Democrat who was vocally critical, Congressman Daniel J. Flood, of Pennsylvania, declared that if conservation were the real aim of the statute, it would be much better to conserve petroleum by using coal.[11]

The Congressmen found, however, when inquiring into the Compact's workings in 1951, that they were questioning a phantom. The Interstate Oil Compact Commission, its defenders averred, had no power to limit production, to fix prices, or even to suggest to the states what ought to be done about such matters. Governor Allan Shivers of Texas testified that if price is an incidental result of conservation, then "I can see no harm in it." Secretary of the Interior Oscar Chapman added that the Compact Commission had been "a useful tool."[12]

Oil state Senators were "appalled," the *Oil Daily* reported, when Congress in 1955 directed the Attorney General to make

an annual scrutiny of the Compact Commission, as a condition
for another 4-year extension of its life. The Attorney General was
directed by the Senate's bill to report whether the Compact's
activities "have resulted in stabilizing or fixing of prices of oil
or gas, the creation or perpetuation of any monopoly or the
promotion of any regimentation in the production or sale of oil
and gas."

Since conservation is the key word in the legal approval of
the domestic oil cartel, U. S. Supreme Court Justice Butler's
opinion in 1932 upholding the Oklahoma statute deserves attention. He held, with unanimous backing from other justices, that
the state law had for its purpose the prevention of the physical
waste of petroleum. In the name of conservation, therefore,
production could be limited to market demand although it would
be illegal to control production to stabilize prices.

THE USES OF TRUE CONSERVATION

"Conservation" is a rubbery word. Some people argue that
true conservation would require the nation to shut in many
of its fields and draw on foreign production. Domestic production
to date has accounted for two-thirds of the world production;
we have been exhausting our own resources at an alarming rate
while vast deposits around the Caribbean and in the Middle East
are barely tapped. The argument here is not so much the senti-
mental desire to keep some of the resource for our children but
the deadly need to preserve intact a ready supply for military
purposes at a time when foreign, and particularly Middle Eastern,
oil may not be accessible.[13]

Or conservation might be considered from the angle of use. Is
it wise to burn up half the domestic resources to fire boilers in
homes, industries, and public utilities when coal is available in
almost inexhaustible quantity? Should not the oil be saved for
automotive purposes and for lubrication? In this country a
quarter of our oil is used for passenger cars, a quarter for other
transportation, a sixth for heating, and a third for industrial and
other purposes.

Conservation considered from either of these angles implies a
sharp reduction in production at home. With these ideas the

industry has no truck. It is for the widest possible use of oil for all purposes, since profits are made on volume of sales.

Considerations of military supply or most essential use obviously had nothing to do either with Oklahoma's conservation law or with its approval by the Supreme Court. The backers of the law were concerned only with the proposition that if too much oil is produced at any time the price structure weakens and with it the profit structure. At the best, the Supreme Court in legalizing the domestic cartel overlooked economic realities and the relentless drives within the industry. At the worst, it was a piece of legal charlatanism indulged in by justices self-blinded to the real issues.

Conservation has another meaning, as used by petroleum engineers. It may be summarized:

(1) There must be no gushers and uncontrolled flush flows by which gas pressure is prematurely lost.

(2) The number of wells must be kept to the minimum determined by the geology of the field. Too many wells drain the field of gas and water pressures; too few can cause loss of oil as it migrates toward the well.

(3) The flow from each well should be adjusted so as to maintain even pressure throughout the field.

(4) The ratio of gas to oil in the flow from each well should be at the minimum which will assure a flow of oil.

Obviously these conservation principles have nothing whatever to do with the market demand figures released monthly by the Bureau of Mines to guide the Texas Railroad Commission and its fellow state commissions in setting allowables for the following month.[14]

The state legislatures, Congress, and the courts, in seeking "conservation" via market demand, were of course, in a backhanded way, really limiting the rule of capture which compelled each landowner to pillage his neighbor's oil before his neighbor could rob him. The law of wild animals as applied to petroleum had to be modified, and the legal fiction of conservation served the purpose. Geologically and economically, the very nature of oil pointed to it as a natural monopoly which demanded technical exploitation at least in units of pools and fields, rather than in capricious units of surface ownership such as lots, farms, and ranches. The truth is that genuine conservation would demand national ownership of petroleum and its exploitation in accordance with a national plan. Since the nature of free enterprise forbids this solution, the only feasible method was to hand the treasure over to the major corporations and to maintain the fiction of public authority by passing the regulatory power to state commissions more easily dominated by the industry than a national commission would be.

The trouble is that this solution violates not only national interests but the principles of classical economics as well. Classical economics holds that the free play of price in the market would harness overproduction by cutting down on exploration, postponing the exploitation of new fields, and checking drilling. As a glut forced down the price of oil products, production would slow until prices readjusted to a normal level. Not only would such a regime permit the related triumph of private enterprise—the rule of capture—to prevail, but also it would give low-cost independent producers and refiners a chance to survive. This, however, would not be to the taste of the major companies who much prefer controlled enterprise to free enterprise.[15]

"Unitization" has long been urged as a real step toward conservation. Under this system, all the properties in a field are brought under common management for "unitized" production. But unless compulsion is used, the system will hardly work in the older fields or in territory where land is cut up among a myriad owners.[16]

Even in west Texas, in cattle range country, it has been difficult to unitize fields. In the new Scurry area, after months of effort, it was possible to get 93 percent of the working interests and 80 percent of the royalty interests representing some 1200 wells in 47,000 acres into a unitized project. This was said to be the nation's largest project for controlled production through such operation. Its goal was the recovery of an additional 750,000 barrels through regulated pressure maintenance.[17]

The major companies have been the most enthusiastic advocates of unitization, as they are apt to hold the controlling interest in fields and pools. To combat the drive for compulsory unitization, the Texas Independent Producers and Royalty Owners Association was formed in 1946. Their warning is "compulsory unitization on the label, but socialism in the bottle"—an imputation embarrassing to the antisocialistic majors.[18]

THE ROLE OF THE TEXAS RAILROAD COMMISSION

The key position in the edifice of production control is held by the Texas Railroad Commission whose state accounts for nearly half the entire domestic production. This Commission's action on the magic market demand figures, flashed from the Bureau of Mines in Washington each month, sets the pattern for the other oil state commissions. Let us take a look at it.

The Texas Railroad Commission, created in 1891 to regulate railroads, had the oil industry dumped in its lap in 1919. The Commission consists of three men elected for six-year terms, with one seat coming up for grabs each two years. Its present members are Ernest O. Thompson, who has held office since 1933, Olin Culberson, in office since 1941, and William J. Murray, Jr., who was elected in 1947.

The Commission meets monthly in Austin, its main mission being to set allowables for the ensuing month. Before the Commission are the U. S. Bureau of Mines figures. Around the Commissioners are the representatives of the major corporations who announce their "nominations" for crude for the following month. Company A says it needs so many thousand or hundreds of thousands of barrels of oil, Company B adds its figure, and so on down the line. These figures are totaled and compared with the Bureau of Mines figures. Government agencies, such as the Petroleum Administration for Defense, may also offer their suggestions, particularly in regard to the needs of the military.

The Commission thereupon decrees the allowables. Fields generally may be put on a 19-day production basis, with east Texas, the major field, cut several days under. This field, the center of small poor boy holdings, has been cut to as low as 13 days a month, and its production generally is confined to about 2 percent of its capacity at open flow. In accordance with the nominations by crude producers and purchasers and with an eye on imports, the Commission enters its decrees.

Obviously, the monthly adjustments upward and downward in allowables have no conceivable relation to conservation as understood by petroleum engineers. Nor are they hitched to any other sensible definition of conservation. Ernest O. Thompson, senior member of the Commission, makes no bones about it. Price, he says, is the greatest of all conservation agents. "You can afford to spend more money to recover $4 oil than you can on $2.50 oil." Consumers, he adds, "are willing to pay the proper price that will assure such protection and provide a hedge against rationing of gasoline."[19] Consumers are not, of course, represented at hearings of the Texas Railroad Commission. Their interests are represented presumably by the major companies, who are in charge of the prices the consumers are "willing to pay."

The Commission has other duties in addition to setting allowables. It sets rules for the spacing of wells and for the conservation of natural gas. Despite Rule 1, aimed against the waste of natural gas, a billion cubic feet were allowed to go to waste daily in the 1930s, with the consequent waste in oil recovery because of lack of pressure.[20] In the 1940s the situation was little better. The Senate Small Business Committee reported that in January, 1948, Texas flared 1475 million cubic feet of gas. The Committee, headed by Senator Wherry, a conservative Republican, observed that true conservation would require that the gas be returned underground, or used, or that the wells be closed in. If such wasting wells were closed, the Committee added, arbitrary prorationing of allowables would be unnecessary.

Well-spacing fares little better. The rule is fine, and a tribute to conservation. The practice is that under the rule of capture, the Commission is loath to interfere with any Texan's God-given right to get at oil; there are so many exceptions that the rule is negated.

Wells are limited in their production within a field, not according to engineering principles, but on a flat per-well basis. Thus each well in a field may be limited to 40 barrels a day. So the enterprising producer sinks another well, and has 80 barrels production. As this is "too much" for market demand, the Commission may then cut the allowable to 30 barrels. Thereupon another shaft is sunk, and production from the three wells is 90 barrels a day. The extra wells are economically needless, cost money that must raise the price to the consumer, and are drilled amid the industry's constant complaint about shortage of oil-field pipe and equipment.

Within the past five years, as domestic production has failed to meet internal needs, the Texas Railroad Commission has been paying more attention to bona fide conservation practices. In new fields, wells are being more adequately spaced and the leg-to-leg derricks are not seen there, as in east Texas. Unitization is encouraged so far as rugged Texan individualism will permit. Wastage of natural gas through flaring has practically been stopped, as vast new markets have opened in the East for this once useless by-product of oil production. Where only a few years ago the entire west Texas oil country around Odessa was aflame by night with flaring gas, today the traveler by air spots only an occasional orange jet in the darkness. The entire Spraberry Trend fields in west Texas were ordered shut in until pipe lines were made available for the 220 million cubic feet of gas that was being flared daily in this one area.

Similar policies have been adopted by the Oklahoma and Kansas authorities. But, one and all, they have been unable to get at the taproot of waste, the rule of capture as applied to petroleum. And month by month the allowables teeter up and down, not through the principles of maximum efficient recovery of crude, but to adjust production to market demand, to assure maximum efficient recovery of profits from consumers.

It must not be thought that all proceedings of the Texas Commission are conducted in a goldfish bowl. In Texas, in the free and easy ways of the frontier, business is done man to man and to hell with the rules. Or, in the words of York Young Will-born, of the University of Texas, who looked into the Commission's procedures in 1943, its activities take place in "an atmosphere of specific personalities and often petty political influences. The existence of the atmosphere of special political contacts and influences is probably the most significant feature . . . of the Commission's activity."[21] The general interest of the public, he complains, can never be brought to bear as well as that of special interests. The Commission does not limit its contact with the industry to hearings and public sessions but seems in constant touch, in private meetings of which the public knows nothing, and of which there is no public record. The Commission, too, according to Willborn, depends for information on employees chosen on the basis of political allegiance and activity. Even those technically qualified to judge a well's potential production are handicapped by relatively insecure tenure. Their salaries, he adds, are only a fraction of those paid by the regulated interests to employees with comparable responsibilities.

Such a reflection leads to another of much graver import. The three men who compose the mightiest state regulatory body in the United States are each paid $7000 a year to pass judgment on an industry doing a $2.5 billion annual business in Texas. Willborn discreetly limited his comment on this to the observation that "men of real honesty and ability are elected at times." Nor would it do to leap to the conclusion that members of the Texas Railroad Commission enjoy any overt income from the huge corporations they regulate. The "bad old days" when Standard Oil kept U. S. Senators and federal judges on its payroll are gone. Today, in Texas, it is notable that many political figures can expect to be retained as attorneys by the oil companies after they leave office. For example, Beauford Jester, onetime railroad commissioner, one-time governor, was counsel for Magnolia, the Socony subsidiary in Texas. Many politicos have ranches on which quite lucrative leases are signed for mineral rights, although the property may be far from any oil field. The large independent producers frequently strike it rich in a new field; just as a favor, friends are permitted in on the company's stock or leases before the news is out. And always there are elections, with campaigns to be financed. Texas is a big state with more than two million voters, and it costs a lot to run for office. No opponent of the oil interests has been successful at the polls in recent years.

It would seem that a state as rich as Texas might well pay its oil Commissioners more than $7000 a year. Oddly enough, there is no agitation for an increase, say, to $25,000, which might redress the balance a bit between a giant industry and Commissioners who receive less in salary than the corporations pay competent drillers. Everybody in Texas seems content with the present situation.

The independent marketing end of the industry, however, has been highly critical of the cartel's domestic operations. The Atlantic Coast Oil Conference and the Empire State Petroleum Association, representing jobbers for the most part, phrased it this way:

> Under this system of price-fixing, using conservation of a natural resource as the basic reason, the power of the state regulatory bodies takes priority over all the laws of supply and demand. Furthermore, it subjects the fundamental supply of the petroleum industry to political actions and pressures. . . .
>
> Too often here of late, the producers and the regulatory commissions fallaciously have looked upon the petroleum industry as a mere handful of the integrated companies, probably because of their nearness to the integrated companies. However, like the old adage of "failing to see the forest for the trees," they have given little consideration to the mass base of the petroleum industry—the independent refiners and marketers comprising thousands of various types of operation.
>
> How can any great industry, with talented leadership at its command, capable of world-wide operations, oppose on the one hand efforts toward national regulation, and at the same time tolerate state coercion, price-fixing and regulations?
>
> To many of us in the lower echelons, this paradox cannot be justified. Will not passive resistance to the misuse of one form (state control) be the means of breeding another (national control) which would undoubtedly have a greater impact on the economics of the industry?[22]

7

Reserves

How long will the oil last?

Considering the industry's eagerness to get all it can out in the shortest possible time, in order to make the greatest possible profit, the answer might seem somber. But the major corporations operate on the assumption that as there always has been enough, there always will be, world without end. There are, nevertheless, pessimists within the bosom of the industry itself willing to say nay.

In this eager age of synthetics, the possibility that petroleum may be exhausted within a generation fails to excite the fears that attended such predictions in the 1920s. Have we not atomic power, solar energy, and other glittering substitutes which will make oil seem as laborious a source for power as we now believe coal to be? Such prospects may soothe those worrying about the needs of the coming generation but they are scant solace to the military men who want the power now, and want it quick. So far, planes, propeller or jet-driven, require petroleum fuel and are unable to draw energy from either the atom or the sun.

The pessimists we have had with us for some time. Back in World War I days, Mark L. Requa, then oil director for the U. S. Fuel Administration, said:

We must either plan for the future or we must pass into a condition of commercial vassalage, in time of peace relying upon some foreign country for the petroleum wherewith to lubricate the highways of commerce, in time of war, at the mercy of the enemy who may either control the sources of supply or the means of transportation; in either event our railways and factories will cease operation, our battleships

will swing helplessly at anchor, and our country will resound
with the martial tread of a triumphant foe.

In 1918, Joseph E. Pogue, then with the Smithsonian Institution, commenting on an estimate of 7 billion barrels potential
supply, saw "no hope that new fields, uncounted in our inventory, may be discovered of sufficient magnitude to modify
seriously the estimate given." In 1919 the U. S. chief geologist
said that the peak of production would be reached in 1921.[1]

Pogue, now director of Gulf Oil and vice-president of Chase
National Bank as well as its petroleum adviser, has changed
his mind since 1918. But even in 1925 the American Petroleum
Institute (API) saw only 5 billion barrels in reserve in this
country. Then came a dozen great discoveries, capped by east
Texas, so that in 1935 API estimated the proved reserve at 12
billion. By 1943 this had climbed to 20 billion, and in 1954 the
figure was 35 billion.[2] Divided by the 2.5 billion barrels used in the
one year 1954, this amounts to a known supply for 14 years. But
oil reserves are a good bit like human mortality tables; if a
person arrives at his allotted age span, he then has a good chance
of living some more. More oil is constantly being discovered.

The official industry attitude was expressed by J. Edgar Pew
of Sun Oil, when, as chairman of the API committee on reserves,
he testified that oil has been discovered when needed, and therefore will continue to be found. There is enough, he said, for the
foreseeable future, and beyond that who can see, who can predict?
(It might be added, who cares?)

This view is questioned by E. DeGolyer, as eminent an authority as one can find on matters of petroleum geology. He contends
there has been a falling off in the rate of discovery since 1938.
The glowing additions to reserve estimates made by API, he
points out, consist more of additions to known pools than ac-
cessions of newly discovered fields. For example, for 1951 API
calculated that 4 billion barrels had been added to known
reserves, but of these only 400 million were in new fields or in
new pools in old fields.

The new oil costs a lot more to discover, too. In 1937, according
to the API, 33.4 barrels of crude were discovered for every foot
of hole drilled; this figure has declined rather steadily to 13.2

barrels in 1954. Back in 1940, it cost $11.80 to drill a hole a
foot into the earth; in 1954 the figure was $17.25. That means that
the cost of discovering and developing a barrel of oil increased
from 63 cents in 1940 to $1.30 in 1954. In 1954 the industry spent
$3.4 billion on discovery and development, against $1 billion in
1940. Footage drilled rose from 97 million to 200 million in the
period.[3]

Another disconcerting tendency is the increase in the percentage
of dry holes (no production) to total wells drilled. The percentage in 1936 was 10, in 1947 it was 27, and in 1953, 37.5. On a
different basis of computation, there were 3.62 dry holes drilled
in 1945 for each producer in "exploratory drilling," that is, outside tested areas. This figure had gone up to 4.3 in 1951. However,
in "new-field wildcats," the most hazardous kind of drilling, only
1 hole in 9 was productive in 1951.

All these discouraging trends, however, are cast to one side
by the exuberance of such experts as Wallace E. Pratt, head
physicist for Standard of New Jersey, author of *Oil in the Earth*
and co-editor of *World Geography of Petroleum.* He believes
that available deposits exist in volume proportional to the areas
of unmetamorphosed sedimentary rocks of marine origin, and the
prospect is indeed exhilarating, for there is plenty of such rock
scattered around the globe. Basing figures on such enthusiasm, it
has been calculated that there are a thousand billion barrels of
petroleum on the continental shelves in less than 600 feet depth.
At such depths enthusiasm will indeed be needed to catch the
fleeing mineral when it taxes the ingenuity of man to find it under
dry land.

Professor A. I. Levorsen of Stanford in 1949 told the United
Nations Scientific Conference on the Conservation and Utilization
of Resources that the world's undiscovered oil resources were
sufficient for 500 years at the present rate of consumption. Although known world reserves then were but 70 billion barrels—
enough for 20 years—there may be as much as 1.5 trillion barrels,
if oil is evenly dispersed throughout the favorable rock forma-
tions. Two thirds of this rock is beneath ocean waters to a depth
of 600 feet. He added that our own success in finding oil within
the United States was a tribute "to its laws of mineral ownership

whereby the individual owns the petroleum under his land and can do with it what he wishes." National ownership, he observed, is a deterrent to exploitation.[4] The ultimate decision on this argument might be the opposite, if it should prove that the United States, within a generation, has exhausted its richest deposits while countries under a different system of subsoil rights are just beginning to develop theirs.

M. King Hubbert of Shell labeled Levorsen's estimates "an exercise in metaphysics," and in that he reflects the judgment of other geologists not so addicted to the more optimistic point of view.

The fact is that while half the nation is underlaid with sedimentary rock which might contain oil, only some 8000 square miles out of the 3 million are actually producing oil. Some million square miles have been blocked out in possible oil provinces but assiduous wildcatting is mostly negative.[5] Oil may also underlie presently known deposits at greater depths, but so far the drill has only been able to penetrate three to four miles and the costs of exploration ascend geometrically as the drill descends.

A good bit of mystery still surrounds the discovery of oil. The highly touted gadgets of the geophysicists missed out completely in east Texas and it was left to a random driller on a shoestring to discover the richest field in the country. The Athabasca tar sands of Alberta are estimated to contain as much oil as has yet been found in the Western Hemisphere, but their presence was unsuspected until prospectors stumbled on a small eroded area. Technologists are at work on methods to extract oil from these sands at an economic cost. Nevertheless the most promising areas in this country have been surveyed and plumbed time and again. No other surface in the earth has been so scratched over; the uncomfortable conclusion will not down that the United States has seen its best days in petroleum and that the center of production will swing within the next decade to other lands whose known deposits have barely been tapped, and whose unknown resources still await intensive exploration.

In part, Jersey's optimism on the future is based on world resources. Its brother company, Standard of Indiana, which has no foreign sources, must squeeze whatever optimism it can from

the domestic scene. Indiana in 1952 forecasted the next 15 years
(about as far as oil men care to peer) this way:

U. S. DEMAND FOR OIL PRODUCTS
(thousand barrels a day)

1951	1955	1960	1965	1967
7,043	8,300	9,180	9,990	10,280

This 46 percent increase in demand will be met, Indiana asserts,
by domestic production, with a 5 percent margin in excess; if
allowance is made for imports of about 10 percent of domestic
production, the cushion would be 18-20 percent.[6] The military
want a 25 percent cushion, but Indiana says they're not likely
to get it. The figures mean that the industry must find 49 billion
barrels of oil, 7 billion more than has been produced since 1859.
The bulk must come from the mid-continent and the Gulf Coast;
Indiana, it is interesting to note, expects about 350,000 barrels a
day production from the offshore lands 15 years from now. This
would be about 4 percent of the total expected supply in 1965—
a far cry indeed from the glowing hopes of some for the treasures
beneath the sea.

Another string to Indiana's bow of optimism is the possible
improvement in the methods of recovery of oil. Present methods
get only a quarter to a third of the oil to the surface. By water
injection as well as gas repressurizing, it is hoped to raise this to
40-60 percent. Indiana also has hopes that the Great Basin of
Nevada-Utah, the Salina Basin of Kansas-Nebraska and southeastern Colorado may become big producers, in line with current developments in the Williston Basin in North Dakota-
Montana-Saskatchewan and the Uintah Basin in Utah. California,
it is conceded, can do no more than maintain its present volume
even by developing offshore fields. That state is using up 10
percent of its resources each year, against a world average of
2 percent.[7]

A longer range is included in the forecasts published in 1952
by Eugene Ayres and Charles A. Scarlott in *Energy Resources—
The Wealth of the World*. They do not believe in the ever-
ascending plateau which Standard of Indiana sees through the
next 15 years; to them it begins to descend in 1960. Twenty years

from now, they believe, production will have petered out—so to speak—to a mere billion barrels a year, half the present figure. But even if production could be maintained at the present level in 1975, there would be a deficit of 4.9 billion barrels, which would have to be imported.[8]

Obviously by that time we would have to quit burning up a third of our domestic production for industrial and household use; then perhaps the demand for motor fuel and lubrication would total only 3.5 billion barrels. Some 1.5 to 2.5 billion (depending on whether production is maintained at the present level or declines to a mere billion) would have to be imported or derived from other sources. The authors do not believe shale oil could account economically for more than 300 million barrels a year, in competition with imported oil. Two hundred million could be processed from coal, as a by-product of more valuable carbon chemicals.[9]

This long glance into the future is the more interesting as Ayres is connected with Gulf's research department. While Indiana's brand of optimism may stem from its dependence on domestic sources, Gulf is half-owner of the fabulous Kuwait deposits along the Persian Gulf, and so Ayres more cheerfully faces the prospect of the need for big imports. The scientific acumen of the Indiana and Gulf research specialists leads them to draw curiously opposing conclusions from data available to all scientists. The Gulf expert seems not to expect too much from shale (so long as Kuwait holds out) while the Indiana experts toil endlessly and hopefully with the problems involved in such synthetic fuels.

Ayres, the Gulf expert, in considering the use of energy by the leading nations, points out that Britain built her empire on coal energy. Back in 1875, Britain was using 30 times as much coal per capita as the rest of the world, and Britain was great. Now its coal use is only four times greater and is declining steadily. For the United States, oil is the main energy fuel. But already our curve of consumption is following the ominous British coal use trend. In 1930 we used 30 times as much oil per capita as the rest of the world; in 1940, 26 times; in 1952, 17 times; and by 1975, he says, we will be with oil about where Britain is with

coal now, using but five times as much per capita as the rest
of the world.

On the other hand, Ayres points out, Russia is climbing up the
grade on her use of coal, oil, and gas; at present it is but 10
percent of our own but is advancing 25 percent each decade,
while we passed our maximum share of world use of oil in 1910.
Even more ominous is the fact that we have already used 61
percent of our proved reserves and Russia has just begun using
hers. She has proved less than 4 percent of her presumed petroleum resources and has consumed, of course, even less. For the
future, these figures portend gloom for the United States. The
Soviet lands are calculated to have one-fourth of all the oil in the
world while we have one-fifth. United States wells have provided
63 percent of world production so far, and in the process 61
percent of our own proved reserves have been utterly consumed.

The world's oil, according to Ayres's estimates, is divided thus:
Middle East, 25 percent; Soviets, 25 percent; United States,
20 percent; rest of America, 20 percent; elsewhere, 10 percent.

From this Ayres concludes that we must import as abundantly
as possible, conserving our own oil, and avoiding "unnecessary"
waste in production and use.[10] The conclusions fit in with Gulf's
foreign policy.

OIL FROM SHALE AND COAL

Far more substantial than the "metaphysical" surmises of some
geologists and the blooming optimism of most of the companies
is the existence in Colorado and Wyoming of enormous deposits
of oil-bearing shale rock, much of it available by surface mining,
and of lignite, a low-grade coal, in North Dakota.

It is over the future of these deposits that a quiet, relentless
struggle is being waged between the industry and whatever remains in the Department of the Interior of public-minded
geologists and economists. The switch from Democratic to Republican concepts within the Department may change this por-
tentous conflict into an easy victory for the oil interests.[11]

The conflict is double-headed. Oil interests which are concerned solely with production fight resolutely any effort to develop
another source of their product. Their answer to haunting fears

of depletion of petroleum is always price; if $2.90 won't entice a barrel out of the earth, then $4 will, or $5. They are not fighting the consumers' battle; they are confident only that there is plenty of natural petroleum—at a price.

On the other hand, the integrated oil companies, and particularly those in California where natural petroleum admittedly has a limited future, and Standard of Indiana, whose massive interests in the Rockies are directly involved, are by no means opposed to the development of shale oil. They merely insist that if there is to be any development, they will do it. Their argument is persuasively simple; if the development of synthetic liquid fuels is profitable, they will make the profit; if it is unprofitable, the government would be wasting money on efforts to hasten the development.

The conflict was brought to the fore by the Synthetic Fuels Act of 1946, which authorized the U. S. Bureau of Mines to operate demonstration plants to test the scientific possibility of refining these shale deposits at an economic cost comparable to crude oil. The Bureau thereupon built a pilot plant at Rifle, Colorado, where costs have been brought down to $2.25-$2.50 a barrel, and nearly a barrel of crude is squeezed from every ton of shale. In northwestern Colorado, the Bureau adds, there are some 200 billion barrels of shale oil.[12]

Union Oil, of California, interested in replenishing its sources, confirms the Bureau in part. Union President Reese H. Taylor estimates that 100 billion barrels are recoverable and that the cost would be under $4.50 a barrel and probably much less once a sizable plant is in operation. Union has proposed the building of a 50,000-barrel-a-day plant, with the Defense Department picking up the tab for possible deficits.[13]

The National Petroleum Council, the government-sponsored oil lobby, spent $300,000 for a report which found that gasoline can be made from shale for 14.7 cents a gallon, against the current wholesale price of 12-13 cents for gasoline from actual petroleum. A bold Associated Press reporter wrote that the industry "was worried that the government has tapped a source of cheap synthetic fuels which some day would cut deeply into its profits. There also was, and still is, another worry—the prospect that

oil made from oil shale will some day bite heavily into the petroleum market."[14]

The price differential against shale gasoline clearly put the
whole project out of bounds, the Council said; if in the future it
seemed that there was any point to developing shale, the industry
would gladly do it—at a profit.

The Council found even less to be said for converting coal into
liquid fuel. It said a gallon of gasoline produced through hydrogenation of coal would cost 43.5 cents. But Ebasco Services, a
New York management engineering firm which studied the
U. S. Bureau of Mines pilot plant at Louisiana, Missouri, said that
gasoline could be produced at 11 cents a gallon, if costs were
properly apportioned among the many products of liquefied and
gasified coal. F. Eberstadt & Co. devised a plan for a $400 million
"Colchem" (i.e. coal-chemical) plant in southern Illinois to
produce 30,000 barrels of gasoline and chemicals daily, with
chemicals as the main economic product. High finance, high
technology, oil, and politics were also synthesized in this project,
commented *Fortune* magazine.[15]

The *National Petroleum News* sniffed suspiciously at the Department of the Interior interest in such projects: "It looks more
and more as though the Department is embarked on a deliberate
campaign to build up popular opinion to the point where private
industry will either be forced, prematurely, to commence com-
mercial-scale production of synthetics or the people will invite
the government to step in." But such sentiments, expressed
October 3, 1951, seemed superfluous after the Republicans took
charge.[16] Among the first acts of the new administration was to
close down the Louisiana, Missouri, plant. Interior Secretary
McKay anounced in 1954 that the Rifle, Colorado, shale plant
would also be closed.

Oil Daily put the matter bluntly:

> The industry is willing to allow "pilot plant" experimenta-
> tion to continue but only on a provisional basis, and only
> with control in its own possession. Even so some petroleum
> physicists and economists admit that within ten years, per-
> haps, and for some areas such as the Pacific Coast, the syn-
> thetic era may be nearer than most people realize. Technical

progress may soon turn up the desired process. The industry is torn between the negative idea that synthetics aren't needed or are uneconomic, and the positive idea that if they become possible, they shall be exploited only by the present corporations.[17]

President Eugene Holman of Standard of New Jersey reduced the argument to one sentence: "When the time comes that synthetics seem necessary for this purpose, we will certainly be making them."[18]

Strangest of all in this controversy is that the war-minded seem so little concerned about the probability that the country would not have sufficient domestic supplies of petroleum products. They seem content to string along with the thinking of the companies with great deposits overseas, that somehow these may be available if and when needed. In fact, the very neglect in expanding energetically the supply of oil products from domestic shale and lignite is another argument for striving for that massive predominance in military power that might make the resources of Venezuela and the Middle East available in wartime.

8

Transportation

UNCERTAINTY and hunches, disorder and ingenuity, rugged individualism and roughhewn independence attend the finding and lifting of crude from the earth. Once tamed, the fleeting mineral is pumped into a line and enters a different world of smoothly grooved controls, quiet and efficient. This is the second grand division of the industry—that of transportation, whether by pipe line or tanker. Here the tumult and the shouting die, and the impassive, imperious order of the major corporations takes over. Half the oil may be *produced* by independents, but at the pipe line toll gate, illusions of independence end.

Whether but a few miles, or half a continent, away from the brawling oil fields, the pipe line station is a world apart. The only sound here is the hum of motors forcing oil along the line to the next pumping station. The station often is located in the countryside, the grounds may even be landscaped, a brook may babble past the neat brick or cement building, an air of rural charm pervade the grounds. Forgotten the raucous whine and grind of the drilling machinery, the sweating toil of roughnecks, gear jammers, derrick monkeys, boll weevils, and tool pushers.[1] Amid the steady thrumming of the motors, a few mechanics move about quietly among dials and valves.

In the oil fields chance still spins the wheel and a wildcatter may strike it rich, a promoter make a killing. But the major corporations stand astride his well or his field and tell him how much he will get, and when. A pipe line from the Gulf-Mid-Continent fields to Chicago costs twenty to a hundred million dollars. The right of way across a thousand miles requires the services of an army of surveyors, engineers, land scouts, lawyers.

Huge pipelayers crawl across the prairie following up the mechanical ditchdiggers. When the line is ready to use, private telephone and telegraph wires and even microwave radio will keep every station in contact with other stations and the head office.

Only the majors can build such arteries for the lifeblood of the industry. Even they sometimes pool their interests in construction and operation of lines which cost as much as $50,000 to $100,000 a mile. The smaller lines, reaching from the fields to points on the main lines, are "gathering lines"; the big lines, many of them with a diameter of 20 to 30 inches, run the crude to the refineries and thence as "product" lines to central marketing points. These lines can carry cargoes of varying products one right behind the other, with little admixture of the different fluids. In 1953 there were 134,000 miles of crude oil and products pipe line pushing 10 million barrels a day, and they were carrying one-eighth by weight of all the freight transported in the United States.

Tankers are the pipe lines of the sea. Ranging from coastwise and river puddle-jumpers of a few hundred tons to the 45,000-ton supertankers traveling at 18 knots and carrying 250,000 barrels, they are the link between the East Coast and the Gulf, Venezuela, and the Middle East. In addition, barges are carrying a swelling tonnage on the inland rivers and the intercoastal canals.

Crude oil and products pipe lines and tankers account for an investment of $2 billion, and another billion has gone into tank cars, trucks, barges, and inland marine equipment. Obviously only the major integrated companies can swing such sums. Of course, the independent producer may move his oil by tank car, at much higher rates, but actually very little crude moves by tank car nowadays. The majors control the great arteries—89 percent by land and 87 percent by sea. By law, the pipe lines are "common carriers" open presumably to anyone who has oil to transport from hither to yon, but little "independent" oil moves in the big lines. In the first place, it is rather pointless, for the price at the end of the pipe line is just as controlled as the price at the beginning. The independent, if he uses the line, does so at the major's convenience, and it may not be convenient if the capacity is all taken. Or the minimum consignment acceptable may be so large as to exceed the independent's storage capacity.

In any event, if the independent producer has access to this common carrier, he pays toll to his competitor, the majors, in the rates charged. This harks back to the "bad old days" of the Standard monopoly when it forced the railroads to give it not only a rebate on the oil it shipped, but also a similar rebate for oil shipped by its competitors. Evidence before the TNEC showed that independent shippers paid double to triple the sums charged by the majors for transporting its own oil. The stern requirements for sizable shipments and the penalizing rates have both moderated in recent years, it is said. But the horse of competition having been stolen, it little matters if the barn door is now locked. In any event the little man has been advised repeatedly to cut his coat after his cloth; if he can't swing millions he can at least open a filling station.

> There is no free market in crude oil [stated Standard Statistics, Inc.], chiefly because virtually all purchases are made through the concentrated pipe line systems.
> The price of crude is thus artificial, and partly because of this, accounting methods and increasing proration, the industry has become geared to the price of crude oil. It is an important determinant of profits and a major factor affecting expansion and development. The division has thus been one of the chief sources of strength for major oil companies, which have emphasized the development of crude oil interests.[2]

Usually the owner of the well has access to but one pipe line; even if several lines are available, the posted price for the field and the gravity of the oil is identical so it can hardly be said that price competition is present when seller meets buyer.

You will look in vain in the daily papers for "market" prices on crude or gasoline. Cotton and hogs, soybean oil and linseed oil, corn and wheat, rubber and tin—nearly every commodity is quoted on the various commercial exchanges. But there is no oil exchange. There used to be, but it was so long ago that few now active in the business can remember so far back. Standard in 1895 announced that it would ignore Exchange prices and pay only its own posted price. After a while the Oil Exchange languished and died, never to be resurrected. The reason is as

simple today as in 1895; Standard then controlled all the pipe
lines and bought 80 percent of all Pennsylvania crude. It was
strictly a buyer's market—the goal of all Rockefeller's scheming.
Today the majors buy an even larger percentage of crude and
control all the important pipe lines. The price posted by Standard
or the leading major in the field is still the only price the independent producer of crude knows, and it is paid when he delivers
his crude at the pipe line receiving station.

The pipe line, Rockefeller discovered, was the throttleneck of
oil. It has also served as the financial governor, capable of adjustment to the majors' requirements. Even when losses are sustained
in production or marketing, the two fields in which independents
are numerous, the artificially contrived profits of pipe lines can
still assure an overall profit to the big integrated companies. The
Interstate Commerce Commission reported in 1933 that pipe line
earnings were "startling in view of the fact that they were made
during a time of widespread industrial depression." From 1929
to 1937 dividends averaged 33.2 percent a year. In the depression
years 1929-1933, dividends of 17 major pipe line companies
equaled 98 percent of total investment, according to the Commission.[3]

The producer, the refiner, the marketer might lose, but the
integrated company, thanks to manipulated pipe line "earnings,"
could not lose. Of twelve majors reporting to TNEC on operations during the troubled depression years, nine reported losses
on refining, seven losses on marketing, one a loss on production,
but none lost on transportation.

The pipe line stands guardian of production control, of prorationing, and of state allowables, the policeman over "hot oil."
All but a negligible amount of oil, whether crude or refined, must
enter the line at some time; as the majors do most of the buying,
oil in excess of "market demand" cannot reach the consumer in
appreciable quantity.

Pipe lines are the enemy of the small refineries in the fields,
and thus serve the majors in another capacity as an instrument
of control over the market. The huge refineries of the Gulf Coast,
the Great Lakes, and the East Coast are made possible by pipe
lines gathering crude all over the Southwest and stuffing it into

the maws of these catalytic monsters. The little refinery loses whatever advantage it might have in being close to the field through lacking access to the bigger markets because it has no pipe line of its own for its product, and must pay toll to its major competitors for using their facilities.

The federal government for a half century and more has engaged in a seriocomic battle with the pipe-line-owning companies. As early as 1906, the Hepburn Act declared the pipe lines to be common carriers, but the companies ignored the law until it was upheld by the U. S. Supreme Court in 1914. The original Senate draft of this law forbade a common carrier to transport goods in which it was directly interested. This would have prevented refining and marketing companies from owning pipe lines, but in the final conference with the House the word "railroad" was substituted for "common carrier," and the oil companies were exempted.

After 1914, the companies were quite willing to be common carriers, but only for cargoes which ranged from 25,000 to 100,000 barrels. By 1922, the Interstate Commerce Commission got around to ordering a 10,000-barrel minimum, but since this applied only to certain specific delivery points, the order turned out to be largely ineffective. In 1928, the Federal Trade Commission reported that Standard pipe lines just hadn't bothered about "common carrying"; and in 1936, the Independent Petroleum Association complained that most companies regarded their lines as plant facilities, and Shell even refused to file tariffs, despite the provisions of the Hepburn Act.

So insoluble seemed the problem of getting permission for independent oil to travel through pipe lines controlled by the majors that the Federal Trade Commission in 1915 recommended divorcement—an heroic operation which had been tried before on the anthracite railroads, and later on the meat packers. The arguments for divorcing pipe lines from their oil company owners seemed so cogent to President Roosevelt in 1933 that he recommended that Congress enact emergency legislation to that end. Congress in fact gave the required power to the President in Section 9 of the National Industrial Recovery Act, as a counterpoise to the "hot oil" ban in the same section. He was empowered to divorce any holding company from control of a pipe line if "by unfair practices or by exorbitant prices [it] tends to create a monopoly." While the hot oil section was promptly and vigorously enforced, no effort was ever made to divorce the pipe lines under Section 9.

The Interstate Commerce Commission later proposed that rates be limited to 8 percent on investment. As this required calculation of the rate of return on a crazy-quilt pattern of original cost, depreciation, cost of reproduction and what not, little could come of the proposal.

In any event, rates of return and prices charged for hauling oil are not of crucial concern any longer, now that the product is firmly controlled through the limitation of production and the strong grip that the major companies hold on the market, from the well to the filling station. By now, no independent dreams that he can get a better price for his crude by piping it to a refinery rather than selling it at the well.

But before the days of legalized control of production through prorationing and allied mechanisms, the pipe line was monopoly's device to force the independent to sell at the well (or build his own relatively less efficient tea-kettle refinery to handle his output). In those days, as Justice Holmes pointed out in 1914, Standard had "made itself master of the fields without the necessity of owning them and carried across half the continent a great subject of international commerce coming from many owners but, by the duress of which the Standard Oil Company was master, carrying it all as its own."

9

Refineries

THE true majesty of the oil industry is best seen in a modern refinery. There, in a sublime industrial cathedral known as a "cat-cracker," just about all that man knows of chemistry is used in breaking up molecules and reforming them. By night, with a thousand lights pricking the darkness along soaring platforms, catwalks, and ladders, the catalytic cracking unit affords one of the magic sights of twentieth-century technology.

Petroleum is a certain arrangement of molecules of hydrogen and carbon which are broken down, rearranged, and set up again in different patterns in these cracking plants. The very names of the processes—polymerization, alkylation, hydrogenation, isomerization—betoken the intricate chemical processes which reshape them. In these synthetic temples without walls or roofs are performed rites known in their entirety only to the high priests of the laboratories.

A far cry indeed from the primitive "tea-kettles" and "coffee-pots" of an earlier era whose operation could be understood readily by a skilled workman. In these, the crude oil was placed in a closed tank and boiled by heat from a furnace underneath. As the temperature rose, the lighter "ends" began ascending as vapors—naphtha, kerosene, and gasoline. They were conducted through a tube into a condenser where they cooled, liquefied, and were drawn off. What was left was residual oil, sold for fuel oil, and heavier sludges for asphalt, tar, and coke.

In the kerosene age which Rockefeller knew so well, gasoline was an unwanted by-product which sometimes adulterated kerosene and made it explosive. Henry Ford changed all that. Gasoline became the prized product. As the primitive process could extract gasoline from only about a fourth of the crude charge, pipe stills were introduced. Through thousands of feet of pipe in the furnace, crude was subjected to heats of more than 700 degrees, sufficient to vaporize all but the heaviest portions of the crude. This had the advantage also of being a continuous process, since crude stock could be charged into the pipes constantly as the vapors rose into the fractionating tower where they condensed at various levels.

This is still the first process, sorting out the various constituents of crude. The non-gasoline products are then subjected to further heat under pressure to change the molecular structure. This is thermal "cracking." If a catalyst is added to speed up the chemical reaction, it becomes catalytic cracking. By these methods about half the crude can be changed into gasoline. Further processing increases the octane content* for aircraft and high-compression engine use. Theoretically, nearly all the crude can be converted into gasoline.

The chemical processes can do even more. By reshuffling the molecules and reshaping them, crude is turned into a storehouse for the fast-developing petrochemical industry which is replacing the coal-tar chemical industry. In many of the refining centers, pipes connect with nearby chemical plants from which flow dyes, drugs, plastics, synthetic rubber, detergents, explosives, and a thousand and one products rubbed by modern Aladdin from his oil lamp.

In 1925, less than 1 percent of organic chemicals were produced from petroleum, but now the fraction is nearing one-half. Chemicals are shifting their base from the middle Atlantic states to the Gulf Coast where new plants are rising all the way from New Orleans to Corpus Christi. Most of the $15 billion invested in expansion of the chemical industry since 1940 has been based on the use of petroleum and natural gas rather than coal tars.[1]

The great cat-crackers, towering a hundred feet and more, are the creatures of the pipe lines which feed them endlessly from hundreds of thousands of wells. The little refinery out in the

* The octane number is the percentage of iso-octane in a blend of iso-octane and normal heptane which will give the same anti-knock characteristics as the fuel sample in question.

field is no match for them. The field may be exhausted; the small refinery may be too far from mass markets and, even if modern, is dependent on a major's pipe line and must pay toll to a competitor to reach the buyer. If it is a topping plant, merely separating gasoline from the residual, it is no competitor at all. If it has neither wells, pipe lines, nor marketing apparatus of its own, it is an orphan of the industry. Everything it buys and sells will be at a disadvantage with the integrated majors and its survival a tribute either to the ingenuity of its owners or to some peculiarity of location.

The biggest refineries—owned by the majors—are concentrated along the Gulf Coast from Baton Rouge to Corpus Christi, along the Great Lakes from Chicago to Cleveland, in the St. Louis, New York, and Philadelphia areas, and in the Los Angeles and San Francisco areas.

The little majors have sizable modern refineries in the midcontinent. Close to their source of supply and near the big Midwestern markets, they maintain a toehold. Skelly and Mid-Continent are typical of these provincial firms which cluster between the Rockies and the Mississippi. But by 1940, all refineries not owned by the majors had disappeared from the Atlantic Coast; the 74 refineries which east Texas had boasted but five years before had shrunk to three. The majors' refineries in all Texas then had an average capacity of 77,000 barrels a day; the independents but 8000. In the nation as a whole, the majors held more than 80 percent of refinery capacity and 90 percent of cracking. In 1950, the Federal Trade Commission placed the majors' share of refining at 83 percent of the total throughput.

What happened in east Texas in the 1930s is recounted by William J. Kemnitzer in vivid detail. His typical refiner owns 20 wells producing 10,000 barrels a day, and he markets through independent jobbers. Because he is stripped for action, unencumbered by high overhead, using perhaps some hot oil bought at a discount, the independent refiner can sell for a few cents under the majors. For that he is called a cutthroat and a chiseler. From time to time the majors will undercut him in price in his market to bleed him of operating capital and make life miserable for him; their only reason for mercy is that his outright ruin might stir up a public fuss.

The little independent hangs on. Then the majors get the Railroad Commission to impose prorationing. His wells are cut to 20 barrels each a day, giving him a supply of 400 barrels instead of 10,000. Now he must pay the posted price for other people's crude. If he survives this and continues to sell, he may be asked to join an "agency" set up by the majors to remove "distress" (cut-rate) gasoline from the market. He is assigned a major company as a "waltzing partner." The major will pay him the going price for his distress gasoline; no longer does he have to dig around for cut-rate outlets. This is a lot easier for the little independent, but in the process his connections with his own customers are broken. He now becomes an adjunct of the major, one of its plant facilities. In another situation, majors may raise the price of crude and cut the price of gasoline. This puts the scissors on the little refiner.

What with one stratagem and another, but mainly through prorationing of allowable production, nearly all the independents in east Texas had thrown in the sponge by 1940.

Integration is thus the key to success. The refinery must control a substantial part of its crude—usually a half; it must have a network of gathering lines in the fields, a big crude line to the plant, and a products line to the markets, and there it must have its own marketing setup, complete with bulk stations and filling stations, these under ownership or control by lease.

How parlous is the margin between profit and loss for the non-integrated company was instanced in 1953 when independent refiners pleaded against a rise in the price of crude. A 35-cent increase in crude or a 5 percent decrease in refined products, they said, would put many small refineries in the red and eventually force them out of business.[2]

Eugene V. Rostow, Yale law professor, contends that it should be possible for the independent refinery to make a go of it. Advanced cracking processes are available through specialized engineering firms; such a firm will even build his refinery, for $2 million or more. Unfortunately, the majors control access to the crude and to the markets, as Rostow concedes. And their control of patents presents a high hurdle.

The long solemn names attached to synthetic processing represent these patents. Until recently many were the private pos-

sessions of the various majors, but they got into such involved
hassles over infringements and what not that they were finally
obliged to reach agreements to license to each other. This came
so close to being a patent pool that the Department of Justice
protested. Standard of Jersey is affiliated with no less than ten
patent companies; some of the majors team together to control
a patent. Most of these are available to the independent refiner,
but at a fee which represents another toll he must pay to his
competitor for the right to exist.

In a more specialized category is Ethyl Corporation, owned
jointly by Standard of Jersey and General Motors. Until recently,
Ethyl had an exclusive patent which obliged everyone—majors
and small fry alike—to pay tribute to it and thus indirectly to
Jersey for the license to use the product. Sun Oil, a holdout for
many years, only recently gave in though it still markets a one-
grade, one-price gasoline.

While the primitive topping plant gets as much gasoline as
it can out of crude and sells the rest for fuel oil, the complex
refineries can adjust their output to market needs. More gasoline is produced upon the approach of the summer season,
more heating oils in the fall for the winter trade. It depends on
the market how much is tapped out for aviation gasoline, sol-
vent naphthas, kerosene, diesel fuels, hydrocarbon gases for
synthetic rubber, plastics, alcohols, industrial fuel oil, finished
lubricating oils, paraffin wax, coke, and asphalt. The proportions can be altered at will, and the more complex the refinery,
the more flexible is its ability to meet the market's needs.

The rising tide of Venezuelan imports and the piping of natural
gas to the East Coast are changing the nature of domestic production. Inland and West Coast refineries have had to shift to
greater output of gasoline, diesel oil, lubricants and specialty
products, leaving the heavy oil market to Venezuela. The majors
with big Venezuelan production—Standard of New Jersey, Gulf,
and Shell—can take advantage of this shift; those dependent
on domestic crude have to make the heavy capital outlay in
refinery equipment that can convert their own residual into more
marketable products.[3]

Gasoline is the industry's big money-maker, for it encounters no competition from any other product. Its disposal at a profitable price is the main aim of the industry. What is left, by and large, is sold for whatever the market will bear. Fuel oil, for example, is competitive with coal; the petrochemicals with coal-tar chemicals.

A good bit of argument has raged around the exact source of the industry's profitability. Is it in the production of crude, in the control over pipe lines, in the refineries, or at the gas station? For the integrated company, all four sections seem to be needed to assure overall profitability. Marketing may be run at a loss but the majors feel that without control over the retail market, profitability will be affected further back in the line. Pipe line profits, while imposing, are merely a bookkeeping affair, for the companies can charge themselves as much or as little as they choose for transporting their own product. Refining is an essential bottleneck of the industry kept out of reach of overweening independents. But the real money, most oil people agree, is in the production of crude, and the rest of the apparatus merely protects that vital source from which all blessings flow. Standard of California, for example, says it costs 88 cents to produce and market a barrel of crude, sold for $2.90.[4]

Although the practical oilman sees profitability mostly in the production of crude and in its sale as gasoline, to the economist such reasoning seems largely metaphysical. For the industry is in truth monolithic and not merely an assembly of parts and divisions. The fact that consumers can be charged prices far in excess of total costs of production, refining, transport, and marketing is the real source of profit. For those companies with access to cheap foreign crude, the profits become colossal.

The practical oilman can justify his own approach to the question of profitability only because at the two ends of the industry, production and marketing, there are a number of independents. Hence there are prices to be set for crude oil and for gasoline and other products; the resulting price pattern leads to calculations as to which sector is the more profitable. But for the integrated majors, the question of which sector is more profitable is merely a matter of accounting—for them it is the entire integrated operation that is profitable.

LEADING REFINERIES

		Crude Oil Capacity (thousand barrels a day)
Jersey Standard (Humble)	Baytown, Tex.	282
Jersey Standard (Esso)	Baton Rouge, La.	265.6
Gulf	Port Arthur, Tex.	245
Texas Company	Port Arthur, Tex.	210
Indiana Standard	Whiting, Ind.	195
Gulf	Philadelphia, Pa.	183
Socony (Magnolia)	Beaumont, Tex.	182.5
Cities Service	Lake Charles, La.	175
Shell	Wood River, Ill.	170
California Standard	Richmond, Calif.	165
Jersey Standard (Esso)	Linden, N. J.	163.4
Sun	Marcus Hook, Pa.	145
Indiana Standard (Pan Am)	Texas City, Tex.	145
Atlantic	Philadelphia, Pa.	142.9
Shell	Houston, Tex.	125
Socony (General Petroleum)	Torrance, Calif.	125
Sinclair	Houston, Tex.	125
California Standard	El Segundo, Calif.	120
Richfield (Sinclair-Cities Service)	Watson, Calif.	115
Sinclair	East Chicago, Ind.	110
Sinclair	Marcus Hook, Pa.	100

("Petroleum Refineries, including Cracking Plants, in the United States," Bureau of Mines Information Circular 7693, U. S. Department of the Interior.) The figures are as of January 1, 1955.

Part III

The Jungle of the Market

10

The Marketing of Gasoline

THE test of the production controls in the oil fields is found in the market. After the crude has been tamed in the pipe lines and processed in the refineries its products flow to some 200,000 filling stations which take in $9 billion a year. If the price for gasoline is the same at every major station in a community, the controls are in good shape and the profits roll in to shame Mammon himself.

This achievement is the crowning glory of the petroleum cartel, justifying its every ingenuity, from the geophysical crews on the prowl in the fields through to the towering refineries. To regiment a market where any free enterpriser with a few thousand dollars may open a filling station is a tribute to the infinite capacity of the dominant firms to assure their dominance.

It looks like chaos: on every sizable Four Corners of the country are posted four stations flaunting the emblem of the majors—Esso, Flying Red Horse, That Good Gulf, Texaco Star, and the rest. Here, hundreds of millions of dollars are thrown around in a seemingly senseless competition to sell gasoline of the same octane rating at the same price, but the annual financial reports show that it is good sound business.

Some 80 percent of the 200,000 stations are directly controlled by the majors. Some are owned outright; others are leased, to escape chain-store taxes in some states, or to avoid the provisions of social security and labor laws. But the lessee, that symbol of free enterprise in the industry, is tied either by contract or understanding to his supplier, and to no other.

This is in flat defiance of the Clayton Act which forbids manufacturing corporations to tie lessees or purchasers to them in exclusive dealer bonds with a view to lessening competition, creating a monopoly, or fixing prices. But the Clayton Act is what the courts say it is, and in fact the exclusive dealer contracts exist in a vague borderland between outright illegality and judicial sanction. The dealer, whether wholesaler or retailer, is a part of the major's marketing apparatus. His real freedom is the privilege of absorbing the losses incidental to the hazards of the market.

Let it not be said that the majors have mastered the market without effort. Indeed the scene resembles nothing so much as a cage of wild animals confronting the trainer who fends off the beasts with whip and blank bullets and forces them to their tasks. Rare that year when the Department of Justice is not prosecuting a major company—or a group of them; when the Federal Trade Commission is not investigating the jungle practices of the market; and there never has been a time when the jobbers were not snarling back at their suppliers, demanding more "margin"—that fraction of a cent which separates them from the ranks of the ruined.

And ceaselessly the majors contend with each other for "gallonage," knocking off a fraction of a cent here to a big industry or utility, indulging in rebates disguised as "service," striving to increase even by a hundredth of a percent their share of the market. In trade organizations, they preach endlessly the need for "ethics," for maintaining at whatever cost a united front to the public on price; on the job, the sales managers prowl the jungle for accounts, for gimmicks to delude the customers, for sly advantages within the letter of the industry's own law.

No wonder the industry feels injured when it is said by the uninformed that there is no competition. Competition rages on every conceivable front, in every conceivable manner—with but one exception: the price of gasoline must be identical in every "ethical" station.

The costs involved in this priceless competition are staggering, but they are borne for the most part by the owners of 50 million autos and trucks. That is their tough luck, not the industry's.

Harry F. Sinclair, a leading magnate, put it succinctly: "We have over-built service stations, wasted manpower, crosshauled

millions and millions of unnecessary miles and thrown away
hundreds of millions of dollars in marketing expenses." A
survey by his company showed that 35 percent of the stations
then in use would be enough to serve the public adequately and
conveniently. But this waste, Sinclair added, is attributable "to
our system of 'free enterprise' which we are fighting to maintain."

Sinclair adduced a survey made by the industry in 1932 which
said the excess capacity of service stations represented an over-
investment of $1 billion, and caused an annual waste of $455
million, the equivalent of 2½ cents added to the price of each
gallon of gasoline. Of 156,000 stations, 111,000 were said to be
unnecessary. A more recent survey made by the industry in a
community of 85,000 revealed 16 bulk plants of which 13 could
be closed; 37 tank trucks where 9 were needed; 315 filling stations
of which 187 were marked for abandonment because of the war
emergency. Another survey, in California, showed 8600 of 12,600
stations to be unneeded.[1]

In the two "open ends" of the industry—production and marketing—there is a notable similarity in practice. If Smith sinks a well
on his property, Jones on the next piece must promptly sink an
offset; so if Esso builds a station on one corner then Texaco must
offset on the kitty-corner. If Gulf builds a new station that
glistens with shiny steel and chrome, then Texaco's station, built
across the street in the style of the late '30s, must be scrapped to
make way for even more flashiness. Actually, the majors spend
tens of thousands of dollars a year just to study the whims of
motorists which cause them to choose one station instead of
another. These learned surveys use the latest in sociostatistical
techniques to determine why a driver prefers to pay 29.5 cents a
gallon in one station rather than 29.5 cents a gallon at another.
It is a fine question, fraught with "psychology," the waywardness
of the human animal, and the glories of "service." It is important,
too, when there is one station for every 200 autos.

The question is even more important when it comes to maintaining major control of the market. The independent marketer
cannot afford the extravagant prices paid for purchase or lease
of desirable locations or for the shiny surfaces and sumptuous
fittings of the new stations. So the majors control some 85 percent

of all gasoline marketed. If overequipment, overdevelopment and overinstallation in pumps and stations equal 100 percent, as the president of the National Petroleum Marketers Association once declared, that is the price paid by the consumer for the lordly profits reported each year by the majors. Not even the crisis in Korea, with its consequent shortage in steel and other critical materials, could stem the waste. Toward the end of 1951, it was predicted that 24,000 service stations would be built in 1952, twice as many as in 1951.[2]

In broad outline, the mechanics of distribution is simple. Refined products flow from the refineries via pipe and tank car to distributing centers. From some 28,000 "bulk stations," tank trucks pick up their cargoes for filling stations and for industrial and commercial accounts. The majors own about 20,000 of these bulk stations. Products not marketed directly by the majors are handled by some 8000 jobbers, of whom 80 percent have contracts with the majors. Jobber margins fluctuate around 2 cents a gallon on gasoline while the retail station margin is around 3½ cents, more or less.

Most service stations bearing a company name are owned by the company and leased to operators on a gallonage basis, usually 1 cent out of his 3½-cent margin. The majors maintain pilot stations to give them a yardstick in gauging market operations. A lessee falling down on gallonage can be forced out quickly —sometimes the lease calls for 24-hour cancellation, sometimes 10 days or 30 days.

Dealers are obliged to carry a full line of company products known in the trade as "TBA" (tires, batteries, accessories) as well as "lubes" (lubricating oils and greases).

In the olden days, the Standard Oil empire was divided into 11 geographical provinces each ruled over by a subsidiary. During the past forty years, the rise of non-Standard majors has altered the pattern somewhat, but in general there are still "price leaders" who call the tune in the various marketing regions. The usual procedure is for a leading major to announce a change in crude or in "tank-wagon" price of gasoline, or in fuel oil. Within a few days, other majors announce that they, too, are changing their prices in accordance with the "market." Sometimes a major, after feeling about, announces a price change and then sits back nervously to see whether its lead will be accepted. This happened in 1953 when Socony, Sinclair, and Atlantic announced an increase in gasoline prices in the New York market. Standard of New Jersey, replete with profits and unwilling to disturb the goose that lays the golden eggs, demurred. Dutifully the smaller companies retreated and withdrew the price advance.[3] In 1948, Phillips upped the price of crude from $2.65 to $3 and Sinclair eagerly followed suit. The Standard companies—Humble and Magnolia—vetoed the increase. Phillips and Sinclair reluctantly rescinded their advances, bitterly blaming companies whose cheap foreign imported oil kept domestic producers in leash. Standard of New Jersey responded a few months later with slashes in prices on heavy fuel oils in order to find larger markets for its Venezuelan product. This cut the domestic refiners' margin on this product by 25 cents a barrel and led to acute embarrassment of mid-continent refiners, caught in the Standard scissors.[4]

In connection with this incident, J. H. Carmical, petroleum editor of the *New York Times*, explained the price situation to his readers with charming candor. Heavy fuel oil had been cut, he related, because many industrial and utilities companies had begun converting to coal. There would be no corresponding cuts in other oil products, he explained, because the Texas Railroad Commission had reduced production allowables there, and the companies themselves had cut production in Venezuela so that "with cut-backs in crude oil production, the industry hopes that it will be able to maintain prices. In this connection, it is pointed out that there are no substitutes for gasoline."[5]

The crosscurrents in price-fixing came under Carmical's scrutiny:

> Involved in the apparent strategy to hold prices, however, is the ability to prevent an excess crude oil production in Texas and Venezuela, while at the same time expanding the output of the Middle East. For political and other reasons, the companies operating in the Middle East feel that it would be unwise not to expand operations there as rapidly as possible.

Although the cost of producing crude oil abroad is much less than in the United States, there is the chance that imports at the present rate may not have a decided influence on prices of any products except heavy fuel oil. This is contingent upon the ability of the regulatory bodies of the oil-producing states to hold production in check so that a large proportion of the excess foreign production may be absorbed here until it can be marketed advantageously outside the United States.

A year later Carmical was able to add a footnote to his comment:

Normally such drastic reductions as were made in fuel oil prices [in 1949] would have resulted in a downward adjustment in gasoline prices. However, since there was no substitute for gasoline and since demand was increasing, the price was increased moderately in an effort to absorb some of the loss from other price reductions. With the regulatory bodies holding crude oil production in line with demand, the gasoline market held generally firm until late in the year when some price concessions were being made.[6]

The *National Petroleum News* was curt with consumer protests over the situation as outlined by Carmical. "Gasoline consumers," it editorialized, "instead of complaining that oil companies are discriminating against them in raising gasoline prices when distillate and heavy fuel prices are being reduced, should thank their lucky stars that there is no OPA around to prevent this natural operation of the competitive free enterprise system."[7]

That didn't mollify Senator Homer Ferguson, Republican, of Michigan, who said: "A cold winter and short supplies of fuel oil tend to boost gasoline prices. Likewise a warm winter has the effect of driving up gasoline prices. Heavy petroleum imports are used to justify a rise in gasoline prices, but an inadequate foreign supply does the same. And so on."[8]

A plausible breakdown of the price of a gallon of gasoline in New York City in 1949[9] showed these proportions, according to an Associated Press report (the industry is chary of giving such breakdowns):

Cost of crude at the well	6.20 cents
Piping to refinery	.50
Refinery labor	.67
Other refinery costs	1.00
Refinery profit	1.63
Tanker, Gulf to New York	1.20
Delivery to station	2.20
Storage, etc.	.57
Distributor's profit	.33
Total	14.30
U. S. tax	1.50
New York state tax	4.00
Station markup	5.70-6.20
Retail price	26 cents

A. L. Nickerson, a director of Socony-Vacuum, was called upon by the Senate Subcommittee on Small Business in 1949 to explain why gasoline sold at 14.06 cents, retail, without tax, in Manchester, New Hampshire, and at 15.20 cents, without tax, in Little Rock, Arkansas, near the heart of the oil country. "Transportation costs can be very misleading," Nickerson explained. "Prices at varying points, at varying times, will be different."[10]

It really is difficult to explain, as the majors are the first to admit. For example, when a company does a business of $6 billion a year and makes a profit of a half billion, produces a thousand and one products emanating from dozens of refineries and tens of thousands of wells in a dozen different countries, it is certainly almost impossible to say what a gallon of gasoline costs. The major companies can't even "reveal" whether they make any money at all on marketing, according to the National Oil Jobbers Council, which said that replies on this point from 24 majors were "unsatisfactory," "evasive" or "unrevealing."[11]

It has been said that this mysterious price system is based on "Tulsa plus." Some gasoline is offered on the "spot tank car" market in Tulsa by smaller refineries, and this is bought by the majors at a price said to be influenced by the "market." Prices along the Great Lakes are then based on this price plus tank car transportation. Of course the oil moves by pipe, and the addition of the cost of transport by tank car is as purely imagina-

tive as the Tulsa spot tank car market, which independents claim
is rigged.

There are also transient offerings of gasoline and other products
by small refineries on the Gulf Coast. This establishes the market
price, plus transportation, in New York harbor. Until recently
this "market" in Houston even ruled the price of Middle Eastern
oil.

Perhaps the subject of price still is not too clear. Let us try
to explain it in another way, then. Briefly, it may be stated that
heavy fuel oils sell at a price competitive with coal. Gasoline,
being noncompetitive, is priced at what the market will bear—
a most subtle calculation. Other oil products sell on calculations
based on their place in a spectrum which runs from genuinely
competitive to naturally monopolistic.

Standard of New Jersey, stuffed as it is with the superprofits
of Venezuelan and Middle Eastern production, does not care,
apparently, to make more than 17 cents profit on each dollar
of sales, for fear it will excite too much curiosity and/or cupidity in Congress and elsewhere. This condemns the smaller majors
and others sections of the industry, dependent mainly on domestic production, to smaller profit margins than they otherwise
could earn. That is why, when the smaller majors occasionally
extend a paw to grab an extra margin on price, they are slapped
back by Jersey, unless it feels safe in increasing its own lofty
profit figure.

As for the consumer, the oil companies feel that counterattack
is better than defense when it comes to explaining the price of
gasoline at the pump. Union Oil, in full-page ads, inserted at a
time when prices had just been upped, asked "WHY AREN'T
GASOLINE PRICES HIGHER?" If the consumer plowed through
to the end of the ad, he felt lucky that he paid only 30 cents a
gallon instead of 50.[12]

11

The Jobber and the Major

SPARKS from the friction between jobber and major illuminate dark corners of the oil industry. The spectacular price wars that break out from time to time, the dealers' strikes with their lurid headlines, the seepage of gasoline into cut-rate stations—all these are outward signs of the desperate struggles of wholesale jobbers and retail dealers to resist cuts in their margins, to maintain these margins or to raise them.

The rule of capture in marketing revolves, for the jobbers and dealers, around margins; for the majors, around gallonage. These factors of margin and gallonage interplay; for the majors are not only producers, refiners, and transporters but also wholesalers and retailers themselves, in competition with quasi-independent jobbers and dealers bound tightly to them by more or less manifest exclusive dealing contracts.* In addition, a fifth of the marketing end is in the hands of "independents," whose independence involves also their dependence on the majors for their source of supply.

These independents are precious, in a way, to the majors, for they prove that competition exists within the industry, that any man with get-up-and-go and guts and a little money can carve himself a slice of the profits. But the independents, whether tied by exclusive dealing contracts or on their own, find their role as free enterprisers rather circumscribed by the fact that their sup-

* According to a compilation by the Oil Industry Information Committee in 1952, there were 44,000 business enterprises engaged in producing, refining, transporting, and wholesaling petroleum products. In the retail field were 188,000 service stations, of which 177,000 were single-unit establishments classified as separate businesses. The OIIC counted 14,000 wholesale bulk stations, 11,000 fuel oil dealers, 5500 bottled gas dealers.

pliers are also their competitors. The district manager of the major
cannot resist the temptation to grab away the independent's juicy
commercial or industrial customers; the independent can hardly
match the major in bidding for expensive leases on lucrative corners, or in building flashy "superservice" stations, nor can he
sponsor operas and symphonies, no matter how his heart throbs
with love of the fine arts.

To defend themselves, the jobbers and dealers have an amazing
patchwork of organizations, local, state, and national. These are
policed in a friendly way by the big-brother majors who counter
the pressures of the harried jobbers with suave arguments to show
how lucky they are to be in business at all. These organizations
might be said to run an accurate fever chart of the market; at
times their caterwauling makes the day hideous for the majors.
They are adroit in catching the ears of Congressmen susceptible
to the cries of free enterprisers being ground into the dust by
monopoly, and they make the most of their Rotary and Lions
Club connections to arouse distrust of "the industry." As this is a
thorn in the side of public relations for the majors, they react with
mollifications, divisions, and insults. But on one point they are
firm: they do not intend to engage in any collective bargaining
with jobbers and retailers. President A. A. Stambaugh of Standard
of Ohio complained in 1949 to the Ohio Petroleum Marketers
Association that they were trying to introduce collective bargaining as a club to beat bigger margins out of the majors. Such
bargaining, he lectured them, excludes the customer from
consideration, smacks of socialism, and leads to Communism.
Nevertheless the angry Ohio marketers, who were just trying to
get a little more profit, went on record as favoring the divorce of
the majors from their pipe lines, if not from marketing altogether.[1]

The majors do make concessions of various kinds from time to
time, when the pressure gets too raucous. The margin may be
upped a trifle, the "lip" of the jobbers' organization may be
greased a bit to tone down his utterances, or stooges within the
organization may be encouraged to cut his throat. Despite
President Stambaugh's resolute stand against collective bargaining with his jobbers and dealers, the struggle shows a marked

resemblance to the troubles the majors have with the union of their own workers.

The situation becomes so bad at times that the American Petroleum Institute, the supreme court of the industry, takes a hand. In its 1951 convention the API invited Otis H. Ellis, of the National Oil Jobbers Council, to the rostrum to speak his piece. It ran this way:

(1) The jobber feels he is a tolerated sector of the industry only because of the existence of the antitrust laws.

(2) Local managers for the majors are mere "puppets," but they are the only contact the jobbers have with their suppliers.

(3) The jobber feels he has nothing to say about his contract. He gets "a mass of words that he either accepts or he gives up his supplier." There are no explanations of changes in the contract. Take it or leave it, he is told.

(4) The jobber deeply resents the majors selling to commercial customers at prices less than are charged to the jobber himself. Is the jobber not to "get any of the cream, but only the crumbs"?

(5) In times of shortage, the jobber feels he is pinched while the major covers the requirements of its own direct customers.[2]

The result of this speech was that the majors invited the jobbers to consult with the majors' managers. Round tables were arranged to permit the jobbers to get their beefs off their chests. This followed good psychiatric practice and permitted the majors a good inside view of who are the real "agitators." While this covered Ellis's Point 2 in a way, none of the other points was dealt with. A good bit of praise was directed toward the National Oil Jobbers Council for cooperating in this healthy venture and it did seem, for a time, that talking out grievances is a fair way of handling them.[3]

The South Carolina Oil Jobbers Association was not satisfied with this approach, however. After all, the margins were no better than before, despite the round tables and the soothing explanations given by the majors' managers. The Association decided, after a survey, that the majors must be divorced from marketing, a stand that won unanimous endorsement from its members.[4]

The oil industry, said the South Carolina survey, is the only example of integration in manufacturing and merchandising in this country. The jobbers laughed at the bugaboo of governmental controls in divorcement:

> This approach assumes that there are no controls today. Actually the controls that exist are perfect for the oil producers and the integrated oil companies. Because these controls are so suited for their purposes they like to make you believe that the oil industry operates under the free enterprise system. . . .
>
> Competition in the marketing end of the oil business by integrated oil companies is unfair to those engaged only in marketing. As the trend toward extension and absorption of the marketing outlets continues, the monopolistic hold on the oil industry grows more complete. The integrated companies are fortified by profits from production of crude oil, refining operations and pipe line and tanker transportation. They thus can use profits from the more profitable branches of the industry to absorb losses in marketing.

The report cited depletion allowances, duties on imported crude, state proration laws, the Connally hot oil act, the Interstate Oil Compact, and the monthly U. S. Bureau of Mines forecast as the means by which the majors are assured profits from the production of crude oil.

The South Carolina jobbers stated that the majors operate their marketing at a loss. "That statement may be challenged but no major oil company has opened its books to disclose the actual costs of operating its marketing division. Where disclosures have been made in required public filing only losses have appeared." If such figures are revealed, and show profits, the report added, they should be checked to see whether the wholesale department is charged on the same basis that is allowed to jobbers, and to make sure that all costs, including advertising, are included.

The *National Petroleum News,* everybody's friend in the industry, warned the little fellows that there are worse perils in the jungle than the majors. It was fearful that "men who are Rotary and Chamber of Commerce leaders in their home towns were seriously talking about asking the government to step in and impose regulation that they knew they were opposed to in principle." The organ admitted that independent marketers read with some grimness the glowing reports about major profits while their own drooped. One group of jobbers had even bought newspaper space to explain that they weren't responsible for higher prices and the fantastic profits of the majors but were actually making more money when the majors' profits were lower.[5]

The trade paper conducted a survey of its own, which resulted in these comments:

The big problem is "maintaining a decent margin between product costs and product selling prices, both of which are set by major companies." (Arkansas)

"Monopoly—big business with unfair tactics and unlimited capital." (Florida)

"Very small margin on TBA in our locality." (Georgia)

"To be assured of a permanent source of supply that is competitive in quality and cost to that of major companies." (Missouri)

"The small spread the major companies allow the jobbers on the products they handle. A major sets the gasoline price in this territory, and we are forced to follow." (New Mexico)

"The majors—I am *agin' 'em*. So much good could be accomplished if they'd break bread with the jobbers, instead of giving backdoor handouts, and those mouldy at times." (Tennessee)

"Major companies are paying prices for property and service station construction that are out of this world for a jobber." (Texas)

"When we started in business, the spread from the refinery to the dealer was 7 cents, of which the distributor received 4 cents and the dealer 3 cents. Today the distributor receives less than 3 cents, and the dealer the rest of the spread." (Pennsylvania)[6]

Divorcement of marketing from the rest of the majors' activities is the big stick brandished by many a jobber organization to put the fear of the Lord into the big companies. When the majors, responding in 1952 to a questionnaire, stated that they could not divorce marketing costs from other costs, the National Oil Jobbers Council drew the obvious conclusion that these operations were conducted at a loss. With mock solicitude, the Council prayed the majors to divorce themselves not only from marketing but from the heavy losses they incurred in that branch of the industry.

The president of the Northwest Petroleum Association condemned "some people in big business—a minority to be sure—who talk free enterprise while at the same time doing everything possible to crush the small businessman, just as though he were a foreign enemy." The independents do not begrudge the majors their fast tax write-offs on new plants and their depletion allowances, "but when that money is used to subsidize marketing losses to put the independent jobber out of business, then he begins to wonder and knows that something is wrong."[7]

Such suspicions left the *National Petroleum News* cold. It pooh-poohed the idea that the money was in the pipe lines, and it was well known that the refineries weren't the source of all wealth because of the number of independent refineries shutting down, and it was notorious that there were enormous losses in production. The money must be in distribution, and the jobbers were barking up the wrong tree.[8]

Nevertheless, the trade paper admitted that "there is too much ill feeling against the major oil companies generating among jobbers, commission agents and dealers for the good of the industry as a whole these days. First thing the majors know the government at Washington will be out slugging at them still more with the various state governments probably joining in." The editor added that "the fumbling and shortsightedness of the top brass of the industry and its disregard of others in the industry" was responsible for a lot of the industry's troubles, including slender margins for jobbers.[9]

Chairman John Harper of the National Oil Jobbers Council harked back to the old issue of deficits in the majors' marketing activities. "Many majors," he said, "are frank to admit they lose money in their marketing divisions, and I don't believe any major's marketing division can stand on its own feet without the use of profits, credit standings and investment capital from other divisions."[10] Jobbers, he insisted, do a better marketing job than the majors.

The National Oil Marketers Association, looking over the controlled petroleum field, was reported as finding that "existing laws, decrees, orders and activities of the federal and state governments regulating the petroleum industry have resulted in the monopoly of such industry by a small group of integrated companies." Consumers, it said, were not protected thereby from "inordinately high prices." The Association hit straight at the heart of the business by urging that state conservation laws be repealed, along with the Connally hot oil act, that Congressional approval be withdrawn from the Interstate Oil Compact Act, and that appropriations be withheld from the U. S. Bureau of Mines to stop it from forecasting so-called market demand.[11]

Paul Blazer of Ashland Oil & Refining, an independent, told the Empire State Petroleum Association that the industry, already "grossly misunderstood" by the public and the government, had better drop price-matching, quality uniformity, pipe line gouging, exchanges of products, and extravagant advertising claims. The majors, he said, are responsible for "twice as many service stations as we need."[12]

The Association condemned the majors for the extravagance by which they dominated the marketing field. Practices such as offering to furnish and install new equipment where the volume did not justify the investment, making improvements in stations at no expense to the dealer, arranging for loans at low rates of interest, giving commercial accounts lower discounts than those allowed jobbers, purchasing or leasing sites and erecting buildings at costs greatly in excess of the potential volume of business—all these contributed to the top-heavy marketing situation at costs the independent marketer was unable to meet, or which tied him irrevocably to the supplier.[13]

Otis H. Ellis, of the National Oil Jobbers Council, warned that the majors themselves were writing the jobbers' recommendations on the subject of divorcing marketing from the rest of the industry. If margins continued to shrink, commercial accounts to be stolen, and similar manipulations continued, the jobbers would have no alternative but to seek federal relief.[14]

The *National Petroleum News* was worried. The majors, it said, seem to think the demand for divorcement comes solely from "uninformed congressmen and from social schemers in the Department of Justice, who are bent on knocking out 'big business,' if for no other reason than because it is 'big.'" The truth is, said NPN, that it is the marketers of petroleum who are behind the demand for divorcement.

"The Independent competitors," it said, "believe that the policy of the majors toward them is ruthless, unthinking, disregardful of their rights and best interests and, with some people, that major policy is even actually planned for the purpose of drying up competition. . . . There is still a widespread belief that the majors make a whale of profits in their producing, pipe lining and refining with which they subsidize excessive losses in marketing for the purpose of driving competition out." Such foolish notions, the trade paper added, indicated "more and stronger competition" as a dire need for the majors themselves.[15]

The paper asked for "top-level" meetings between the majors and the National Oil Jobbers Council. "The majors have stepped on the Independents so many times over the past score of years, dating back into the code days, and made them sit for hours on the hard cold benches in the outer hall, that it might seem gracious if the American Petroleum Institute made the first overture."[16]

The majors, indeed, ought to quit flaunting those strident signs proclaiming the Socony Flying Red Horse, That Good Gulf, Esso, and so on, for it gives people the impression that they dominate the industry. How much better it would be if the signs displayed "Johnny Jones Oil Co." in much larger letters. On an auto trip from Cleveland to Boston, the editor said, the only signs he saw of the existence of competition in oil were a jobber's truck climbing a hill in Pennsylvania and a small sign under a bridge in Hartford. It's things like that, he said, that give the public the impression there is no competition.[17]

The independents continually debate all the differing ways of belling the cat. Some are for divorcement, others for cutting out the various federal and state laws limiting production. The Georgia Independent Oilmen's Association asked for federal price controls all along the line, fixing margins by law.[18] They also put the finger on major policy of undercutting jobbers by direct sales to commercial accounts and discrimination against them in times of scarcity. "We want the public to know," the

Georgians announced, "and the major companies to remember, that our segment of the petroleum industry received no part of the many price increases of the past. . . . The sooner we begin calling names, the more impressive we can be in bringing about fair play on the majors' part."[19]

The North Carolina Oil Jobbers Association discussed a proposal to set up a refinery of their own to escape the rigid market control of the majors in that sector. The Ohio Petroleum Marketers Association said it would be satisfied with nothing less than a half-cent rise in the margin to save "the jobbers from business extinction and to correct a very unpleasant attitude toward suppliers."

The Tennessee Oil Men's Association plugged for a three-point program including higher margins by "any governmental or legal means available," possible divorcement if relief could be had no other way, and refusal to support the industry's propaganda service unless the majors played ball.[20]

In neighboring South Carolina, the organized jobbers pointed out that divorcement had worked in the meat and movie industries. The jobbers' secretary said that, as a former marketing official for majors, all that had been asked of him was "to keep out of the red." "Shooting par on the course was considered pretty darned good," he said.[21]

The official paper of the Wisconsin Petroleum Association seemed to have lost its patience:

> For the past two years we have been flooded with literature, pep talks and what-not about public relations and that petroleum is progressive. NUTS! What's progressive about an industry that stymies and stifles its very backbone, the fellow on the firing line, the independent marketer. What we need is a better industry relations program and then the public program will take care of itself.
>
> Too long now we have attempted to settle the issue by diplomacy, tact and every other peaceful means in the book, but to no avail—what we need now is another good "Madison Trial" with some good, forceful governmental control. This looks as though it might be the only way to settle the problem.[22]

In 1949, Senator Gillette of Iowa introduced three bills to divorce the majors from their transportation and marketing divisions. He said that independent jobbers were "practically unanimous" in support of the measures. The Iowa Independent Oil Jobbers Association backed him up, and the jobbers' division of the Kentucky Petroleum Marketers Association said they would support the National Oil Jobbers Council in seeking divorcement.[23]

As the issue of divorcement became critical, the *National Petroleum News* pondered the need for integration. Would it not be better for the majors to survive three-fourths integrated than to be broken altogether in some political blowup?

"Those who say," it counseled, "that the oil industry must be completely integrated close their eyes to some most obvious facts and the strange thing is that some college professors of economics, who more and more are being called on by major oil companies for advice, seem to be the most blind to some of the facts. Such professors say the majors cannot allocate to company functions various parts of their equipment investments, operating costs and inventory. They just wave their hands and blandly say, 'it can't be divided.'"

But the majors had their reasons to fight divorcement. Marketing might be unprofitable, but the losses incurred in that branch of the industry nourished the price structure by which the rest of the industry maintained its overall profits. A. L. Nickerson, of Socony-Vacuum, knew that. He was alarmed by the divorcement propaganda and denounced it as "socialistic experiments" which give "aid and comfort to our enemies" in these trying times. "Our government," he said in 1950, "cannot afford to indulge in political manipulation and socialistic and ideological experiments under today's conditions. They must be immediately and ruthlessly eliminated. . . . If the divorcement of marketing is but a step in the ultimate drive for complete disintegration of the industry, it assumes a distinctly dangerous and subversive aspect."[24]

The Socony man had put his finger on a sore spot. Where would this talk of divorcement end? Morris Parker indicated the terminal point. Vice-president of the Central West Oil Corporation of South Bend, Indiana, president of the Indiana Independent Petroleum Association, and a member of the National Oil Jobbers Council, Mr. Parker put it in these words:

> We independent marketers do feel that the concentration of capital which is taking place in the producing, transportation and refining branches of the industry will ultimately bring about a condition where the major companies can, if they so will, take profits that might be hard to justify. If such a situation comes about, it will surely bring nationalization of the industry.[25]

Chickens, it seemed, were coming home to roost. The marketing end of the industry, snubbed and rebuffed by the majors, saw no hope in the industry or in its representatives, the American Petroleum Institute and the National Petroleum Council.[26]* The *National Petroleum News* minced no words:

> The jobbers have been so snubbed by the API in the past . . . that the API has had little or no support worthy the name from Independents. . . . The API, considered as a representative chiefly of the major companies, cannot possibly have the standing it should have as if recognized as representing also and fairly the Independents. . . .
> The top brass in the industry and in Washington should also re-study jobber representation on the National Petroleum Council which does not carry the influence today with the Independents that it should by any means. So far as the jobber is concerned—15,000 of them—the Council may more accurately be said to be looked upon as an adjunct of the API.[27]

The trade paper in 1952 had run an editorial bewailing Humble's heavy expenditures for new equipment and begging that the government be more generous in depreciation allowances. F. C. Weiss, a Toledo distributor, wrote his own comment, published in *National Petroleum News*:

> You're breaking my heart! Let's all get together and pass out the crying towels and weep for the poor, poor Humble Oil & Refining Company, who only made $169,480,000 last

* The formation of the NPC is discussed below, page 180.

year. What about the poor Jobber—who ended the same year in the red? Where is HE going to get the money to replace HIS equipment?

Since World War Two, the Jobber has sat back and watched the Major Oil Companies raise the price of gasoline to the consuming public a total of seven cents per gallon. How much of this has been passed on to the Jobber?

I can only speak for my own company—NOT ONE DAMN CENT![28]

Perhaps the final word should be left to Otis H. Ellis, spokesman for the National Oil Jobbers Council. The Council's questionnaire to the majors about their marketing costs had elicited from one company the statement that perhaps "marketing economics" would not permit higher margins—in other words, why should the majors pay higher margins to independents when they could do the whole job themselves and keep the margin? If that is true, exploded Ellis:

> I will then reverse my position on divorcement, on depletion allowances and my current beliefs on so-called "free, competitive enterprise" and do battle with all the facilities at my command before the Federal Trade Commission, the Department of Justice and the Congress of the United States to tear apart the power of integration which is the only thing that could ever cause such a condition.[29]

In 1955, as in many a previous year, a Congressional committee was investigating the source and reason for the anguished wails in the marketing jungle; the jobbers' organizations were protesting over margins and the loss of fat commercial accounts to their supplier-competitors and were filing complaints with the Department of Justice and in federal courts; and Ellis was again announcing: "I was never closer to changing my mind about divorcement than I am right now."[30]

The majors' "greed for gallonage" nullified the laborious educational work of the American Petroleum Institute among the little independent dealers and continued to raise up, within the ranks of the industry itself, a potent disaffected faction. Here were allies, indeed, in any determined push in the future to challenge overweening monopoly.

12

Trouble in the Market

THE strangest show this oil industry has ever seen," commented *National Petroleum News,* as it reviewed the 1950 dealers' strike in New Jersey. The dealers, tormented by price wars, not only shut up shop but formed cavalcades which visited gasoline stations still open, persuading them—sometimes at gunpoint, according to the trade paper—to close, too. They then paraded to Trenton to demand that the governor do something about price-cutting.

The strike, warned *National Petroleum News,* was a sheer conspiracy to fix prices. Small business men needn't think *they* can agree to raise prices just because they're small, they were told.[1]

The governor named a commission to look into the dealers' grievances. It reported:

> General retail price levels of graded and branded gasoline are somewhat artificial in nature and not responsive to the governing economic law of supply and demand. The relative stability of prices under "normal" conditions, and the lack of price reduction when a surplus market exists, tends to prove the fact that prices are governed more by mutual understanding between associate, affiliate and even competitive marketing agencies than by economic factors.[2]

The commission concluded that, the retail price level "being built upon artificial support, it is not unlikely that gasoline price wars are the result of the collapse of this price structure agreement. . . . The public benefited through lower prices" although "the dealers themselves are in an unenviable position." The commission offered slight solace to the dealers. "Though their income from the sale of gasoline has visibly declined due to the closing of the gap between cost and sales price through the pressure of competition, it is a matter between the dealer and the company he represents and not a problem calling for some form of governmental control."

National Petroleum News was perturbed that three conservative businessmen who composed the governor's commission should have so misunderstood the price situation. More must be done, it urged, to "explain how competition works in marketing at the service station. . . . The industry has only itself to blame for leaving too much to the lively imagination of committee and public."[3]

Price wars are the other side of the fixed-price coin. At times a fever breaks out in the usually well-controlled body of oil marketing. The causes are many. Near the oil fields, supplies may be seeping outside the controlled channels. In and around great metropolitan centers, a temporary surplus may need to be disposed of without injuring the permanent price structure. In such cases the majors, rather than let their regular dealers cut prices, may sell their surplus cheaper to unbranded dealers. In congested areas the prospect of heavier turnover may induce some dealers to entice more trade through price reductions. Or, as the *National Petroleum News* says, the jobber's or dealer's margin may not be narrow enough to keep him from having "big ideas" about increased gallonage through price-cutting. Or the supplier may give subsidies to certain dealers which encourage them to increase gallonage, in the covert war constantly waged among the majors themselves. And when the majors make direct deals with big consumer accounts at prices below those to the dealers or jobbers, these latter may cut their own prices in revenge.[4]

In Providence, Rhode Island, a price war started in May 1951. Gasoline selling normally at 25.5 cents dropped as low as 19.9. Majors subsidized their dealers to the tune of 3 cents a gallon to join in the war. Congressman Fogarty suspected that the purpose might be to "eliminate competition through below-cost sales followed by higher prices as soon as competition is wiped out."[5]

Members of the Rhode Island Independent Retail Gasoline Dealers Association, and many who had not joined that group because it "never accomplished anything," formed themselves into a local of the Teamsters Union to put a halt to the price wars that are "ruining us." This curious twist to unionism, in which the authority, stability, and financial resources of an immense labor organization were invoked to give the dealers cohesiveness they could not otherwise attain, was by no means an isolated instance. The Teamsters Union has shown itself eager in various localities to take in dealers without too much regard to their status as employers and/or employees. After all, to be technical about it, is a dealer under an exclusive dealing contract an employee or not?[6]

Sometimes a price war is aimed at an independent refinery. Such was the case in Memphis, in November-December 1952, when it was determined to hamstring the Delta cooperative refinery there, owned by the Missouri Farmers Association. The co-op was installing a catalytic cracking unit which would increase its daily throughput from 1700 to 3000 barrels. Such an expansion costs a good deal of money; if the co-op's expanding market could be throttled it would be financially embarrassed at the very time it needed working capital.

The majors' filling stations cut their retail gasoline prices 6 cents below the price charged by the co-op for wholesale quantities. The co-op stood pat and refused to cut its price. And its retailers descended upon the major stations with tank trunks and said, "Fill 'er up." That was the idea of Mrs. Josephine McKinnon, a widow running a bulk (wholesale) plant. In addition, Mrs. McKinnon yelled for the cops. They arrived from New Orleans — investigators for the Federal Trade Commission. Thanks to the spunky widow's initiative, pictures were flashed across the country showing the independents' tank trucks parked in the majors' stations. When the storage tanks ran low, the station managers refused further delivery. Filling stations, according to the lawyers, are not public utilities and need not sell to customers, and need give no reasons.

While the war lasted, it was estimated that motorists saved $450,000 on their purchases, while the majors invested $350,000 in subsidies to their dealers to permit them to cut prices. The losers were the Missouri Farmers Association and its dealers; they were not put out of business, merely crippled badly. That was the intent of the strategy — a warning to the farmers not to expect to save too much money out of their oil co-op.[7]

During this price war in Memphis, a group of major dealers in Nashville published an ad that "private" brands of gasoline, those not sponsored by the majors, are inferior. The ad caused some commotion in the industry where it is well known that certain majors supply unbranded gasoline, identical with their own branded product, to independents. The purpose is to increase gallonage and to get rid of temporary surpluses without disturbing the branded market; the effect often is to help the unbranded or private-branded product undercut the majors' own branded dealers, much to their disgust.[8]

Perhaps the sorest point in the entire country in gasoline pricing is Los Angeles. Here, in a heavily populated center without adequate public transportation, harboring within it the great oil fields of the Los Angeles Basin and a spate of small independent refineries, the price controls of the majors are sorely tested. Over the years they have been closing in on the independent refineries, driving them out of business or absorbing them. Early in 1950, one of the area's periodic price wars broke out.

Said the Service Station Dealers Association of San Fernando Valley, in ads in the press:

> When you've got too much of a product, you drop your price and sell for less. Get rid of your surplus and give the public a break. Right?
>
> Wrong! say the major oil companies. Keep right on selling for the same price to the service station dealer, but make HIM sell for less. Take away so much of his paper-thin profit that he can't afford to stay in business—and threaten him with cancellation of his lease if he complains! . . .
>
> Our worst competitors today are the corporations who sell us "gas." Don't ask US why—we don't understand it either. But it's happening.[9]

Several months later, as the price war still continued, the secretary of the Serve Yourself Gasoline Stations Association complained bitterly to the Department of Justice.* "The majors,"

---

* In the self-service stations, customers help themselves to the gasoline. The attendant—sometimes a girl dressed snappily as a majorette—merely checks the gallonage and makes change.

he said, "have devised a formula to damage us. It is a conspiracy by them to knock us—the independent self-serves—out of business." Tank wagon prices remained unchanged despite the retail price war. The majors' formula, he said, consisted of rebates, competitive allowances, and rental benefits given individual dealers, so that the listed tank wagon price was not the true price. In some cases major lessees were selling at 18.9 cents a gallon when the tank wagon price was 19.6.[10] He urged self-serves to help themselves and organize. "Recognizing that government aid is a forlorn hope and that members are faced with actuality, they had best take the threat of the majors seriously."

An obvious way out of his plight is for the independent to throw in the sponge and affiliate directly with a major. That is what Milton Oil did in 1952 in the Missouri market. This company marketed through 500 stations swinging the "Dixcel" brand name. That, incidentally, was one factor in Harry Milton's decision to abandon his independence and become a part of the Cities Service marketing setup. His 48-inch signs cost $25 apiece, but they were obsolete; Cities Service would supply 72-inch signs costing $300 apiece.

As part of Cities Service, Milton feels he can expand into fields otherwise closed to him. "The average jobber," he explained, "can't expand with a private brand and carry out an advertising program in line with that of a major company. The private brand jobber will lose out, and the majors will gain."

The majors won't supply independents when there is a shortage, Milton said, and the marketers' former reliance on independent refineries is near an end because these small companies can't afford to compete with the majors in the octane race that requires expensive modernization of their plants.

Cities Service brings the advantages of a national advertising program, of a steady supply of oil products, and its national credit card, sales-training, and promotion programs. So "Dixcel" signs came down and Cities Service signs went up—just another incident in concentration.[11]

State governments have looked into the mysteries of gasoline pricing and reported their bafflement. Often the investigators look for conspiracies in which the majors sit down together and arrive at a fixed price, formalized in a document which could be used in a court proceeding to end the monopoly. What they actually find is something too ectoplasmic to display before judges.

In North Carolina, for example, interest was aroused in the uniform price situation because periodically there were brief and violent price wars which disturbed jobbers and dealers and gave the public the idea they were being overcharged. In 1951, the governor appointed a committee to look into this.

Majority and minority reports were filed. The majority stated that it looked mighty "suspicious" that prices were always the same everywhere in the state, except for occasional price wars, but there was no proof of conspiracy, aside from inferences which might be drawn from the practically simultaneous price changes announced from time to time by the majors. The majority recommended that the state antitrust law be amended so as to remove the need to produce written evidence of agreements to fix prices.

The minority was more outspoken. The antitrust law was found to be "impotent in the face of what, in effect, is a growing monopoly that yields unprecedented profits." It advised that the state utilities commission be given power over gasoline prices similar to its authority over other utilities. The state's attorney general went even further in proposing that simultaneous price changes that followed the market leader and also posting identical prices be regarded as prima facie evidence of violating the antitrust act.

The governor's committee said that the nine majors operating in North Carolina had reported a 21 percent increase in profits, nationwide, that their profit was 1.27 to 2.53 cents a gallon, and that net earnings ranged from 8 to 13 percent of gross revenue. Esso, with 30 percent of state sales, was found to be the dominant company, and its prices the standard. It was estimated that North Carolina car owners paid $2 to $3 million more each year for gasoline than did consumers in Virginia.

One member of the committee, a retired Standard of New Jersey manager, demurred from the view that there was any discrimination in prices. Said he: "Government interference with the right of a businessman to price his product according to his best judgment is incompatible with free enterprise."[12]

The Michigan legislature was also curious about the price structure, said in that state to be dominated by Standard of Indiana. The secretary of the Michigan Petroleum Association testified in 1951 that he doubted that the majors conspired to fix prices, but added that "I must confess that the manner in which an individual refiner or supplier arrives at a given price for any certain locality or for a certain class of customers has always been clothed in a great mystery."[13]

So often has the sovereign state of Texas instituted antitrust proceedings against the major oil companies, and so fruitless have they been, that it is darkly hinted that the suits are hardly more than shake-down rackets, aimed to loosen oil lobbyists' purse strings in crucial elections.

The latest was instituted February 21, 1949, by Attorney General Price Daniel, later elevated to the U. S. Senate. He charged that ten companies made uniform, noncompetitive price raises in gasoline six times after OPA controls expired in July 1946. In 1948, eight companies cooperated to resist a rise in crude, of which they are heavy purchasers.[14] Daniel stated that the ten companies control 90 percent of the retail outlets in the state, under exclusive dealing contracts. Although each company brags of the superiority of its own gasoline, they often exchange in accordance with the convenience of the market. Texas gasoline, he charged, is sold along the Atlantic seaboard at prices lower than in Texas. The same price rules throughout Texas despite differentials in freight rates.

The *National Petroleum News* snorted that Daniel was relying on "kindergarten economics" to prove his case of uniform price being an evidence of monopoly. This is a common practice, it added, of representatives of what the trade paper called the "peepul." If the state won its case, how would the ten companies determine, the paper asked, who was to be "low man on the totem pole"? The case was still on the docket in 1955, awaiting further service in the cause of Texas politics.

In neighboring Arkansas, Governor Sid McMath asked for state suits against the "big oil dealers" for fixing gasoline prices. He said that five large companies had been charging 2 cents a gallon more in Arkansas than in bordering states, costing the consumers $40 million from 1947 through 1951.[15]

In 1955 the Montana legislature authorized an investigation of gasoline pricing practices. The sponsor of the bill complained that Montanans had to pay tank car charges from Tulsa, Oklahoma, on oil produced and refined in Montana.[16] Whether the Montana investigation would shed more light on the mysteries of gasoline pricing than those in New Jersey, Michigan, and a dozen other states was questionable. The majors, buttressed behind learned economists who proved that healthy competition in an open market produces identical prices, befuddled both the investigators and the legislators. When public indignation flared too high, the majors usually eased off a bit on price pressure and cozened up to independent dealers, until the storm passed over. It was difficult indeed for hosts of little dealers and for bewildered legislatures to grapple with a price system dictated from New York by a tight little group of billion dollar corporations.

Part IV

Intimate Relations

13

The Majors and the Public

IN AN industry which is confirmed in its allegiance to the one-price system and has no bargains to offer, institutional advertising serves the double purpose of keeping the advertiser's name before the public and combatting popular fallacies on subjects of price, profits, and bigness.

Such advertising, Standard of Indiana is convinced, sells products as well "as performing its primary function of subtly presenting the case for free enterprise." Not that Indiana uses such "hackneyed phrases" as "free enterprise," commented the *National Petroleum News*. For example, one ad was headed "How to Stay Happy After Your Wedding Day." An Indiana employee and his bride, an ex-Indiana girl, had found the secret because their future security was based on working for the company. No direct attack need be made here on the government's fatuous "social" security.[1]

There's nothing to be ashamed of in profits, says Indiana, when you mail out dividend checks to 40,000 women stockholders. It pays to be born in America, proclaims another ad as it shows a plump baby and various folks—pensioners, workers, stockholders, customers—all members of Indiana's big happy family. As for profits, they "help pay for the new tools our employees use," and so customers benefit from better products. That's their dividend.[2]

The theme of people's ignorance is a favorite one with the institutional advertisers. This reflection on the world's most expensive educational apparatus points up their own indubitable service to enlightenment. Americans, according to Sun Oil's public relations chief, do not understand their own business system and have to have it explained to them. The relationship of prices and profits, for instance, "poses a major task for industry."[3]

Standard of New Jersey takes the sober magisterial approach in public relations. It prefers to speak of meeting "the oil needs of free people" rather than to dwell on weddings and going to church. Typical is a statement on "Jersey Abroad," a public interest advertisement, three pages long, for the readers of the *Saturday Review* and *Harper's*. The statement shows that it takes a big company a long time to work out projects such as Venezuela and Arabia. "Jersey is against cartels . . . conducts its business affairs in an open and straightforward way . . . advocates vigorous competition . . . believes in the free flow of goods and services" and is contributing to economic development of all countries in which it has interests.[4]

Such a leisurely style is appropriate to Jersey, but when the Department of Justice files a suit aimed at divorcing marketing from the other activities of such companies as Standard of California and Union, their ads pull no punches.

"What's this 'integration' they're attacking you for?" asks a bewildered fisherman. Standard of California explains, fisherman-style. He catches his fish and sells them in his own store just as Standard catches its oil and sells it in its own stations.[5]

"What have *I* got to lose if they break you up?" asks a bespectacled citizen. Standard shows a laboratory, an Arab mounted on a camel alongside the wells, a filling station, and a bomber being fueled. "We believe we perform them *best* by being *big*," Standard explains.[6]

"Who *really* owns Standard?" asks a suspicious bystander who may have heard something bad about Rockefeller. Not the caricature of a tycoon of Big Business shown in the ad, replies Standard, but 115,000 stockholders, few of whom could be called rich. In the ad are a minister, a nurse, a professor, an employee, and other ordinary folks.

Union Oil prefers a more general line. "What's bad about profits now?" it asks. For the past twenty years, the ad says, profits "have been so lambasted by left-wing propagandists that a great many honest Americans were beginning to wonder if maybe there wasn't something evil about them after all." But the ad shows that most profits are reinvested to provide more jobs for workers and better products for customers, and only 40 percent goes to the stockholders.[7]

Summing up its ads on the Department of Justice divorcement suit, Standard of California asked its stockholders, employees, and customers to "lend support and understanding in our common struggle against this effort to smash your company, your industry, and your historic freedom." The suit was described as a "phase of the developing political war of extinction against the successful American institution of large business." At the "end of that road is governmental domination of every aspect of American life—the forfeit of freedom."[8]

A good bit of the ad copy is self-congratulatory in a circuitous way. A two-page oil industry ad showed big and little companies bidding for land leases in North Dakota. This ad inspired the *New York Times* editorially to commend the role of the profit motive in encouraging North Dakota oil exploration. This in turn inspired the Oil Industry Information Committee to reprint the editorial, adding laudatory references to the *Times*, the profit motive, North Dakota, and the oil industry.[9]

The *New York Herald Tribune* published an oil industry ad which consisted of a news story from the same paper telling "How U. S. Oilmen Met Peak Needs in '51." "A risky business," said the subhead, although in that year profits had never been better for the majors. The ad kindly referred to the *Herald Tribune* as a "great American newspaper" and said that "it salutes the oil industry."[10]

Such advertising approached perpetual motion in self-laudation. It was a factor in leading *Fortune* magazine to survey institutional advertising to see whether it was worth while. *Fortune* estimated that corporations were paying $100 million a year in defense of free enterprise (the oil industry quota is about $10 million), and "it is not worth a damn."[11]

The campaign, said *Fortune*, "is psychologically unsound, it is abstract, it is defensive and it is negative. Most important, in a great many aspects, it represents a shocking lack of faith in the American people, and in some cases, downright contempt."

As for the "facts" in the copy, said *Fortune,* they frequently were not facts at all "but conclusions." Not since the war when we were told that GIs were fighting for apple pie and refrigerators "have we been insulted with such noxious interpretations of the American Dream."

The truth seemed to be, so far as plain people are concerned, that the institutional ads don't make much difference in the long run. Most people read ads with prices in them—and the oil industry is deficient in such copy. As for the rest, it at least furnishes work for a growing subindustry and nourishes those dependent on printing for a living.

In times of prosperity, people take the enterprise system for what it is worth to them and worry little about whether it is free or controlled. In times of adversity, the ads, if remembered at all, will be a sour subject for reflection. Those for whom history begins with today's newspaper will be influenced, but they would seem to be a weak reed for the oil industry to lean on in stormy times.

More to the point in winning friends if not in influencing people is the industry's radio and television program. Leader in this is the Texas Company, the only company marketing in all forty-eight states. While the Standard firms most certainly blanket the nation, each one serves mostly its own province. So it is left to the biggest of the non-Standard units to sponsor the most ambitious effort to reach the public. This it did for several years by sponsoring "Mr. Television" himself, Milton Berle, on a telecast to 25 million viewers every Tuesday evening. The nation's delight in Mr. Berle's entertainment meant "money in the bank," Texaco told its dealers.[12]

If Berle was for the millions, including the kiddies, the Metropolitan Opera broadcasts on Saturdays in the winter were for the elite. Eighteen matinees were broadcast over more than 250 ABC stations from two to five in the afternoon, and later if the opera lasted longer. Texaco could be pardoned its pride in receiving a certificate from the National Federation of Women's Clubs for its service to culture. Music-lovers were grateful too, not only for the broadcasts, but for the brief commercials which did not belabor the point of Texaco's contribution.[13]

Cities Service favors semiclassical air music shows and has spent $18 million on them in 1300 networks programs over the past 25 years. Its current Band of America program lists at $1 million a year, a third of its advertising budget. Standard of New Jersey, Pure, Sun, Richfield, Shell, and Socony favor spot newscasts; Atlantic, Standard of Indiana, Tide Water, and Humble go for spot and regional sports shows.[14]

Pure Oil has sponsored Hans V. Kaltenborn for 14 years on a national hookup, although Pure is regional in its market. But the Dawes family is interested in public service as well as oil, and Kaltenborn's blasts against the creeping socialism of the Democrats and the unions are right up the Dawes alley. Quite a few Pure dealers have protested that Kaltenborn isn't good for their business, but he suits the Chicago Republican family just fine.[15]

Radio and TV are admirably attuned to the needs of such corporations. For one thing, there is no back talk from the listeners, and, at the moment of broadcast, no competition for the listener's ear or eye. As only those with millions can sponsor such programs, there is little likelihood of radio and TV listeners absorbing incorrect ideas. In the American way, the corporations foot the bill for the nation's entertainment and information and can properly call the piper's tune. Here there is little need to bow before the shibboleths of objectivity for it is frankly a commercial proposition, even if draped in terms of public service. The commentators hired by the oil corporations are inevitably well to the right of center and there is no likelihood of their hiring others either toward the center or the left.

Word of mouth is still the best propaganda, and Socony takes advantage of it through a speakers' bureau. In one year 317 Socony men spoke at 463 meetings to 69,000 persons. Cultivating friendly relations with the press is a "must" and cocktail parties to meet the new executive or to hear an impressive announcement are routine. So, too, the reception given visiting journalists, as when Standard of New Jersey was host at a reception for delegates at the Inter-American Press Conference.[16]

More ambitious are such efforts as Continental's to mark the expansion of its big refinery in Ponca City. This is out where the

West begins, close by the Cherokee Strip of Hollywood fame. So Conoco gathered in some fifty oil, finance, and business writers by plane from various sections of the country for a general jollification. Unfortunately the editor of the *National Petroleum News*, also invited, engaged his confreres of the general press in conversation. He was dismayed to find that even among this top layer there were many who did not understand the mysteries of price. They believed that prices were "arbitrarily imposed on a long-suffering public and without any rhyme or reason." The trade paper editor returned to his office wagging his head over the failure of the majors, even at such a brilliant spectacle as the Ponca City affair, to make it all clear. The business writers perhaps understood that one reason prices must go up is to underwrite such publicity expeditions as they had just enjoyed.[17]

More for the "family" of employees, stockholders, and customers are the house organs published by most companies. *The Lamp*, quarterly organ of Standard of New Jersey, is the most elaborate of these, a handsomely produced magazine reflecting company achievements and policies. Many companies also go in for films, some explaining the industry's technical processes for school children. The most celebrated company film is *Louisiana Story*, filmed by Robert Flaherty for Standard of New Jersey. It deals with a boy's life in the swamps; Jersey's tidelands operations are purely incidental. More pointed is Texaco's *Man on the Land*, aimed at farmer audiences and plugging oil-consuming farm machinery as well as progress "in a competitive atmosphere."

IN THE SERVICE OF ENLIGHTENMENT

It is no more than right that an industry which has so often expressed its concern over the economic ignorance which beclouds the American populace should extend a helping hand to education. In this the perpetual mendicancy of the universities joins with the federal tax structure to encourage corporations to be generous.

Leader in this effort to throw a financial bridge across the chasm between corporations and the higher learning is former Chairman Frank W. Abrams of Standard of New Jersey. In association with his confreres of General Motors, U. S. Steel, Container Corporation, and Armstrong Cork he has formed the Council for Financial Aid to Education, Inc. Corporations, says Abrams, are giving about $235 million a year but they could give $1750 million within the 5 percent tax-deductible limit allowed them. The beauty of this is that a company can give away $5500 at a net cost of only $1000—Uncle Sam, in the 1954 tax law, making up the rest while the corporation takes the credit.[18] Standard of New Jersey in 1954 gave $1 million to 138 institutions of higher learning.

The reward is not simply the virtue of supporting a worthy cause, Abrams remarks. He sees great danger ahead for the Republic and for "stockholders' investments in corporations" unless we have "prudent and mature people on whom we can rely. . . . In my opinion it is not good business to withhold from these institutions needed support."[19]

Addressing the Association of American Colleges, the Jersey chairman stressed the need for supporting education. "The peace, prosperity and security of the nation may depend as much on the way we treat our teachers and our religious leaders as it does on any other single influence. We must offer them more than bread and butter and a chance to do good. The American people insist that the legal persons which we call corporations have responsibilities to society. In our view, the American people are right."[20]

Nor, from a practical point of view, was it right, Abrams said, for corporations to be free riders on the back of private education, eagerly bidding for trained graduates in engineering and other specialties while contributing nothing to their tuition.[21]

One annoying detail remained to be adjusted; in many states an irate stockholder can sue members of the board personally for giving away the corporation's funds, and unfortunately some such law in New Jersey itself hamstrung Jersey's eagerness to be of assistance. It was hoped the states would take an enlightened attitude toward this, for, as Abrams explained, many directors are men of modest means.

There was nothing in the law to prevent Jersey from assisting colleges burdened with excess teachers. The company hired ten such and assigned them to Standard Oil staff duties while paying their salaries directly to the colleges. The effect of this experiment, Abrams said, would be "to help broaden the experiences of the educators and to inject fresh thinking into the day-to-day work of the company." The program "could make a contribution toward relieving any unemployment problems in the academic ranks during the next several years, as well as greatly improve the understanding between the campus and industry. . . . What we are doing, we hope, is a modest start toward building it."[22]

National Petroleum News applauded. "We can't think of a gap that needs closing more, for a pretty sadly misunderstood industry, or of a better way of spanning it for everybody concerned." One of "Jersey's professors" is at work on community attitudes, another is developing a program on stockholder relations, while a third is drafting a new policy manual for the employee relations department.[23]

Another way of helping the universities is to farm out research. According to Abrams, 25 percent of the industrial research being carried on in colleges is paid for by the oil companies.[24] Six oil companies have contributed $1,325,000 to Massachusetts Institute of Technology for a five-year research program in the fields of nuclear science, physics, chemistry, and chemical engineering.[25]

Abrams and his colleagues in other branches of big industry warned that failure to support higher education would mean federal intrusion. "Already," warned the *National Petroleum News,* "there has been talk of government subsidies for the colleges— and fear that through subsidies the freedom and independence of the schools will be curtailed. We're not suggesting that the petroleum industry could alone turn back such a tide. . . . They could just help."

Senator J. William Fulbright, Democrat of Arkansas, looked darkly on the implications of the program. At the National Book Awards dinner in New York in 1955, he cited a Socony personnel pamphlet distributed to college students seeking corporate employment after graduation. "Personal views," warned the Socony pamphlet, "can cause a lot of trouble. The 'isms' are out. Business being what it is, it naturally looks with disfavor on the wild-eyed radical or even the moderate pink."

Red-faced, Socony announced that the pamphlet had been revised and the offending section removed. But it had circulated for seven years on college campuses without protest from the custodians of Academe until the Princeton *Alumni Weekly* spotted it.[26]

At the higher levels, it could hardly be said that the industry applied outright McCarthy methods. There was Yale, for example, one of whose law professors had published a book highly critical of the monopolistic tendencies in the industry. Instead of denouncing Dr. Rostow for his *A National Policy for the Oil Industry*, the American Petroleum Institute neatly countered by financing, through Yale University Press, a study of competition within the industry. Two oil men and four highly respectable professors were chosen, "nonpartisan" and "unbiased," and told to go ahead on studies of production and conservation, integration and prices and price mechanisms.

The first monograph to be published, by Ralph Cassady, Jr., professor of marketing at the University of California at Los Angeles, confirmed API's contention that there is a good bit of price maneuvering and shaving in the retail market. The monolithic nature of crude pricing in Texas, Venezuela, and Arabia—the gist of the matter—entered not at all into enthusiastic reviews of the book in the trade press. Indeed, the professor conceded there might be a bit of price-fixing, but it was on the part of small, marginal retailers in certain shaky areas. If there was anything to complain of, he surmised, it was that competition might actually be "too intensive."[27]

While Columbia's loss of its president, Dwight D. Eisenhower, was the oil industry's gain when he campaigned against federal ownership of the offshore oil land, the great university lost little in its understanding of the industry's problems. Eisenhower was succeeded by Dr. Grayson Kirk, a director of Socony-Vacuum. Dr. Kirk announced, after his elevation, that he saw no incompatibility in holding the two posts. Soon thereafter Courtney C. Brown, in charge of Standard of New Jersey's higher public relations, was named dean of Columbia's Graduate School of Business.[28]

Many scholars were at last turning their attention to the

neglected industry, thanks to generous grants. Dr. Paul H. Giddens of Allegheny College, whose *Early Days of Oil* was widely distributed to schools and libraries with the compliments of the Pennsylvania Grade Crude Oil Association, was commissioned in 1947 to write the history of Standard of Indiana. "The opportunity," he said, "to make an objective and independent study of this company, free from all censorship whatsoever and with access to all company records, was so unusual that I accepted the invitation."[29]

To celebrate its 50th anniversary, the Texas Company in 1952 commissioned a biography of itself by Marquis James. Biographies of oil luminaries such as Mike Benedum, former Senator Tom Connally, Ernest O. Thompson of the Texas Railroad Commission, Hugh Roy Cullen, and W. L. Connelly, a veteran Sinclair man, pour from the presses.

But as yet there is no general history of the oil industry—a curious commentary both on the industry and on learning. Carl Coke Rister, who wrote a Southwestern oil book by courtesy of Standard of New Jersey, is at work however on a centennial history of the industry scheduled for publication in 1959; Northwestern University also has projected a similar volume.

Two Harvard Business School scholars have produced a mammoth book on *The Growth of Integrated Oil Companies,* with emphasis on the period since 1911 when the Standard Oil trust was disintegrated. They concluded that refining companies just about have to be integrated; those that are so knit together have 93 percent of the country's refining capacity, 85 percent of the pipe lines for gathering crude oil, 81 percent of the crude trunk lines, and 92 percent of the product pipe lines. Small refineries have dropped from 28 percent of the nation's refining capacity 30 years ago to but 15 percent now.[30]

Standard of New Jersey financed the writing of *Oil: Titan of the Southwest,* by Carl Coke Rister and its publication in 1949 by the University of Oklahoma Foundation. Humble, Jersey's subsidiary in Texas, is sitting for a full-length portrait by Kenneth W. Porter, the biographer of John Jacob Astor.[31]

Magic Oil: Servant of the World, written in 1951 by Dr. Alfred M. Leeston of Southern Methodist at Dallas, is a "refutation of the critics of the Petroleum Industry and free enterprise." To celebrate its golden anniversary, Gulf Oil published *Since Spindletop*, by Craig Thompson, a lavishly illustrated history. "Through the cooperation of the employes of the Shell Oil Company," *The Oilmen*, a photographic story of the industry written by Thomas Hollyman, was published in 1952. *Black Bonanza*, a history of Union Oil of California, "bringing you the romance and color, the fabulous story of Oil," was written by Frank J. Taylor and Earl M. Welty, combining scholarly research and journalistic flair.[32]

Standard of California has done more for education than any other oil company. It operates at all levels from the primary school to the university. The need for this was shown by a survey in 1948 which indicated that a third of West Coast teachers thought Standard was a "bad" company. So it started a program of furnishing grade and high schools with a variety of educational tools, such as motion pictures of the industry, literature, model building kits, and such like.

In 1951 a dozen colleges were invited to send faculty members to San Francisco for two weeks "in residence" with the company. They were shown the company's great installations across the bay in Richmond and given generously of the time of senior as well as junior executives for discussion of company affairs. Their only fee was to submit reports of their impressions.[33]

As a result, said *Oil Daily*, the educator-guests have "become thoughtful and influential friends." One even offered to help "stamp out anti-business propaganda in the teaching profession." A new survey showed that now only 13 percent of West Coast teachers think that Standard is "bad." So gratifying was the progress that the company intends to continue the program for two years, with staff members of more than fifty colleges.

Standard operates through an education section set up in the public relations department. In one year it sent out 6000 model kits of an oil field, the next year it sent out refinery kits. Thirty-six students are given $500 scholarships to colleges to "promote future American leadership in democracy." Sixty-six Future Farmers of America and 4-H Club scholarships worth $200 to $350 have been awarded deserving students.[34]

After three years of trial and error, OIIC's program for in-filtrating the nation's high schools was ready in 1954 for its permanent phase. The goal, to carry the industry's point of view to ten million high school students, is regarded as the most important part of OIIC's work. From small beginnings in 24 pilot counties, the industry's propaganda was expected in 1955 to reach two to three million students.

14

The Majors and the Consumer

To SINGLE out the distinctive merits of different brands of gasoline of much the same octane rating and to persuade the public to buy one instead of the other is a challenge to human ingenuity. Copywriters for the oil companies have risen manfully to the challenge. Magic "additives" to gasoline have been paralleled by magic adjectives.*

In 1953, Shell announced "the greatest gasoline development in 31 years." Shell's TCP, it was claimed, gave "up to" 15 percent more power and "up to" 150 percent longer spark plug life. Cities Service met the challenge with "the world's first 5-Dimensional gasolene" which dared the motorist's car to knock. The same company boasted that it maintains laboratories of trained "oil psychiatrists."

Not to be outdone, Esso (Standard of New Jersey) urged motorists to "try the *best* gasoline you can buy." As befitted the imperial might of Jersey, this was emblazoned across the nation's magazines and billboards as "TOTAL POWER"—an ominous if unintentional tribute to that puissant corporation.

Standard of Indiana watched the battle of the adjectives and announced for its East Coast Amoco: "Excuse Us! Count us out of the additive race because Amoco-Gas is the one gas that needs no additive." Indiana added the admonition: "—and it leaves

* The "additive" advertising campaign appeared in the press beginning in the spring of 1953. Additives are chemicals added to gasoline to affect its efficiency as a fuel. Tetraethyl lead is an additive to overcome "ping" or "knock" in the engine. As this additive leaves deposits which cause "pre-ignition," other additives are used to prevent pre-ignition. Among them is tricresyl phosphate (TCP).

145

no metallic deposit." In another dark hint to the car owner, Indiana said that its gasoline is made of "pure petroleum." Out of a delicate regard for business ethics, it did not explain what the other companies used.

Standard of Ohio bragged that it had "Uncaged today . . . the new multi-million dollar fuel that brings your car a kind of performance never before thought possible. Marathon 'Cat' gasoline gives your car jungle-cat smoothness and power." But Phillips "66" claimed that "when it comes to 'quick get-away' this gasoline's got it." Socony has "maximum car power"; Sinclair produces the "world's first anti-rust gasoline"; while ordinary Shell is so powerful that the engine jumps right out of the car. "It's activated!" shouts the happy driver.

Texaco countered with Top Octane Sky Chief Supercharged With Petrox, which actually results in an "increase in maximum performance of engine life of 60 percent." Sun announced that its ordinary gasoline "will give more miles per dollar of top engine performance than premium-priced gasolines." Tide Water Associated had a Sky High Power Flying-A Ethyl. Standard of Indiana, avoiding the crowded gasoline expletives, boasted new oils "so revolutionary that they can save motorists up to two gallons of gasoline in a tankful."

Members of the National Petroleum Association were worried and confused. While Shell and Texaco were backing additives, Standard of New Jersey, Sun, and Atlantic said the need was for more volatile gasoline and oil. Ethyl diplomatically plugged for both additives and more volatility. The laboratory men were concerned, it was reported, about whether "additives and other oomph panaceas are here to stay, or will ruin even the best of high-compression engines."[1]

J. H. Carmical, of the *New York Times*, said smaller refiners would be unable to meet the competition of the new gasolines. Oil executives, he reported, were reserving their judgment before reaching "solid conclusions" on the value of additives.[2]

Tide, the advertising magazine, surveyed the battlefield of supercharged adjectives, and counseled that the oil companies were "courting the same ad dangers as cigarets." Describing the oil effusions as "some of the most exaggerated advertising of the day," *Tide* warned that the industry might lose public confidence.

President Reese H. Taylor of Union Oil summarized the situation for his cohorts: "I might state that we are steering clear of the rash of gasoline additives described everywhere in newspapers and on billboards. Our research boys gave all of those so-called wonder chemicals a thorough going-over. They find that the wear and tear on motors, the deterioration of valves, and so on, resulting from the use of such additive-fortified gasolines more than discounted the benefits, if any. We found there was no substitute for good gasoline."[3]

When dypermatic adjectives and cosmobolonic nouns had been stretched beyond the limits of imagination, Standard of California called a halt. In its invasion of the New England market, Calso observed that "champions don't need gimmicks . . . we refuse to take any Dynamic Stance and brag about the way molecules have been re-arranged by cracking to produce Calso." The company conceded that "there isn't any other way to make a gasoline that will give you the maximum in efficiency, mileage and economy, so why pretend it's an exclusive process?"

As for the octane business, "you won't find us prating about octane. To claim that your octane is higher than that averaged by a number of brands is no more than so much razzle dazzle." And so it was confessed that "we know that Calso gasoline is good— that it's better than most, surpassed by none."[4]

Satirizing the advertising of other Midwest companies, Naph-Sol, an independent, said that "no 'gas' will give an engine more power than was built into that engine by the designers. . . . No uranium, baloneyium or atomic pandemonium is concocted by Zephyr scientists (formerly called oil men) to jet propel your auto. . . . Zephyr's scientists confess they are still using the old-fashioned basic ingredient for good gasoline. . . . Let's face it, folks, all you need to power that family limousine or 'struggle buggy' is just good Zephyr gasoline!" Naph-Sol reminded motorists that most cars require "just regular grade gasoline."[5]

Advertising Age sympathized with the plight of oil industry writers in expanding "nothing" into "something." Four varieties of "nothing" were listed: (1) Exaggerated promises of benefits, factually unsupported; (2) "entertainment" of the cute or clever species; (3) innocuous and meaningless generalities; and (4) claims too technical for laymen to understand.

In a compilation of "100 greatest advertisements," only one oil company ad made the grade. *Advertising Age* admitted that the industry's problem was tough, because there was so little to talk about, as between one brand and another. But even the institutional advertising, it said, credited the average motorist with "the intellectual curiosity of a groundhog."[6]

Octane ratings are subject to some confusion as there are two methods of calculating them—the motor test and the laboratory test. The average octane number of premium grade in 48 cities in January 1953 was 82.5 on motor test and 90.78 on laboratory test. Tetraethyl lead content, which is something else again, was 2.1 cubic centimeters a gallon, lower than the October 1952 rating of 2.25 cc.

The average octane number of regular gasoline was 79.08 by the motor method and 84.3 by the research laboratory test. Lead content of regular was 1.78 cc.[7]

Octanes and lead content vary a good bit from region to region, if not in the same locality. According to the continuing survey made by the DuPont company, main supplier of tetraethyl lead, premium octanes ranged in 1953 from 78.2 in Calgary, Alberta, to 85.2 in Corpus Christi, Texas; and lead content ranged from 1.05 cc. in Salt Lake City to 2.85 cc. in Vancouver, British Columbia. For regular gasoline, the octanes ranged from 75.1 in Salt Lake City to 81.5 in New York City, while lead content ranged from 0.43 cc. in Salt Lake City to 2.34 cc. in Shreveport, Louisiana. It will be noted that the octane rating for regular gasoline was higher in New York City than for premium gasoline in Calgary and that there was more lead in regular gasoline in Shreveport than there was in premium gasoline in Calgary.[8] The DuPont survey conceded that a third of the regular gasoline sampled had as much or more lead than the premium, and two samples of premium had no lead whatsoever!

Reader's Digest, in its April 1949 issue, raised quite a fuss when it published an article advising motorists to stick to "regular" if they wanted to save money. The writer, Harland Manchester, quoted the American Automobile Association as authority for the statement that the "mass delusion" about premium gasoline costs motorists $200 million a year. The federal government, he said, had instructed drivers of its 71,000 vehicles that engines are designed for satisfactory operation on regular gasoline.[9]

The purchasing agent for the state of North Carolina looked into the situation and decided there was little difference in the two grades and that it was "tommyrot" to fear that unbranded or "off-brand" fuel would hurt engines. "In fact," he said, "there's a very good chance it's precisely the same gasoline that's pouring from that big-name tank up the street."[10]

Within the family, Ethyl is frank about the reason why motorists pay 2 cents a gallon more for a trade name. Boasting in the trade press of its tremendous growth in sales since it started in 1923, Ethyl asks:

> Did you ever stop to consider what caused this tremendous growth? One reason we can think of is the continuous year-in and year-out advertising and promotion of "Ethyl" gasoline by Ethyl Corporation. For example, there's been a constant flow of magazine, radio, and now television messages to car owners. . . . In 1952, Ethyl magazine advertising reached 48 million people every month. . . . In the years ahead millions of new car owners will come into the picture. These people, too, must be sold if this market is to be maintained. That's why Ethyl's plans for the future include an expanded advertising and promotional effort, plus a wide variety of dealer education programs.[11]

The *Reader's Digest* article also quoted the request of the U. S. Treasury Department's Bureau of Federal Supply to all departments to change oil only in the spring and fall, or at 4000-mile intervals, whichever comes first. Autos making stop-and-go runs in cold weather or driven often in sand or dust should change more frequently.

But the industry urges motorists to change every month or every 1000 miles, whichever comes first. At this point the oil companies lock horns with the auto companies who resent aspersions on their engines. The car manufacturers say 2000 to 2500 miles or twice a year, whichever comes first. The *National Petroleum News* was perturbed by such friction and suggested a "high-level" rapprochement between the two industries on the issue. The oil paper emphasized that it "doesn't advocate that the automotive engineers be 'gagged,' but it does raise a point of how the oil industry plans to counter-balance the publicly-expressed opinions of these men."[12]

The oil industry's best answer to the Treasury Department's recommendations is that federal cars are driven by professionals and cared for by mechanics, and thus not to be compared with privately driven cars. Ordinary drivers are not to be trusted to judge whether their motors are enjoying normal use, and the thousand-mile change is an insurance policy against engine trouble.[13]

Oil never wears out, it just gets dirty, says the Association of Petroleum Re-refiners, which maintains that 12 million barrels of motor oil are wasted each year by being thrown out. The U. S. Air Force and many airlines and railroads buy re-refined oil. The point is made that this is superior to "new" oil because it has been subjected to an extra refining process. The re-refiners go the auto companies one better by claiming that there is no need to change oil in an auto before 10,000 miles.[14]

As if this weren't bad enough, the industry has now been subjected to an attack from within. Union Oil has invaded eastern markets with its Triton, the "amazing purple motor oil" which, it is claimed, has been sealed in motors and driven up and down the Pacific Coast for 30,000 miles without showing more depreciation than "ordinary" oil after 1000 miles. "Visitors from the East Coast even took it home with them and continued buying it by mail." This, Union said, led it to give all eastern motorists the privilege of buying Triton.

In any event motorists are abandoning the thousand-mile-change habit, if they ever had it. The proportion of oil sales to gasoline sales at filling stations has declined from 1.62 percent in 1947 to 1.31 in 1952. The public, cried the *National Petroleum News*, must be educated on how frequently oil must be changed, and station attendants must be instructed to "lift the hood" whenever possible. The first problem here is to activate the attendant into suggesting the need for a change, and the trade paper was properly vexed with the perversity or laziness of station managers and their employees for not using their tongues, eyes, and hands to suggest that "the oil is dirty, sir."[15]

When branded gasolines in a community sell at the same price, what causes the motorists to use a certain brand? This exercise in the higher mystique has engaged the attention of experts in the industry and has even excited the curiosity of DuPont, whose petroleum chemicals division set National Analysts, Inc., on the hunt for clues. These sleuths made 21,000 observations of motorists at 1193 stations and followed up with 3100 home interviews.

The disconcerting results made public in 1953 showed that only 12 percent of the customers chose their stations by brand. Some 40 percent chose them for convenience, another 31 percent because of friendly treatment. Older and higher-income motorists want service; the younger and lower-income prefer friendship. Of those who scatter their buying among various stations, the majority drop into any handy station. Some 40 percent on the road actually don't care whether the gasoline is branded or not, but it can hardly be said that advertising is sheer waste, for 41 percent seek a particular brand. For 20 percent, the nearest location on the right hand side of the road is O.K. Price was a negligible factor—less than 3 percent hunted for cut-rate gasolines, a tribute to the efficacy of price control.[16]

The campaign for brands was formalized during World War II by Brand Names Foundation, loyally supported by the majors. This foundation had as its main aim the fight against grade labeling, such as Grade A, B, etc., favored by some government people. Instead of these grades, in the case of gasoline "the customer is offered an ever-present, instantly-available range of choices among brands," the Foundation reminded consumers. They were not obliged to buy gasoline according to octane rating and lead content; such information of course was available in the DuPont surveys, but without the brand names. As a result, the refiner "does not have to fit his ideas into some set of government-approved specifications, and the customer alone is the final judge." Not having a DuPont laboratory at his elbow, the customer was subjected to a large margin of error as final judge; but to err is human.

Brands "are symbols of a way of life." The Foundation provides educational materials for home economics and social studies classes and for women's clubs. "In the past," it observed, "schools, women's clubs and other thought-molding groups have been among favorite forums for attacking the brand names and trade-mark system." The Foundation sponsors oil industry contests to pick the leading Brand Name Service station of the year.[17]

It would be pleasant to believe that all the glamour put into the shining "service" stations assures the motoring public of first-rate service, even if the price of gasoline is the same in all of them. Unfortunately, that isn't true. F. A. Bean, an oil marketer, is something of a one-man survey institution on such matters. He has written on the subject for *National Petroleum News* for many years, and his survey of a 5000-mile trip in the southeastern states is typical.[18] The trade paper was so impressed with his survey that it was republished in pamphlet form for the industry. It is summarized here:

Bean entered 78 service stations, but passed up four times that many because from the highway he could see dirt, disorder, or loafers. Of the 78 stations entered, only one could be rated as first class in every respect.

The stations entered were dirtier, had poorer service and less merchandising ability than he had noted in his survey 18 months before. When attendants spotted his out-of-state license, they gave him the minimum of attention because he was not likely to return. The managers and attendants "know absolutely nothing" about the products they handle. The salesmanship was the poor-est of any line of business he had ever known.

Bean, as an oil man, made it a practice to talk to managers and executives of companies along his route. A jobber with 100 sta-tions told him, "Gasoline is gasoline, no matter where you buy it. Octane does not mean anything." A station supervisor said his regular gasoline has a 92-octane rate and premium was 100! An assistant division manager, asked why premium gasoline should be bought, answered, "The company will make more money if you do."

Another executive, asked about various tests of his motor oil, said "such information is secret and highly competitive and could not be given out." Another dealer said his supplier gave him all this information, but he never read it. Another didn't know what the tests meant but was sure 40-cent oil was better because it cost more.

At two stations, gasoline loaded with dirt and water was pumped into Bean's car. Both were branded gasolines, but the suppliers took no responsibility for their dealers.

Despite the violet-rayed toilet seats and other advertised features of service stations, Bean rated the stations as a whole this way on cleanliness: good to excellent, 23.8 percent; fair, 30.7; poor to bad, 46.1. As for the "restrooms," 61.5 percent ranged from dirty to downright filthy. Only 6 percent were perfect and the rest somewhere in between clean and dirty.

In 39.6 percent of the stations, service ranged from poor to terrible. In only one station was the service what it should be. The usual method of cleaning a windshield, Bean found, was to run a dirty chamois through dirty water and a dirty wringer and then to smear the glass. Fortunately none tried to smear the side and rear windows. The only repairs needed on Bean's entire trip were caused by service station carelessness. In a freezing spell, Bean had his radiator tested in five different stations and still didn't know whether it was safe. Only two stations out of 78 made any effort to check the battery without request. Getting the right battery Bean found to be a man-sized job. Only two stations carried good drinking water; at the others it was assumed that all motorists prefer to buy cokes, whether they like them or not.

At 57.6 percent of the stations, no effort was made to check the motor oil; only one suggested a change of oil. At 64.1 percent of the stations, Bean decided it would be unwise to leave a car for complete lubrication; however, two stations he felt would be competent turned out otherwise, so Bean admitted his percentage was too low. At a fine station blazoning the name of a major, one attendant said it would take 45 minutes, another 30. But the car was returned after 15 minutes' work. It's impossible, said Bean, an oil man himself, to lubricate a car properly in 15 minutes. So another station was tried, where it was found that the first station had not checked the brake fluid. Then the car was driven to a sales agency where it was found that the two previous stations had not opened either the differential or the transmission.

Although at the season every oil company had radio programs stressing "winterizing," not a single station offered to do any of it. What with the poor service and the gypping, Bean got quite bitter about the majors:

All of these companies are continually telling the motoring public how good they and their dealers are. If they were half as good as they try to make the people believe, the motorists would soon find it out and put on an advertising campaign that would save the oil companies a considerable part of their present advertising expense.

In his overall judgment, Bean found only one-sixth of the 78 stations better than fair (and he passed up more than 300 stations as not even worth trying). Stations rated fair were 29.6 percent, and those poor to bad were 53.8 percent.

While Bean's trip was confined to the southeastern states, his previous trips had covered the eastern part of the country and a large part of the West. "Only slight differences can be seen between various sections of the country. The motorist who is spending the money is not getting a fair break when he patronizes them and he knows it. . . . If the oil industry, like some other industries, does not begin to police itself, someone, probably some governmental or state agency, will do it for them."

So much for "service" stations, the crowning glory of America's motorized civilization.

15

The Cooperative Challenge

Is THERE a way to produce and market oil which will give consumers a break and avoid the evils of monopoly? The cooperatives say that they hold the key.

Theirs is not a theoretical approach to the problem, but one hammered out of necessity and improved by experience. It occurred to local farmers' co-ops in the early 1920s that it would be a good idea to add motor oil and lubricants to the products handled in their stores, and pass on the advantages of wholesale purchases to their members. As the farms became increasingly mechanized, oil products became a major item in the business of local co-ops and many added gasoline pumps and even distributed gasoline in their own tank trucks. As the business grew, the co-op wholesalers began doing the purchasing for the locals, adding to the savings.

Three factors helped boom the farmers' co-op oil business. In the 1920s, the majors were enjoying marketing margins of 6 to 9 cents a gallon, or 30 to 40 cents on the dollar, far more of course than the cost of manufacture. Most of this margin the co-ops were able to appropriate for their members. The majors tended to slight the rural areas in favor of mass markets in the urban centers, thus giving the co-ops a chance to get their foot in the door. And the quality of available lubricants was so unsuitable for farm machinery that the co-op wholesalers were practically forced to set up grease and lube plants to assure their members against the ruin of tractors and other equipment.

The leading farm organizations, the Farm Bureau in the Midwest east of the Mississippi and the Farmers Union west of that river, and the Grange along the Atlantic seaboard and in the north Pacific states, encouraged the growth of the oil co-ops. Here and there the majors retaliated, slashing retail prices below the wholesale level to stamp out competition. In such situations, the co-ops often suspended their oil business until the war was over; backed by the wholesale enterprises of the big farm organizations, and by the general non-oil business they handled, most were able to survive and flourish.

In the late 1920s and early 1930s, many co-ops realized 10 percent or more on each dollar of oil products sales. Indiana co-ops saved 3.5 to 3.7 cents a gallon on gasoline. Since 1935, savings have declined to 5-7 percent, and in 1950 averaged about 4 percent. The very decline was evidence of success, for it reflected the lower margins which the majors were forced to accept in the rural areas because of co-op competition. Beyond success in price-reducing were the improvement in the quality of the products handled, the full measure assured co-op patrons, and the honesty in transactions.

By the end of 1950, there were 2230 local co-ops handling oil products through 2685 bulk plants, 2000 service stations, and 5660 tank trucks. They supplied a million farms with more than 2 billion gallons of fuel, about a fifth of the total consumed by farmers in the areas where the co-ops operate. In all, co-op oil accounted for but 2.1 percent of total domestic consumption, and the co-op investment of $178 million in all branches of the oil business was only about 1 percent of the total invested by the 30 principal oil companies and amounted to one-third of Standard of New Jersey's yearly profit.

While these figures reveal the meager share the co-ops have of the nation's total oil business, nevertheless in certain areas it is impressive. In Illinois, for instance, 40 percent of the farm oil business is handled by the co-ops. The U. S. census figures for 1950 reveal that one-sixth of all the high-volume gasoline stations in the country (handling over $300,000 a year each in sales) are owned by co-ops.[1]

The most striking example of success is furnished by Consumers Cooperative Association (CCA) of Kansas City, Missouri, headed by Howard A. Cowden. In 1929, this co-op entered the lube market with a capital of $3000. CCA built up a flourishing busi-

ness in oil products, thanks to the large margins it was able to
turn to account, and to the quality of its lubricants and greases.
In 1939, CCA built a small refinery in Phillipsburg, Kansas, the
first complete co-op refinery in the world. Compared to the giants
of the Gulf Coast it was insignificant; what was significant were
the 27,000 cooperators and townspeople who attended the barbe-
cue that marked its dedication. But hardly had it gone into operation than the little plant had to close down, for lack of crude.
CCA's report for 1940 told the story:

> A major company which had shown no interest in oil pools
> in the area, and which had refused to connect its pipelines
> with such pools, became eager to do so when construction
> began on the cooperative pipeline. . . . It paralleled our pipe-
> line for 12 to 15 miles and every effort was made to keep the
> cooperative from getting oil well connections enough to meet
> our demand for 3,000 barrels of crude a day. . . .
>
> Our crude difficulties had their origin in amendments to
> the State's oil proration act. . . . Our nominations for crude
> oil in April totaled 90,000 barrels. . . . The State Corporation
> Commission made only 26,000 barrels available. CCA im-
> mediately filed an application . . . for a rehearing. It was
> dismissed, however, when it became evident that special
> allowables were difficult, if not impossible to obtain, and
> when it developed that the Commission could not, under the
> law, allocate allowed but unused oil quotas. . . .
>
> In the meantime, with some 50,000 cooperative members
> in Kansas, CCA was bringing pressure on the State Ad-
> ministration to help work out the problem. . . . Suppliers who
> furnished CCA with various commodities—suppliers who
> also had producing wells near the cooperative refinery—
> were induced to turn over such oil to the co-op refinery.
> Word got out that the Justice Department at Washington
> was looking into the monopoly aspects of the case. . . . When
> the logjam finally broke, there was a rush to sell crude to
> the cooperative. . . . It was then that directors of the whole-
> sale voted to build a 22-mile pipe line extension giving us
> 90 or more connections altogether.

After that, the co-op began to reach back all along the line
to the oil in the earth and do its own drilling. Today, it owns
nearly a thousand wells.

"Heretofore," Manager Cowden said in 1946, "it [oil] has been drained away to make multimillionaires of a few men. Farmers have grown poor, oftener than not, farming the earth's top surface. They haven't realized as much as they should have out of the oil pumped from the 'subsoil.' Now that they're farming their 'subsoil' cooperatively, running it through pipe lines and refineries owned by cooperatives, they're going to reap advantages that were never possible under the old system of private profits."

The Phillipsburg refinery paid for itself within two years. One windfall was the discovery that petroleum prices are pegged on so-called basing points in various producing areas. CCA was able to save fictitious freight charges.

World War II hit the rural areas hard. With oil in tight supply, the majors saw no need to favor those areas which had depended on co-op wholesales and stations and had forced a reduction in the majors' margins. Let them shift for themselves, was the majors' attitude. In self-defense CCA and other oil co-ops were forced into acquiring refineries to assure their members of oil supplies. CCA bought a small plant at Scottsbluff, Nebraska, and when the two refineries could not meet the demand, several wholesales joined with CCA to buy a 17,500-barrel-a-day plant at McPherson, Kansas. In 1944, a fourth refinery was bought at Coffeyville, Kansas, which could also process lubricating oil. This found a ready market through exporting to European co-ops.

Other co-ops were also forced to buy refineries, many of them little old "tea-kettles" available at bargain rates. Even so, the savings were so large that rapidly these antiques, when materials became available, were transformed into modern plants, many with the latest thermal and catalytic cracking units. The largest are Texas City Refinery Company, backed by several eastern co-ops; National Co-op at McPherson, owned by CCA and several other regional co-ops; CCA at Coffeyville; Farmers Union at Laurel, Montana; and Indiana Farm Bureau at Mt. Vernon: each has crude capacity of more than 10,000 barrels a day. Plants at Coffeyville, Mt. Vernon, Laurel, McPherson, Levelland, Texas, Louisville and Fort Worth each have thermal cracking capacity of 3000 barrels a day or better. But all the co-ops together had a capacity of only 157,000 barrels a day in 1954, compared with

Standard of Jersey's single Humble giant at Baytown, Texas, with a capacity of 282,000 barrels. The co-op throughput in 1954 was about 1.8 percent of the total runs to stills in the nation, although co-op refineries handled a fourth of all throughput in Kansas.

CCA, biggest of the oil co-ops, sold $64,700,000 of oil products in its fiscal year 1953-54. Other big petroleum co-ops are Farmers Union Central Exchange and Midland Cooperative Wholesale in Minnesota, Illinois Farm Supply, Indiana Farm Bureau Co-op, Pacific Supply Co-op in the Pacific Northwest, Missouri Farmers Association, Cooperative Grange League Federation Exchange in New York state, and Farm Bureau Co-op in Ohio. Few, however, are integrated from well to market as is CCA.

The value of the refineries to farmers has been literally beyond price. It was not so much that farmers saved money, in the 1940s, as that they were able to get any oil products at all, at a time when the majors were concentrating on more lucrative markets. From 1940 to 1949, net savings of co-op refineries ranged from 15 to 30 cents on each barrel processed, and in 1947-1948 were 50 to 65 cents a barrel. From their savings they were able generally to pay off purchase costs and part of the cost of modernizing the old plants they had bought. But the squeeze caught the co-ops in 1949-1950 when the majors cut prices on fuel and heating oils from Venezuela. Several co-ops lost money and others barely got by. Since then their dependence on domestic sources of supply has handicapped them in competing with companies having access to Venezuela and the Middle East.

To assure themselves of protection from the price vagaries of the crude market and the pinching off of supplies in tight periods, the co-ops have been forced into production. By the end of 1954, they owned 2927 wells, a modest figure of .6 percent of all domestic wells. Those in refining and production produce less than a fifth of their requirements. To assure a safe position in supply, they should own at least a half of their needs in crude, and control another quarter. But prospecting for oil is a hazardous and expensive proposition, and only CCA can afford a staff of geologists and exploration crews.

Most oil co-ops follow the honored Rochdale principle of one vote to a member, despite the number of shares owned. The shares are usually in $10 and $25 denominations, and dividends are usually limited to 4-5 percent. Earnings, distributed annually on the basis of the total of the member's purchases, are called patronage refunds. Actually the refunds have been modest as the co-ops have had to plow back a large share of their savings into new equipment to continue meeting the towering competition of the majors.

In their bid for a bigger share of the market, the co-ops suffer sharp disabilities. Their slight representation in production means that they must pay the posted price for their raw material and are therefore at the mercy of the price structure on crude built by the majors. The lack of adequate pipe line and other transportation of their own binds them to circumscribed markets and forces them to pay toll to their competitors if using their lines, or to pay the uneconomic rates charged by railroads for tank car service.

As farmers' organizations, the co-ops are bound to a limited market and one that is more expensive to serve in rural territory, compared with the majors' choice territory in congested urban areas. Even more important, the cooperative sector of the industry rises only by tugging at its own bootstraps. Barred to co-ops are the major securities markets where the big companies can float multimillion dollar issues. The Farm Credit Administration offers certain financing services, but they are severely limited by statute and red tape.

The co-ops therefore depend largely on their own members for laboriously raised shares in small denominations. And their very success in lowering prices charged by the majors has tended to slow down their own financial appeal to farmers; in addition, the fact that they must plow back so much into expansion lowers materially the amount of refunds they can make on members' purchases of supplies.

In spite of all, however, the co-ops prospered, in their limited way, under a friendly administration in Washington which supported farm prices, and afforded limited credit facilities. The Department of Justice was able to restrain mayhem in the market to some degree.

Several domestic and foreign co-ops joined with CCA in 1947

in founding the International Cooperative Petroleum Association. With headquarters in New York, and an office in London, this group conducts international trade largely on a wholesale or brokerage basis, although it has hopes of getting into production and refining if the opportunity presents itself. In 1950, it had 21 member co-ops in 15 countries.

ICPA was an outgrowth of CCA's first shipment of motor oil to Europe in 1934. Because of the stranglehold of the British and U. S. companies, the European cooperatives find themselves stymied in their attempts to assure a supply of oil. The cartel has a fixed price, and the co-ops are welcome only to whatever marketing economies they can achieve. In 1937, President Cowden of CCA proposed at the International Cooperative Alliance meeting in Paris that a world oil co-op be formed. World War II put the quietus to such dreams for the time being.

In 1945, Cowden was in London at a meeting of the International Cooperative Trading Agency with his idea. A committee of five, including representatives of the English, Scottish, Swedish, and French co-ops, set up the organization in 1947.

In the meantime, no fewer than 21 cooperative deputations from 13 countries had visited CCA headquarters in Kansas City, and shipments of motor oil in large quantities followed to France, Sweden, Australia, South Africa, and Holland. The Swedes have established a national petroleum co-op with a terminal at Malmö and plan to build a refinery; the Norwegians have a similar co-op.

CCA has imported crude oil from the Middle East and other regional co-ops have bought crude owned by the Venezuelan government. Through an odd quirk of history, CCA has actually exported oil products to Iran, itself normally one of the biggest producers; this happened as an aftermath of the Anglo-Iranian controversy.

To meet co-op competition, the majors rely on occasional price wars, as in Memphis,* to whittle down co-op profits; generous discounts to big farm accounts to cut the savings which might otherwise be made through patronizing the co-op; and lower margins generally in the rural areas to keep the co-ops fairly well hamstrung. Even more important, the economies that come

* See page 125, above.

through control of production, through great refineries and a nationwide pipeline and tanker system, assure the majors security against the little fellows, whether co-ops or small independents. Against the somewhat condescending attitude of the majors toward the little co-ops, the latter have the advantage that their struggle evokes wide farm support. This support becomes vocal in Congress and has influence on the Department of Justice. While it can do little to unlock the door for wide and rapid expansion, it does assure them of a chance for survival and growth.

The industry prefers the flank attack, not on the cooperatives as such, but on their "tax advantages." The National Tax Equality Association conducts a constant propaganda campaign on the theme that co-ops escape taxation because their "profits" are distributed to their members as patronage refunds.

This aims at the very heart of the cooperative idea. Co-ops sell at the going market price and refund the savings to their members. These savings—patronage refunds—are income to the members and not to the co-ops. If they are heavily taxed as co-op income, then the co-ops lose their main incentive to remain in business. This the National Tax Equality Association sees quite clearly, and so it presses for its program.

The co-ops use the analogy of the farmer in the pre-machine age who raised his own horses and the fodder for them, without a tax either on raising horses or fodder. Now he uses tractors and other equipment which he must buy, and feeds them with oil products which must also be bought in the market. Shall he be penalized if he prefers to "raise" his own tractors and his own fuel, through his own cooperative?

The National Tax Equality Association sponsors a constant campaign, one feature of which is "canned" ads. *National Petroleum News* explains that "these ads can be run by individual companies, or can be jointly financed by a group or association. The ads can be run in your name or that of any group or in the name of the National Tax Equality Association."[2]

These lobbying activities find little favor with Congressmen from farm areas. Conservative Chairman Daniel Reed of the House Ways and Means Committee has denounced the tax equality group in scathing terms, particularly after its lobbyists campaigned against him in the upstate New York constituency which he has held since 1918. "The activities of this organizaton are nothing less than wholesale racketeering, principally for the benefit of an unscrupulous bunch of professional lobbyists and agitators," he said. The league was organized by a firm of Chicago "industrial consultants" and has received substantial contributions from the oil companies and big utility and milling interests.[3]

The issue flames up from time to time, as in Colorado, when CCA won the state highway bid for 35,000 gallons of motor oil in 1952. Standard of Indiana protested, saying that supplying state needs was outside the scope of a farmers' co-op, which should confine itself to doing business with its members, and that the bid was unfair competition because of CCA's tax status. CCA denied that it enjoyed any tax exemption whatsoever; what is "unfair," it contended, is either that CCA is a more efficient lube oil producer than Standard of Indiana, or is willing to sell closer to cost. State authorities ruled that Colorado should seek the lowest cost regardless of the seller and that there was no law forbidding it to deal with co-ops.[4]

A CHECK ON THE CARTEL

Cooperators contend that their movement is the only effective check to monopoly. They point to the failure of the antitrust laws to curb the power of the majors and assert that continued concentration in the industry may produce nationalization, to which they are also opposed.

Howard Cowden, head of CCA, says that the oil industry is a top example of monopoly in this country. Citing the figures of the percentage of control exercised by the majors over production, transportation, refining, and marketing, he points to their vast profits as the rewards of such control.

> The lamentations of the "little fellows," including the independent refiners, oil jobbers and retailers, are abroad in the land [says Cowden]. They have made a wailing wall of small business committees of both the Senate and House. Wherever these committees have held hearings there has been a veri-

table parade of "broken and bleeding" entrepreneurs who
have given testimony as to what monopoly tactics are doing
to them, not alone in the petroleum industry, but in nearly
every industry under the sun. These "free" enterprisers don't
need the expert opinions of Gallup, Crosley or Roper to
foresee their fate if the present trend continues. . . .

Small business, whether cooperative or otherwise, faces
a staggering aggregation of wealth and power in practically
every field. How, then can we best save the nation from
an oil monopoly?—and I would substitute the word "world"
for the word "nation"—because the oil monopoly is not only
national but international in scope. . . .

Consumer cooperatives offer the little fellow a means for
combatting the mammoths of business—a means of arresting
the growing concentration of wealth and power in the
wrong hands. But to do it effectively the cooperatives must
make a tremendous growth.[5] *

The co-ops have made approaches to the independent jobbers
to throw in their lot with them, and the idea has met with a
favorable response in some quarters.[6] Inasmuch as the co-ops
themselves seem unlikely to generate the great sums for investment needed to approach in size even the smaller of the majors,
the idea of an alliance between independents in marketing and
the co-ops is alluring. The co-ops have the experience in production and refining needed to liberate independent marketers from
dependence on their present suppliers.

The cooperative [concludes Cowden] is the only thing
I know of that can come to grips successfully with the great
business combines. It is the only program I know of that will,
by fairly peaceful and evolutionary means, give ownership
and control of life's essentials to people of small means—
people who, as individuals, working alone, are crushed
already. It is the only business movement I know of that
takes into account in its operations such abstractions as the

* In the spring of 1955 the House Subcommittee on Small Business once
again was investigating the legion of complaints from gasoline retailers
against control of the market by the majors. It was evident that Cowden
was not speaking only for the cooperatives when he cited marketing practices in the industry.

public interest. A consumer cooperative incarnates the public interest.

The way out for the little man is fairly clear, it seems to me. Millions of them need to make the positive approach toward monopoly control through consumer cooperatives. They need to get ready to carry the ball. If they are prepared to do that they can be fairly sure that their force of numbers will provide them with an active antitrust division to "open up the line." It is quite possible, too, that there will be less and less work for an antitrust division as consumers build organizations strong enough to take care of themselves on every occasion.

Cooperatives, Cowden adds, do not seek a monopoly for themselves. He points to Sweden where the co-ops have about 12 percent of the business generally and find that this is sufficient to hold in line the prices charged by private profit corporations.

16

Unions in Oil

FREE enterprise and monopoly alike have offered a rugged road for employees to travel in the oil industry. The companies prefer to deal with their men as individuals; the men, seeing that corporate organization pays off, prefer to act together. The overwhelming majority of refinery workers, most pipe liners, and some drillers are organized in unions. The largest is the Oil, Chemical, and Atomic Workers International Union of the CIO, formed by merger in 1955 of oil and chemical unions, but a substantial number are enrolled in independent and AFL unions.*

Standard of New Jersey never cared for unions. In the old monopoly days, they were not tolerated; in the 1920s, employee-management plans were favored. After the National Labor Rela-

* According to the American Petroleum Institute 1954 survey of employment, the industry had 1,648,000 employees. Of these 305,000 were in production, 129,000 in transportation, 211,000 in refining, 242,000 in wholesale marketing, and 761,000 in retail marketing. Average weekly earnings in refining were given as $94.19 ($2.31 an hour) and in production $90.39. Hours average 40.9 a week.

The World Petroleum Statistical Yearbook, 1953-1954 edition, gives a different breakdown. According to the Yearbook, there are 90,000 in exploration, 59,000 in drilling, 125,000 in production, 26,000 in transportation, 150,000 in refining, 28,000 in natural gasoline (made directly from natural gas), 29,000 in marine, and 241,000 in general office and administration, for a total of 747,000. In retail marketing, 853,000 are listed and in wholesale marketing, 96,000. The total overall is 1,696,000. Adding 90,000 in services and 144,000 in equipment and supplies, the total oil industry employment adds up to 1,930,000, according to the Yearbook.

According to API, investment is about $20,000 for each employee. But if only production, refining, and transportation are included, investment rises to $41,000 for each employee.

tions (Wagner) Act in 1937 outlawed these as "company unions," the Standard organizations changed slowly into independent unions.

Whatever unionism existed in the early days was confined to the oil fields where sporadic efforts at organizing dotted western Pennsylvania and Ohio. These culminated in the early 1900s in an AFL international union which soon expired. Unionism never dug in at the Rockefeller refineries or pipe lines; if a man was dissatisfied, he could quit or be fired. For its seaboard refineries, Standard imported workers in the early 1900s from southern and eastern Europe and even from the Levant. Rebellions—they could hardly be called strikes for they were spontaneous, unorganized, and leaderless—broke out in the New York harbor refineries during World War I. They were broken savagely by Standard's guards and the police and deputies of Bayonne. Following so closely after the "Ludlow massacre" of the wives and children of striking Rockefeller coal miners by the Colorado militia, these uprisings stirred liberal-labor partisans throughout the country and plunged the Rockefeller name to its nadir.

It was after this that Standard acquired its "new look." Dismayed by public opprobrium, Rockefeller's associates called in a young social worker specialist, W. L. Mackenzie King, to overhaul labor policy. He advised paternalism—pensions, stock purchase plans, welfare work, and an employee-management relations setup. The future prime minister of Canada outlined a system which became known as "the American way" in labor relations in the 1920s. The employee-management plan was particularly astute. It provided for elections by employees to a council, composed 50-50 of management and worker representatives, to consider such matters as health, safety, and recreation. By this device Standard was enabled to determine the natural leaders among its employees, to drain the promising ones off into management through promotions, and to afford the men a safety valve on grievances and the executives a listening post. The plan was widely adopted in other industries after being pioneered by Standard and became the pattern for what was later known as "company unionism." This policy, coupled with generous benefactions and Ivy Lee's public relations work, gilded the Rockefeller name and placed a halo about the aged head of the man who had once been the most detested figure in U. S. industrialism.

The burgeoning industry in the Southwest had little use for the new Rockefeller stratagems. The rugged enterprisers of Texas and Oklahoma had no need for such machinery when an inexhaustible supply of cotton-choppers was available for both field and refinery. During the labor shortage of World War I, however, unions did spread from California eastward, and a new AFL international union was founded. A strike for the eight-hour day in Texas was crushed by a mixture of force and starvation in 1917; four years later, the life was stamped out of the California unions. Nevertheless, the union effort did win the eight-hour day and left memories of mutual aid among the employees.

The postwar golden era, for employers, came to a sullen end in the Great Depression. Distress had darkened the oil fields. Then came Roosevelt, hope, and Section 7a of the National Industrial Recovery Act with its declaration that workers had the right to organize unions of their own. As if by magic, unions sprang up from coast to coast. A band of men who had kept the AFL charter alive in California headed for Washington to present labor clauses for the NRA petroleum industry code. The American Petroleum Institute had overlooked Section 7a in its proposed code. Harvey Fremming, the union leader, forced its inclusion, along with the 36-hour week to reduce unemployment.

But when the Blue Eagle died, the unions found Section 7a of little help. Only a handful of strong locals survived, mainly in refineries, awaiting passage of the Wagner Act in 1937 to protect them in their right to organize. Under this law, and with the encouragement of the new industrial unionism of the CIO, the organization slowly revived; and in 1940, under new leadership, it became the Oil Workers International Union. Once again, a world war provided the stimulus for growth; the labor shortage, the need to avoid strikes, the elections provided by the National Labor Relations Board, helped the union organize most of the Gulf Coast refineries—the heart of the industry—and to wipe out the North-South wage differential.

After the war, the union, in a series of national strikes, successfully challenged Standard's control over the industry's wage policy. The spectacle of Standard "reopening" its contracts with its own unions to give them the gains won elsewhere by the CIO organization gradually undermined company unionism. The 50-50 employee-management councils had awkwardly converted themselves into employee affairs after the Wagner Act, but even so the National Labor Relations Board repeatedly outlawed them. Each time, the Standard unions reorganized and eventually in the 1950s became more or less genuinely independent of company control. By 1952, the Standard of Indiana union had joined with the CIO union in a national strike; by 1954, units of the Standard of New Jersey organizations were meeting with the coalition of CIO, independent, and AFL unions to plan a new setup to absorb nearly all the organized oil workers north of the Rio Grande.

Inordinately clever in technological processes and corporate organization, the companies—even Standard—could not muster the wit to thwart their men's desire for independence. The rugged opposition of companies such as Shell, Texas Company, and Gulf played into the union's hands; the suaver attitude of the Standard companies merely delayed the day of reckoning. Standard of Indiana went so far as to encourage a company-wide federation of its own unions, the better to fend off CIO. The Indiana Standard union nevertheless joined the national 1952 CIO-independent-AFL walkout, which occurred during the Korean war (California was exempted from the strike call so as not to interfere with war supplies). The *National Petroleum News* was indignant. "In the armed forces such 'strikes' are called 'mutiny and insurrection'; yes, and even 'TREASON,' as harsh and awful as that word is." Later, the trade paper declared: "This country is fast getting to the point where a victimized and irate citizenry will get out their own guns and do battle with those who are seemingly doing all they can to cripple our own living at home and also sabotage the efforts of our armed forces in a real war that is getting worse and worse."[1]

The Standard of Jersey unions did not join the national walkout in 1952, but it could hardly be said that their attitude was too reassuring. Sadly, *Fortune* magazine reported that labor relations at Jersey "have deteriorated lately, even to the point of jeopardizing the companies' sensationally long record of industrial peace."

The Standard unions, *Fortune* feared, were getting downright class-conscious. "Sometimes they have the impression that if Jersey were to pay everybody $10,000 a year (as it could afford to) it would be sinking to a new low in labor exploitation." It looked as if Standard might have to "acknowledge and accept union leadership and organization as an asset."[2]

Such problems affect the companies mainly in their refineries. There, labor is a highly stable force, sheltered behind exacting seniority and tenure rules which practically assure the employee a lifetime job. The proportion of wages to the value of the product refined is trifling (about 2½ percent of the retail price of gasoline); the labor operations highly mechanized.

There is no such stability in production, the last refuge of free enterprise in the industry. Constantly shifting exploration creates an enormous mobility of labor in drilling; drilling crews roam the entire oil country from Texas to Alberta. This fluidity has defeated union efforts at organization. The other end of the industry, marketing, is equally difficult to unionize. It is characterized by small units—bulk stations and retail outlets; racketeering finds a foothold here where honest unionism can hardly pay off because of the high costs of organizing scattered groups and negotiating and enforcing contracts for them. The AFL Teamsters Union has made some small headway in this field, but the CIO union has had little luck.

Should the big Standard unions eventually join with the other unions, such an organization would be able to extend its strength from refineries and pipe lines into both production and marketing. This kind of prospect, with its threat of national bargaining, as in coal, steel and auto, is the industry's bugbear. As *National Petroleum News* put it, O. A. Knight, president of the CIO union, "is now in a fair way of becoming just about the most powerful figure in American labor history."[3] The new Oil and Chemical Workers Union, the trade paper pointed out, would have a position similar to John L. Lewis's United Mine Workers. But oil, far more than coal, is the dynamic force of all U. S. industry and transport. A shift of power over such a force from owners and managers to workers would in itself be a major revolution in democratic controls. The industry shudders at the prospect. But it has been remarkably ineffective in the past twenty years in combating the rise of self-organization among its employees; its technological skill has not been matched by any equivalent social intelligence when it comes to dealing with people— whether they be workers, consumers, or voters.

The prospect, in oil unionism, is for a further merger of the CIO oil-chemical union with the AFL chemical workers and with various independent unions which grew out of the company-sponsored organizations of the 1930s. Such mergers, affecting nearly a million employees in a basic and highly strategic industry, would rank the consolidated union as one of the most powerful, potentially, in the country, far more powerful than the declining United Mine Workers.

If the corporations maintain their present hostile attitude, such a union would be obliged to continue along the militant path of the present CIO union. Given the anomaly of the persistence of rugged individualism among the corporations outside the Standard orbit, there would seem to be a built-in guarantee of continued employer hostility toward unions. So long as improvements in working and living conditions can be won by unions in such conflicts, it hardly seems likely that the oil union will veer from the "business union" orientation of most of American labor. When progress is no longer possible along the traditional path, the oil workers, among the highest paid men in all industry, may well be among the leaders in pioneering some other way toward their betterment. If that would mean nationalizing the industry, the union would have to look only to the precedent set in its own founding convention in 1918 when it urged nationalization of oil along with other basic industries.

Part V

The Industry and Government

17

The Menace of Government

IN BROAD daylight the oil industry is aggressive, self-confident, even brash in claims of "know-how" and "do-all." The world is its oyster and the industry intends to enjoy the savor of it.

But the night is filled with fears and alarums, with lurking bogeys and octopi that twine their arms noiselessly around the industry, pulling it down to disaster in the slime from which oil was made. It is a nightmare in which the industry struggles hopelessly for survival. Like a dreamer gorged with too much wining and dining, the industry's moguls fancy they see the hobgoblins of socialism and communism dancing crazily over the Capitol and the White House. Even when the dawn came at last with Eisenhower and it seemed that the weary sleeper would awaken into a bright new day, nameless fears continued to clutch at him.

The root of all these evils was people. People hated, or were supposed to hate, such concentrated power; they envied, or were supposed to envy, the enormous heaps of gain accumulated out of a natural resource; they demanded, or it was feared they might demand, that popular control be tightened around private power. In a democracy the people's minds must be won and such evil and covetous thoughts expunged or at least denied expression. "Business," said President Reese H. Taylor of Union Oil in 1953, "must never assume . . . that our economic system is understood and admired by the majority of the American people."[1]

The American Petroleum Institute, at the close of World War II, pondered the problem and came up in 1947 with the

175

solution—the Oil Industry Information Committee. As a starter, the Committee polled the market place to find out, statistically, what was in people's minds. From a cross section of 10,276 persons came these results:

Only a minority, 41 percent, thought there was a good deal of competition in the industry; a fourth thought the companies were keeping newer and better products off the market; a fifth, that the companies were making too much money; a tenth, that the industry was pretty bad, what with oil scandals, monopolistic tendencies, and international involvements; 17 percent thought the government should get tougher; 15 percent actually believed in federal ownership.[2]

George H. Freyermuth of Standard of New Jersey, then chairman of OIIC, put it in these words: "There is a great vacuum represented by men's minds. We can't let others fill the vacuum. We have got to create the knowledge to fill people's minds. That is what OIIC is trying to do."

This the OIIC contrives to achieve through an extensive advertising program to reach key newspapers and magazines, through widespread pamphlets, leaflets, and posters, through thinking up catchy slogans such as "PETROLEUM IS PROGRESSIVE," and by answering attacks upon the industry that come from press or platform. This heads up in a grand annual climactic known as Oil Progress Week, in which the industry praises itself at luncheons and banquets, in parades of oil trucks and banners, in testimonial editorials furnished to newspapers.

Alas for propaganda! By 1954, OIIC discovered, more people favored government regulation of the industry than in 1950. More people, 42 percent, against 30 percent in 1950, thought that gasoline prices were too high. And of these, 77 percent blamed the major oil companies which, they believed, control the industry. The figures were vouched for by Opinion Research Corporation of Princeton, in a survey conducted for OIIC.

The trouble was, said President H. S. M. Burns of Shell, that "so many people won't listen to our story." The industry's big job was still to "banish the myth of monopoly."[3]

Supervising the industry's public relations is a tough job. No matter what is done to win friends and influence people, there will be kibitzers critical of the slow progress and eager to proffer free advice. For instance, the rather elaborate luncheons, dinners, and banquets that adorn Oil Progress Week seemed to the *Oil Daily* mostly wasted: "We're just talking to ourselves." In 1951 it was made *de rigueur* at the Waldorf-Astoria affair that each oilman bring a friend from outside the industry, free of charge. The *Oil Daily* feared that "a few theories, some money, seasoned by speeches, luncheons and public spectacles" may prove to be "the most costly flop possible in public relations."[4]

And why, oh why, did the industry have to brag of its bigness when so many jobbers and retailers were listening? "It was remarked," observed the *National Petroleum News*, "that this playing up of BIGNESS at a time when government and radical people, including many jobbers and gasoline dealers, are attacking business, just because of its BIGNESS, is a bit incongruous."[5]

The fact is that many of the state jobbers' and dealers' organizations "sit out" Oil Progress Week. They regard it as a show put on by the majors and are ready to take part when they are assured a cut on some of the profits. The *National Petroleum News* had other afterthoughts on the propaganda campaign. When OIIC was set up, the diagnosis revealed the public's poor opinion of the industry, "whereupon a poultice of much advertising was applied generally." But a deeper diagnosis, the paper said, would have shown that "thoughtless, heedless and sometimes ruthless handling of the competitive situation" was the real cause for the public's "poor opinion." The majors should quit buying out independents; if necessary, the majors should finance the sale of independents to other independents to stop the constant mergering. "This oil business is so stupendous, not just big, that its political dangers will constantly increase unless a better over-all policy to provide and protect competition can be developed and applied."

Simple denials of price-fixing just won't do, the trade paper warned. Comic strips and industry self-praise don't help the man in the street to understand why gasoline prices are uniform. This matter of explaining uniform prices "is going to call for some of the best brains that are thoroughly familiar with the workings of the industry. These brains will probably have to give full time to the task and for a long period, for the task is a big one and will continue perhaps for some years."[6]

A job for Lewis Carroll's seven maids with seven mops again!

In a flush of candor, the trade paper even absolved the government and the people for being responsible for the incessant attacks on the industry:

> The major companies that have put up the money for the API's $2 million a year advertising campaign, have overlooked the plain fact that the hue and cry against them has been raised in one way and another by the competitors who believe they have been done wrong by the majors. There has not been a substantial attack on the big companies since before the "dissolution suit" of the old Standard nearly 50 years ago, that did not originate with some competitors, in producing, refining or marketing, who thought they had been treated wrongly by some or all of the majors.[7]

At other times the *National Petroleum News* feels there is some dark, malevolent force at work. "It is hard to pin down just what that force is. Obviously messing up the industry in this country and in the rest of the world would be pleasing to the Communists. Yet repeatedly in these past years it has been evident also that there are others than Communists who have designs on the oil industry."[8]

Somehow these "others" seem always to worm their way into high position in Washington—so much so that it might be thought that the government is as much "agin the industry" as the industry is "agin the guvment." It makes little difference which particular government, Republican or Democratic. *Any* government is a challenge and a menace to an industry which prefers to govern itself. Both Theodore and Franklin Roosevelt were anathema. Even under Eisenhower, contended the *National Petroleum News,* "maybe all the screwy prosecutors have gone home from Washington by now but we have heard tell of some allegedly 'good' Republicans who could be just as fanatical against big business as any New Dealer ever thought of being."[9]

The feeling that it was fighting the inevitable not only added a note of terror to the industry's outbursts but caused it to turn against that most rock-ribbed of Republicans, the late Senator Wherry of Nebraska. His committee's investigation of the industry back in 1947-1948 was rendering service to no one, said the *National Petroleum News,* "except the Commies and others who seek to destroy our competitive enterprises and our democratic government." If his investigation continued, the industry would be justified in "fighting for a fair deal regardless of Wherry's blatting or his 'sicking' what he thinks is his 'Gestapo' on to the oil men and threatening them with jail." At another time he was accused of "emulating Joe Stalin."

As for the Republican Congress of which Wherry was whip, "if ever a Congress gave the industry unshirted hell, it was the 80th. . . . What was bad, almost frightening, was the seeming glee with which they moved in." Actually the 80th Congress took no action against the oil industry, beyond authorizing the Wherry probe.[10]

W. Alton Jones of Cities Service, serving as president of the American Petroleum Institute, put the matter succinctly: "The threat to freedom transcends partisan political lines. The donkey in power is no more an exponent of communism while traveling the road to complete totalitarian rule than the elephant which bellows pontifically that he will do it better."[11]

In fact many of the oil executives seem to prefer fighting Communism at home rather than abroad as it involves less taxation. But if war came, as the *National Petroleum News* put it: "Make no doubt about it, this will not be just a war against an immense and powerful foreign power, but it will also have to be a war against a sinfully and even traitorously wasteful bureaucracy in this country."[12]

From all this an uninformed visitor from abroad might conclude that the United States stood on the verge of civil war, that its government, an adjunct of the Kremlin, would first have to be overthrown before Communism could be vanquished abroad, and that this country was passing through a twilight of socialism into the darkness of dictatorship. The alarums come from high and low in the industry and seem to have a marked paranoiac tinge.

18

The Majors and Washington

THE industry and the government maintain liaison through the National Petroleum Council, the only government-sponsored private lobby in Washington. This makes for convenience. If the government needs a national oil policy, the Secretary of the Interior has but to inform the National Petroleum Council, which obliges. That such a policy is somewhat cloudy at the edges does not detract from its hard core of devotion to the principle laid down by John Jay in the Republic's infancy: "Those who own the country ought to govern it."

The liaison, for the government, is maintained through the Office of Oil and Gas of the Department of the Interior. This division enforces the Connally hot oil act, one of the bases for the industry's production and price-control machinery. It also inherited the odds and ends left over after the demobilization of the Petroleum Administration for War, an agency headed by the Secretary of the Interior but not a part of the Department itself.[1]

The National Petroleum Council was set up in 1946 under Secretary of the Interior J. A. Krug. Its members are selected by the Secretary, presumably from a panel submitted by the American Petroleum Institute, and they are paid by voluntary contributions of the members themselves. This rather curious financial arrangement presumably means that the corporations which employ those designated to serve on the Council also pay them, and contribute to the support of the Council's staff, but no financial report is made public.

Even so, certain sectors of the industry are suspicious of the NPC, for various reasons. The independent marketers regard it as an American Petroleum Institute creation; on the other hand the *National Petroleum News* criticized the Council because it is a "governmental" body. If the government wishes to know the industry's desires, let it consult the API directly; the Council may be a trap to ensnare the industry and subject it to bureaucratic control.[2]

The acid test came when the Petroleum Administration for Defense was set up October 3, 1950, during the Korean crisis. There is a long-standing tradition in Washington that governmental boards should be headed by government officials, even if most of the membership comes from industry. There is strong Congressional support for this attitude. The industry, on the other hand, is adamant against a bureaucrat running a board so intimately concerned with the problem of mobilizing oil for the cold war. The bureaucrats, if chairmen of the board and of committees, could set the agenda and determine what could be discussed.

Secretary of the Interior Oscar Chapman carried his battle to the White House. He told President Truman that the industry insisted upon control of PAD, or there wouldn't be any PAD. An ingenious compromise was worked out by which Chapman himself served as chairman of PAD, an independent agency set up outside Interior, while practical control was placed in the hands of the deputy chairman. This turned out to be Bruce K. Brown of Pan-Am Southern (Standard of Indiana).[3]

Another crisis followed immediately. The Department of Justice insisted that PAD employees must be paid by the government for doing the government's work. But Bruce Brown and other top-flight men would not work for government wages; they demanded that they receive their regular corporation salaries from their quondam employers while on leave of absence. Once again Chapman had to go to the White House to settle the issue, and won. There was really no choice—either corporation-paid PAD executives, or no executives. The Department of Justice, with its antiquated God-and-Mammon ideas, retired to lick its wounds.[4]

The industry had corrected a mistake made early in World War II, the *National Petroleum News* recalled. At that time, too many incompetent men had been placed in high authority within the Petroleum Administration for War. "Part of this was due to the thoughtlessness of business management in giving the government the men it could do easiest without. . . . Some of such last type people in World War II seemed to vent a certain vindictiveness toward their employers and other businesses." Toward the end of the war, this was corrected and "industry had gotten so many of its good men in command of necessary government activities that the damage to industry by bureaucracy was at least slowed down considerably."[5]

The National Petroleum Council elects its own chairman without government dictation. The present chairman is President Walter S. Hallanan of Plymouth Oil, who served as temporary chairman of the Republican national convention in 1952. Nevertheless the House Judiciary Subcommittee on Monopoly was critical of such a practice, on the principle that it was not wise to allow industry men to "head industry divisions which govern activities of their companies or their competitors. . . . There is no reason why the National Petroleum Council or its sub-committees should operate under procedures which differ materially from those established after mature consideration and deliberation for other advisory bodies to the government."[6]

The oil shortage in 1948 brought on a good bit of soul-searching about a national oil policy, which is the particular concern of the National Petroleum Council. There was none, and the fact of the matter was that few people outside the industry knew enough about it to formulate one. The industry had achieved a major victory by monopolizing the knowledge about itself. This led the *New York Herald Tribune* to complain:

"There is no country in the world which has the body of technical doctrine regarding petroleum in all its aspects which is possessed in the United States. There is no country which is so thoroughly geared to the power supplied by petroleum. Yet, thanks to the mixture of unsupported argument, official reticence and sheer hypocrisy which befog the subject, there can be few peoples so poorly informed of the global implications of oil production and distribution as the Americans."[7] (Once again the American people were being berated for their economic ignorance!)

The government, feeling apparently that it had no experts of its own to turn to in the crisis, appealed to its official lobby, the National Petroleum Council, for advice. Secretary Krug had warned of the danger of burning up our oil for heating and making our decisions "on a narrow dollars and cents basis." Krug, like his successor, Chapman, was for "rapid development of a synthetics fuel industry" to "safeguard America's future." He said it might require government financing.[8] At this time Wallace Pratt, Standard of New Jersey expert, was warning that domestic production should be cut back and imports from the Middle East encouraged. He was even for conserving Venezuelan production against the time when Middle Eastern oil might not be available in war.[9]

The report to be submitted to the Secretary of the Interior on a national oil policy by the National Petroleum Council was fore-shadowed by Joseph E. Pogue, vice-president of Chase National Bank and a director of Gulf Oil. He was soothing, and decidedly against any federal expenditures for synthetic oil plants. No further federal laws or administrative machinery are required, he said, but merely a continuation of an efficient and enlightened private industry unhampered in its individual enterprise by government regulations. The government, however, should lend friendly diplomatic aid to companies with foreign investments.

The regulation of production could well be left to the Texas Railroad Commission and its confreres and to the Interstate Oil Compact Commission. There should be no meddling with the mechanism of price by bureaucratic agencies; in fact there should be no peacetime controls at all.

United States nationals should be encouraged to develop oil in foreign countries, with the Navy in charge of the sea lanes; we should come to terms with Mexico, so that United States capital could be put to work on oil there, and we should be friendly with Venezuela.

The government must give up its claim to offshore oil; depletion allowances must be continued to encourage the search for oil; there should be easier terms for private development of federal oil lands; there should be no "distorted" views in the Department of Justice about integration and monopoly.

As for synthetics, private industry, contrary to Secretary Krug's fears, would develop them when needed. There should be no massive stockpiling of oil supplies. The Federal Power Commission's power over natural gas must be clipped.[10]

The National Petroleum Council's policy for the nation was submitted several months later, on January 13, 1949. It covered much the same ground. In case of war it recommended that control over prices be lodged with a Petroleum Administration for War rather than in an OPA.[11]

The report was accepted with thanks by Secretary Chapman and became, to all intents and purposes, the official national oil policy.

Somewhat later a report on the same subject was submitted by the Library of Congress, on request of Secretary Chapman. This report sounded an alarm about the wasteful use of the nation's oil resources and urged speedy development of a synthetics program. The *National Petroleum News* exploded at this impertinence:

> What in h—— business is that of the bureaucrats who work at the Library of Congress? Since when were they equipped to have an intelligent opinion on the subject and who asked them for it? We vote that they be admonished to get back to keeping their card indexes and to blowing the dust off the ends of books as they serve them out to their betters—the long-suffering taxpayers.[12]

Economic ignorance, particularly in regard to oil, was to be the unchallenged prerogative of the American people.

THE OFFSHORE OIL LANDS

More oil lies under the continental shelf than has ever been found under dry land, according to competent geologists. The continents are bigger than the maps show. In recent ages the seas have flooded over sections of the great continental platforms. These slope out gradually to a depth under the seas of about 600 feet, and then drop sharply into true oceanic depths.

Off the coast of Texas, Louisiana, and Florida, this continental shelf extends in places a hundred miles or more into the Gulf of

Mexico; off the California coast, it disappears a few miles out in the abrupt drop to the Pacific deeps. No one ever gave a thought to these submarine lands until geologists began to wonder about the great sedimentary deposits beneath the waters.

If no one really knew who owned the oil beneath the ground in the early western Pennsylvania fields, the doubt was even greater here, for no one even knew who really owned the submarine soil. The early operators were at least able to clutch at the rule of capture—the law concerning ownership of wild animals. But on the continental shelf there was literally no law at all. While that to which no man had ever claimed ownership might seem indisputably to belong to all—the nation—the courts had never touched on the issue beyond the low-water mark of the tides.

At stake was treasure beyond all previous loot in history. E. DeGolyer, the Dallas oil geologist, estimated in 1949 that there were 15 billion barrels of oil off these coasts accessible by techniques within the grasp of man. At $2.65 a barrel, it would be worth nearly $40 billion, and the natural gas another $10 billion. This of course was only an informed guess, as DeGolyer would be first to admit. The real value might range from half that to ten times as much. If it were possible to devise some method of drilling in waters more than 100 feet deep, the wealth recoverable might increase to half a trillion, but such speculations are in a class with the estimates of the trillions of gold in sea waters—if it could be economically recovered.

Drilling under water is no dream. At Long Beach, California, wells were sunk in the 1920s along the tidelands; in the 1940s, the Mississippi Delta offshore lands began producing oil, and of course Lake Maracaibo yields most of the Venezuelan production.

Something like Topsy, the notions of submarine ownership just grew up—and very gratifying it was to the corporations. They were delighted to deal with the various states, and the states were no less delighted to get the revenue on leases and royalty. Nobody much bothered about law. It was of course undoubted that the nation's sovereignty extended to the three-mile limit, the range of a cannon ball in the old days of sail. But that concerned only the waters.

The issue was put up to Harold Ickes after he became Secretary of the Interior in 1933, and he allowed, in an offhand way, that the states had a right to lease the submarine lands off their shores —an opinion that was to plague him in later years. President Roosevelt was more curious as reports came to the national capital of the success that Superior Oil was having off the California coast in perfecting deep-water drilling techniques. He asked Ickes and Harry Hopkins to look into the matter seriously. They reported it was a moot question that had never been decided by the courts.

By unanimous vote, the Senate, on August 19, 1937, passed a joint resolution vesting ownership of the offshore lands in the federal government and directing the Department of Justice to file suits against interlopers. This resolution was approved by a House committee but never reached the floor of the House itself. President Roosevelt asked Congress to set aside the offshore lands as a naval reserve, but no action was taken. The war postponed further federal action, but the corporations had been alerted.

The battle for the greatest unclaimed treasure in history was about to begin. On one side was the federal government, at first irresolute, then harried by war problems, and finally joining the fray when the battle had already been well lost. On the other side were the four states with oil off their coasts—rich deposits already proved in the case of Louisiana and California, mostly prospective in the case of Texas and Florida. In one light, it seemed to be the immemorial struggle between federalism and states' rights. Viewed differently, however, it hardly seemed to the advantage of forty-four states to give away a national patrimony to four.

The tocsins rang for what is certainly one of the most curious episodes in all American history. The Republican party was to split the solid South; the Democratic party itself was to be rent in twain; the Texas Democratic party was to support the Republican presidential candidate, and his vice-presidential mate was to be tarred with the oil brush; the GOP, which had posed for generations as the exponent of the federal principle, was to turn states' rights; even the hallowed name of Thomas Jefferson, foe of special privilege, was to be invoked in defense of Dixiecrats.

To the corporations the issue was vital. It wasn't that it mattered so much whether they paid lease and royalty to the states or to the federal government, for the terms probably would be much the same. The specter that haunted them was federal control. If Washington owned the lands beneath the seas, some administration might follow Roosevelt's urging and declare it a naval reserve, to be held for the future.[13] Or, worse yet, it might follow the advice of Leland Olds, the former Federal Power Commissioner who had been driven out of office by the natural gas interests. He proposed that the government, instead of leasing the submarine lands to private corporations, might set up a public corporation to provide a yardstick by which it could determine what are reasonable costs and prices.[14] Another possibility was that the national government, in its development policy, might endanger the delicate production and price-control system so easily imposed on state commissions in the oil states.

Indeed, the more the corporations looked at the prospect of federal control over this vast watery realm, the more alarmed they became. Not even a conservative regime in Washington would be free of the Congressional pressures generated on behalf of independent factors in the industry and of consumers. It was not wise to leave control in Washington, no matter who headed the government or how safe he was in his views. It was around Washington that "creeping socialism" crept, not Austin or Baton Rouge or Sacramento; nobody knew what a federal government which had $40 billion in oil treasure might not be tempted to do with it.

Divide and rule was the handy motto here. Better four states easily subjected to corporation pressure than one federal government. The corporations need never say a word; their official lobby, the National Petroleum Council, could play possum all the day; the cupidity of the four oil states could be depended upon to make the fronts, to furnish the oratory, the political dynamics. The corporations need not open their mouths, only their coffers.

THE BATTLE IS JOINED

Luck was with the corporations from the start. They were able to fasten the word "tidelands" to the issue, a propaganda windfall of paramount importance. The press, from ocean to ocean, spoke of "tidelands oil," and, as everyone knew, the lands washed by the tides belonged, by innumerable court decisions, to the

states. The federal government was accused of trying to grab
these tidelands. To be sure, it was explained, belatedly, that it
was the land under the waters from low-water mark out to the
three-mile limit that was under dispute. But the press generally
was not interested in such niceties, once the label had been applied. Tidelands oil it was, and tidelands oil it remained.

Already, on September 20, 1945, the House had voted to con-
firm the four states in their rights to offshore oil, with only 11
dissenting votes, and the Senate had concurred. But there were
enough votes in the Senate to uphold Truman's veto.

After the war, the Department of Justice was considering filing
a suit against California for title to coastal oil. The proposal went
unnoticed until, early in February 1946, President Truman told a
press conference that he would continue to support Ed Pauley, a
California oilman, for the job of Undersecretary of the Navy. This
came after Secretary Ickes had testified that Pauley, former Democratic national treasurer, had "advanced the rawest proposition
ever made to me." It was, Ickes said, that $300,000 could be raised
in campaign funds in California if the Department of Justice
would delay its suit.[15] The smell of oil was already rising like a
miasma from the "tidelands."

Truman said Ickes might be mistaken. The testy old curmudg-
eon, seeing "a small dark cloud on the horizon which might grow
into a major scandal," resigned in a 2000-word letter. "I don't
care to stay in an Administration where I am expected to commit
perjury for the sake of the party. I do not have a reputation for
dealing recklessly with the truth."[16] Later Truman withdrew
Pauley's nomination, but Ickes was out of the Cabinet and the
smell of tidelands oil was polluting, not the Republican, but the
Democratic party. The era of government by crony had arrived.
The Democrats had lost the $300,000 from the oilmen and had
gained a noisome reputation.

Tardily, ten years after the Senate had voted for federal ownership, and more than a year after both houses had decided to give
the disputed lands to the four states, the Department of Justice
filed its suit in January 1947 against California. On June 23 of
that year the U. S. Supreme Court ruled 6-2 that the federal government had "paramount rights" in California's coastal lands.

But, the court added, Congress could, if it wished, turn the lands over to the states.

As the court's decision affected only California, Texas rushed in to lease its marginal lands, reaping a harvest of $8,300,000 in bonus payments and rentals on leases. Later Mississippi leased 800,000 acres beneath the sea. Louisiana already had her arms deep in the golden-black harvest.

The Dixiecrat movement flared throughout the South in 1948, fueled by oil. In Texas it was headed by a Humble (Standard of New Jersey) lawyer; in Alabama, the top Dixiecrat worked for several of the majors; in Louisiana an oilman, Leander B. Perez, led the secession. In Texas, Jesse Jones, former Governor Coke Stevenson, and H. R. Cullen, all heavily immersed in oil, nourished the states'-righters.[17] The beneficiary of the Dixiecrats was to be Thomas Dewey, the Republican candidate, the golden boy of New York finance and particularly of the interests that clustered about Chase National Bank and Standard of New Jersey.

The *Atlanta Constitution* reported that the money which financed the Dixiecrats was supplied by the oil companies. "The sordid connection between this fact and the Southern delegations' feverish support of a platform plank indorsing the tidelands oil grab is too obvious to need further discussion," commented the Alsop brothers in the *New York Herald Tribune*.[18] Ellis Arnall, former governor of Georgia, declared that "the oil lobbyists staged and controlled the Dixiecrat convention at Birmingham, and manipulated its steering and platform committees like puppets."[19]

After the doughty Truman had turned the tables on the prophets in the 1948 elections, he took sweet revenge by ordering suits filed against Texas and Louisiana for trespassing on federal property.

Senator Tom Connally of Texas exceeded himself. "The federal government raid upon the tidelands," he thundered, "is a big step toward national socialism and a severe blow to states' rights generally. The next step to be taken by those who fathered the tidelands controversy will doubtless be to take over and nationalize the entire oil industry."[20]

Ickes, who by now had forgiven Truman his Pauley indiscretion in view of his stand for federal rights, backed him in 1948 and then called for federal aid to education from funds to be derived from the offshore oil lands. In his best prose style, Ickes jabbed at two favorite foes, the Republican House Leader and the Senator from Nevada:

> Joe Martin and Senator McCarran and their ilk, whose hearts tenderly throb for the rich and powerful oil companies, thought that God had laid by these rich petroleum deposits for the benefit of the Rockefellers, the Pews, the Mellons, the Sinclairs and those slippery patriots of Texas and Louisiana who financed the Oilycrats in the hope of a touchdown against President Truman by a sneak play.[21]

Ickes for the remaining four years of his life turned himself into a one-man committee to fight for federal rights to oil. "A steal of public property of the greatest magnitude in American history is already off to a fast start," he warned. "The Teapot Dome episode is mere penny-snatching to what is being attempted today with the connivance, or at least with the somnolent indifference of public officials in high places. Such a cynical attitude toward what, if the police do not arrive in time, would be the crime of the American centuries, I have never witnessed. Even the newspapers, for the most part, have refused to be interested."[22]

Ickes was aiming at what he termed the prolonged sabotage of the federal case by ranking officials in the Departments of Justice and Interior, among them Tom Clark, later advanced to the Supreme Court, and Julius Krug and Oscar Chapman, Secretaries of the Interior, themselves Ickes's former understudies.[23]

On June 5, 1950, the U. S. Supreme Court sustained its California decision by ruling that the federal government held paramount rights to the Texas and Louisiana offshore lands, too. Louisiana's bid for sovereignty out for 27 miles was found no more valid than California's, the justices voting 6 to 1.[24]

But on the Texas case the justices split 4 to 3, Jackson and Clark as former Attorneys General not participating. The majority held that Texas entered the Union on an equal footing with the original thirteen states and thus held no special status in its claim to a boundary 10½ miles out to sea. The wording of the majority opinion on the rights of national sovereignty afforded full rein for the legal profession to read dire interpretations, as fitted their predilections. Nor was it lost on Texas that, after all, the majority decision was signed by a minority of the full court membership.[25]

The interpretations to be placed on the Supreme Court's opinion of the paramount rights of national sovereignty alarmed the American Bar Association and threw state, county, and township into fear for their very lives. Nothing was sacred, they cried out—the federal juggernaut could roll over the rivers, the bays, the harbors, the filled-in land upon which Boston and New York stood, the precious iron ore under Lake Superior.

When the Department of Justice followed up the decisions by asking an accounting for revenues appropriated by the states from federal leases on federal oil lands, Congressman Ed Gossett of Texas blew up:

"The power-hungry, power-mad boys who run the Departments of Justice and Interior have surprised nobody in their proposed decrees in the tidelands cases. They would gladly rob the states of their last vestige of sovereignty. Solicitor General Shylock Perlman will continue to do everything within his power to exact from Texas and Louisiana the last pound of flesh."[26] Later, Gossett quit Congress to become an avowed lobbyist.

The *Dallas Morning News* sponsored a series of articles on "The Big Grab," which was not an attack on the oil interests. Rather, "the federal grab of tidelands has clouded title to property all over America. Its implications are tremendous." The series was aimed principally at Harold Ickes, who after all had been carrying on the battle almost singlehanded. The *News* series, carried in leading newspapers across the country, stung Ickes to reply:

> The Capitol today is swarming with greasy-fingered oil lobbyists who, as usual, have crackling greenbacks to spend ad lib in quarters where they will do the most good. What they dearly want, at whatever price, is another quitclaim bill which would convey ownership of the offshore oil lands away from all of the people, thereby losing the taxpayers literally billions of dollars that might be used on the education of their children. Slick operators want to enrich them-

selves at the expense of the children. They are not willing even to set these publicly owned undersea lands up as a reserve for our armed forces or to dedicate them to the payment of the public debt. Ruthless greed has never paraded so wantonly in hideous nakedness. Human nature can be seen at its worst in Washington today where devoted Senators and Representatives are supposed to be working for the public welfare in deference to their oaths of office. Mammon is in the saddle while civic virtue runs to cover. Oil continues to befoul the pure stream of our democratic power.[27]

The House bill was sponsored by Congressman Walter, Democrat, of Pennsylvania, co-sponsor of the McCarran immigration act. His bill not only yielded federal rights to the three-mile limit, but gave Texas a 10½-mile limit and then, to show the government's generosity, threw in three-eighths of all oil revenues which might be derived from the continental shelf to seaward of the state limits. The bill passed by a vote of 265 to 109.

The *New York Times* commented that the bill was a "gift to three individual states of a national resource of major economic and strategic importance. The Walter bill is entitled the 'Submerged Lands Act.' It seems to us that it would be more appropriate, so far as the American people are concerned, to call it the 'Submerged Rights Act.' "[28]

In the Senate an "interim" bill had been introduced by Senator O'Mahoney which seemed quite generous to the states. For five years, the states could veto federal leases which imperiled their own state leases, which were confirmed. They would also be confirmed in the revenues already obtained, and for five years would receive three-eighths of federal revenues from oil obtained from the continental shelf beyond the three-mile limit. Senator Lister Hill and ten others sponsored a bill to turn over federal revenues from the offshore oil lands to all the states for schools. This bill was indorsed by the AFL, the CIO, the National Grange, the National Farmers Union, the American Council for Education, and other organizations.[29]

Senator O'Mahoney fought a delaying action, but the showdown came April 2, 1952, when the Senate adopted, 50 to 35, a substitute bill vesting ownership in the states, submitted by Senator Holland of Florida. The debate was enlivened by the appearance, for the first time in memory, of an outright lobbyist on the floor of the Senate. Senator Holland was able, with only a handful of fellow members present, to get a suspension of the rules to permit Walter R. Johnson, $18,000-a-year representative of the state attorneys general lobby, to assist him on the floor in his three-hour speech. Holland, after all, did not pretend to be an expert on the matter of oil lands. Later, Senate leaders promised it would be the last time a lobbyist would be permitted on the floor.[30]

In conference, the Senate and House agreed to limit states' rights to three miles offshore, and the bill was sent to the White House. President Truman had already indicated his displeasure. He would not back down, which "is just what the oil lobby wants. They want us to turn that vast treasure over to a handful of states, where the powerful private oil interests hope to exploit it to suit themselves." Smarting under the mink-coat-deep-freeze attacks of his opponents, he exploded: "Talk about corruption! Talk about stealing from the people! This would be robbery in broad daylight—and on a colossal scale."[31] He vetoed the bill.

TO THE VICTOR THE SPOILS

The Truman veto of the tidelands oil bill became a prime issue in the 1952 presidential campaign. The Republican nominee didn't pretend to know too much about the intricacies of domestic politics, but his managers did, and they assured the Texas Regulars that he was right on oil. In Detroit one June day when asked what he thought of the Supreme Court's decisions confirming federal rights to offshore lands, he expressed great surprise about the decision but assured the press he believed in obeying the court.

This sent a tremor deep into the heart of Texas. Three days later, in Denver, he showed that he had been briefed on this issue. He declared that on the one hand he believed in federal control over national resources but on the other hand saw no conflict between that and "vesting of title to tidelands in the states."[32]

By the time the candidate got to Louisiana, which had the biggest stake in the offshore lands, he had learned his lesson pat. The script handed him, which he proceeded to read, said: "The attack on the tidelands is only a part of the effort of the Administration to amass more power and money." As for his opponent's compromise, this effort to "dole out to the tin cups of the states whatever part of the revenue Washington decided might be good for them . . . I would call the Shoddy Deal."

"The policy of the Washington power mongers is a policy of grab. . . . If they take the Louisiana, Texas and California tidelands, then what about the Great Lakes? They have been held to be open sea. A good part of Chicago has been built on lands once submerged by Lake Michigan. What of the inland lakes, rivers and streams in Oklahoma, Iowa, Illinois and Kansas? What about the iron ore under the navigable waters of Minnesota and the coal under the waters of Pennsylvania, West Virginia and other states? What of the fisheries in Florida; what of the kelp in Maine; what of the real estate built on soil reclaimed from the once submerged areas in New York and Massachusetts?"[33]

Some of his eastern supporters winced, but there was a good chance, his managers told him, of carrying Louisiana as well as Texas.

In California, the state whose offshore oil deposits were second only to Louisiana's, oil was in the thick of the fight. Earl Warren, the Republican-Democratic governor, who had also been campaigning for the presidency, was suspected of being a federalist. Warren retorted that the "independent oil crowd" in California was pouring money into a campaign of "vilification." He named President W. M. Keck of Superior Oil, the company that had pioneered in offshore drilling, as the leader of the lobby, and Jack Smith, a wealthy oil operator, as his "slippery messenger boy." The "independent oil crowd" answered cheerfully that they had financed Warren's campaign for governor in 1942, and what was he complaining of?[34]

"Tidelands" oil waters ran deep in California politics. It was charged that Warren's candidacy for the presidency was only a blind to thwart the high ambitions of Senator Richard Nixon, the boy wonder of Golden State politics. The "independent oil crowd" took a hand in financing Nixon's crusade against Communism and federal ownership of the offshore lands. Their activities provided the crowning sensation of the national campaign when it seemed for a time, after he had won the vice-presidential nomination, that he might be repudiated by the head of his own ticket. The adroit Nixon was able to avert this castastrophe by his famous TV appearance but doubts would not down and continued to plague him after his inauguration.

THE EISENHOWER ADMINISTRATION

Estimates of the cost of the 1952 presidential campaign ranged all the way up to $100 million. Frank Edwards, the former AFL radio commentator, said that the oil interests contributed half that sum, and all to the Eisenhower forces. There was no way to contest the statement, for no one in authority cared to flash a beam into the dark recesses of corporate financing of political parties.

In the Southwest, the oil crowd worked through the state Democratic parties which were subverted into arms of the national Republican party. In California, there was no need for such subversion. Richard Nixon, Eisenhower's running mate, had the enthusiastic support of the West Coast oilmen. It was more than vocal, as an examination of the donors to his private crusade fund revealed.

For the industry, the victory meant mainly the removal of federal control from the offshore oil lands, valued by E. DeGolyer, a leading petroleum geologist, at around $40 billion. The natural gas end of the industry rejoiced in coming Republican control of the Federal Power Commission; all greeted the prospects of a businesslike administration of the Federal Trade Commission. The top majors could look forward to a better understanding of both their domestic and foreign cartel practices in the Department of Justice.[35]

Unfortunately, there was Congress with its usual quota of "socialistically minded" Republicans, some now in seats of authority. These were mostly eastern and Midwestern Congressmen from oil-consuming rather than producing states who were likely to listen to constituents, whether independent marketers or just consumers. The situation was acute enough for the late Senator Tobey, Republican of New Hampshire, to warn President Eisenhower:

"I know the pressures we Republicans are under from the oil and gas interests. . . . But I do think we should be discriminating and intelligent as to the political end results in the rate and extent of our yieldings to our allies."[36]

Of prime importance to the bigger majors with foreign investments was the appointment of Chairman Winthrop W. Aldrich of Chase National Bank as Ambassador to Britain. It meant that a Rockefeller brother-in-law would be in London to safeguard Standard Oil interests and to afford liaison with its only foreign rivals—the Shell and Anglo-Iranian interests.

An oilman was named to head the Navy Department, the nation's biggest oil customer. As manager of the famed Waggoner oil and cattle interests in Texas and a member of the National Petroleum Council, Robert B. Anderson had firsthand knowledge of the industry's problems. He understood personally the industry's desire for a 27.5 percent depletion allowance and could enlighten the administration. Thanks to President Truman's Parthian shot in placing the offshore oil lands in a naval reserve, he was in immediate command of this treasure until it could be transferred to Texas, Louisiana, and California.[37]

At the head of the Department of Justice was Herbert Brownell, who favored "realistic" enforcement of the antitrust laws.

Even so, Eisenhower was warned by the *National Petroleum News* that the opposition, weakened, would become more "severe and vicious." In their struggle to regain power in 1956, this crowd "will, of course, be aided in every way by all the subversive forces of the world, whose march to world conquest has at last been halted by Eisenhower's election."

There was the enemy within still to be contended with, and even worse, the trade paper warned, "the hard core of the Federal bureaucracy continues New Deal at heart and is still very much of a factor to be reckoned with. Perhaps it will even be necessary on occasion to take out after the President himself or some of those he has brought to Washington and placed in high position."[38]

"THE TIDELANDS ARE OURS"

With the election won, the states' rights forces proceeded to the kill. The only question now was how much would satisfy them. The three-mile limit set by the vetoed Holland-Walter bill was clearly inadequate. Leander Perez, the indefatigable Louisiana oilman who led the fight in his state, announced that nothing less than 60 miles offshore would satisfy states' rights now.

Confidence in the inevitable results of the Republican victory gave way to outraged indignation when President Truman fired his parting shot at the "oil lobby" four days before leaving the White House. He proclaimed the offshore lands part of the U. S. Navy oil reserves, under the jurisdiction of the Department of Defense. The idea was by no means novel; President Roosevelt had suggested to Congress in 1937 that the coastal lands be set aside as a naval reserve.

In his final blast, Truman upped the value of the new naval reserves to $250 billion. He stated that 22 known oil fields off the coasts of three states had proven resources of 492 million barrels and were estimated to contain 15 billion barrels. "It has been, and still is, my firm conviction that it would be the height of folly for the United States to give away the vast quantities of oil contained in the Continental Shelf, and then buy back the same oil at stiff prices for use by the Army, the Navy and the Air Force in the defense of the nation."[39]

Truman hardly met the main issue. He did not indicate that he believed in federal operation of the naval domain in oil; the federal government would lease the lands under the sea to the same interests as the states would, and the oil would be marketed in the same channels as oil obtained from other wells. The main difference would be that the royalty—usually around 12½ percent—would be paid to the federal government instead of to the states. The price, under the scheme of production and price controls enacted during the Roosevelt-Truman regimes, would be the same for Uncle Sam as for other comparable bidders no matter to whom the "tidelands" belonged.

The House bill, as approved in committee, gave title of the offshore lands to the states but provided, if its constitutionality were challenged, that the states could have the right to develop the resources anyway. All bays, harbors, sounds, straits, channels, and islands were to be counted as within inland waters, and the three-mile or 10½-mile limits were to be drawn from a line outside them. Besides, the bill authorized the states to levy production

and severance taxes on oil and gas produced seaward of their
three-mile and 10½-mile limits but generously gave the right of
"first rejection" to the federal government, in case it wanted to
buy oil from its erstwhile lands. Later the House, after cutting
out the sections pertaining to production taxes and policing of
the continental shelf, passed the bill by 285 to 108 (the 1951 vote
had been 265 to 109).[40]

As debate wore on in the Senate the wealth of the "tidelands"
grew to astronomical proportions, up toward a half trillion. Senator Douglas, Democrat of Illinois, gave a $300 billion estimate
and said that this sum, in $1000 bills, would be as high as 300
Washington Monuments. Others began dividing such sums among
the states to indicate how much they were losing by giving away
federal property. In such cases it seemed to be assumed that $100
billion worth of oil—or whatever the sum—could be reclaimed
from beneath the Gulf without cost. When Senator Holland of
Florida, sponsor of the states' right bill, said that the states would
be surprised at how little they might receive he was nearer the
truth. Those who were cutting up the pie forgot that usually the
owner gets only an eighth of the petroleum and the companies
get the rest, out of which they pay the costs of exploration and
drilling.[41]

The prolonged debate changed few votes. The Senate bill went
through by 56 to 35 (the 1952 vote had been 50 to 35).[42]

Federalist papers such as the *New York Times,* which had
battled the "giveaway," consoled themselves that at least the federal government had retained control of the lands to seaward of
the state limits. In this the federal stake was considerable, particularly off the Louisiana coast. Although this state had claimed
"historic" boundaries as far as 27 miles from shore, it actually had
to yield to a three-mile limit (the limit of the Louisiana Purchase).
But the Mississippi delta lands slope out gradually and there are
wells now as far as 20 miles from shore in 60 feet of water.

Alabama and Rhode Island challenged the right of Congress to
give away their interest in offshore oil to three or four favored
states, but the Supreme Court, 6 to 2, followed the election returns
on March 14, 1954, by barring the challenge of the two dissident
states. The marginal lands were so much real estate, the majority

held, which Congress could give away if it so pleased. But to Justice Black it seemed that Congress could hardly sell or even give away the Atlantic and Pacific Oceans while Justice Douglas surmised that "powerful political forces are marshalled" to wipe out for "the benefit of a favored few" the theory that the nation had paramount rights to lands under the seas.[43]

Now it remained only to drive the victory through to its logical conclusion. The vast deposits of oil shale in the Rockies, of lignite in the Dakotas still under federal control—another threat to private enterprise—they, too, must be handed over to the states so that the oil corporations would be relieved of the menace of dictation or competition from Washington. If a price tag of hundreds of billions was hung over the "tidelands" oil, the tag on these resources read as high as a trillion dollars. That seemed a bit fantastic, but no more so than the sight of a great nation giving away the marginal lands around its coasts.[44]

The ultimate objective was stated by Senator Hugh Butler of Nebraska, when the new Secretary of the Interior, Douglas McKay —a former governor of Oregon—was being questioned for confirmation. "I would like to say here," said Butler, "that when the tidelands question is settled—and I hope it will be rather definitely before too far in this session—there are plans for the introduction of a bill that will make the same theory applicable to public lands now held by the federal government within the states." McKay reminded the Senators that as he had always been "one of the states' rights governors, I don't expect to change my philosophy of government because I go to work for the federal government." Complimented by Senator Daniel of Texas, he responded, "I hope I don't disappoint you."

19

The Province of Texas

TEXAS is the premier oil state, with nearly half the production and more than half the proved reserves of the nation. Everywhere in Texas it is oil: the vast fields of west Texas are exceeded only by the enormous wealth of east Texas; the petroleum riches of the Gulf Coast are paralleled by the immense gas pools of the Panhandle; north and southwest Texas add to the lavish cornucopia which nature turned upon this state. And it all belongs to the corporations!

Robert W. Calvert, chairman in 1947 of the Texas Democratic party and as conservative as most Lone Star politicians, put the matter bluntly when he introduced a member of the Texas Railroad Commission to the Lions Club in Hillsboro.

"It may not be a wholesome thing to say," he announced, "but the oil industry is in complete control of the state government and state politics." The oil industry had become so big that it controls "economic, political and social life. The income from the oil industry is so great and the avenues and outlets of its influence so numerous and so far-flung it can bring about any governmental program behind which it unites and defeat any program against it."[1]

The truth of that statement is challenged by no one in Texas. Six corporations among them produce or buy more than 80 percent of all the state's golden flow. Humble (Standard of New Jersey) alone produces 15.5 percent; Pan American (Standard of Indiana), 6.9; Gulf, 6.6; Magnolia (Socony), 4.8; Texaco, 4.7; Shell, 3.5 percent. As these companies generally produce only about half their requirements, the percentages should be roughly doubled for consumption.[2]

The key company is Humble, dominant in the Texas Mid-Continent Oil & Gas Association, but its associates are so big that it might be said that Humble is only first among equals. Their chief executives are interlocked in a tight ring that controls the oil, sulphur, natural gas, utilities, real estate, and banking interests of the Lone Star State.

Almost as important in Texas affairs, though, are the big independent oil producers, men mostly of modest origin who struck it rich by uncovering oil fields. Of these Hugh Roy Cullen of Quintana Petroleum is the archetype. One of the most successful of wildcatters, he discovered the Thompson field on the Gulf Coast worth $20 million. Then the O'Connor field, also on the Gulf Coast near Victoria, made him one of the biggest of all independent oil operators. Estimates of his wealth range around a billion dollars.[3]

Not knowing what to do with so much money, Cullen turned public-spirited and created the Cullen Foundation, said to possess $160 million, to be used primarily for health and educational purposes within the state. The University of Houston is his darling, beneficiary of some $20 million of Cullen cash. When he adopted it, the school was an institute of little standing; today its campus is among the most splendid in the nation. Congressional investigating committees need never worry about communistic or socialistic ideas permeating its crisp new buildings. As a reward for a rousing football victory, Cullen gave the university another $2,250,000 in 1953.[4]

Cullen's public spirit runs over into politics, too. He has engaged in vitriolic imbroglios with his fellow Houstonian, Jesse Jones, whom he regards askance as an "internationalist."[5]

Cullen, a good Dixiecrat, joined with Glenn McCarthy, another oil operator, to sponsor General MacArthur's invasion of Texas after his return from Japan. The trip was none too successful, but the deficit didn't bite deeply into such fortunes.[6]

In 1951, Cullen bought an interest in the Liberty Broadcasting Company, with 431 stations in 43 states. John T. Flynn, a leading anti-internationalist, was placed in charge of news and com-

mentaries, and "internationalist" commentators either left or were
dropped.[7]

Old Senator Connally, despite his sterling services in behalf
of Texas oil, was obliged to walk the plank in 1952 when Cullen
turned thumbs down on him. As chairman of the Senate Foreign
Relations Committee, he was suspected of internationalist dal-
liance. The majors, although sorry to see the old man dumped
so unceremoniously, fell in with the argument that it is better to
have a young man with years of officeholding ahead of him
rather than an aged fellow "who won't last much longer."[8] His
successor was Price Daniel, then state attorney general, who
had had an antitrust suit pending for three years against ten
major companies. This he suddenly dusted off before announcing
his candidacy, although he hadn't mentioned it for 18 months. In
this way he convinced the populace of his abhorrence of
monopoly; for Cullen and his fellow oil operators, he announced
undying devotion to 27.5 percent depletion allowances, the
main source of their fortunes. With this he coupled adherence to
the Taft-Hartley Act, to show his contempt for unions, and
proclaimed that he would fight "civil rights" to the last gasp.
Cullen's Liberty Network and Fulton Lewis, Jr., plugged Daniel
and he won an easy victory after succeeding in the redoubtable
enterprise of making Connally look like a liberal.

Associated with Cullen in this effort to rejuvenate the U. S.
Senate was the rather mysterious Haroldson L. Hunt of Dallas,
who is reputed to enjoy an income of $1 million a week, thanks
to the 27.5 percent depletion allowance on his oil properties.
Similar tycoons of the depletion allowances are Clint Murchison
and Sid Richardson, of Dallas and Fort Worth respectively. Most
of these operators get away from it all on their vast cattle ranches
and some even have hideaways in Mexico complete with private
airfields.[9]

Hunt, like Cullen, is a public-spirited man not averse to using
some of his money for tax-free educational purposes. His *Facts
Forum*, of Dallas, publishes a news magazine, conducts opinion
polls, and sponsors nationwide radio and TV broadcasts. Because
of their "public service" nature, these programs get more than a
million dollars a year in free time from 222 stations. A former

moderator for *Facts Forum* now sits on the Federal Communications Commission, while a former research worker is now Mrs. Joseph R. McCarthy.

Facts Forum is resolutely nationalist and promises that "no part of its earnings shall ever inure to or for the use of the United Nations." The opinion polls feature such questions as "Did pro-Communists in the United States bring about the Korean war?", "Are subversive movements gaining in the schools?", "Are books deriding patriotism favored in book review sections?" In news reports, broadcasts, and opinion polls, *Facts Forum,* in presenting both sides of questions, tends to lump liberal and conservative views on one side and its own ultra-nationalist, extreme right-wing views on the other. It decries the notion that the United States is a "democracy" when as a matter of fact it is a "republic."[10]

Senator Joe McCarthy, Republican of Wisconsin, was featured both as a performer and a prophet on Hunt's *Facts Forum* broadcasts. Interesting light was thrown on *Facts Forum* by an incident that occurred in 1953. Frederick W. Collins, *Providence Journal* staff man in Washington, was invited to take part in a McCarthy canned broadcast. Victor A. Johnston, executive director of the Republican national senatorial committee, served as go-between in arranging the broadcast, which was to net the *Providence Journal* man $125. Collins finally decided not to appear, but he later asked Johnston about Hunt's connection with the broadcasts. According to Collins's report:

> He said Hunt is a very rich guy who is anxious to spend his dough to elect senators and representatives he likes, and that it was all wrong to think he was trying to make McCarthy President. Hunt, he said, has an income of two or three million dollars a week, and he, Johnston, was just trying to help him spend the money on "our kind of guys." There is nothing vicious about Hunt, he said. . . .
>
> So what it all comes down to is that McCarthy has latched on to someone who has two or three million dollars a week coming in, and that a result is going to be McCarthy's frequent appearance on television shows which are canned under his auspices and shipped around the country for

release as straight discussion shows. It might be worth keeping that in mind the next time Facts Forum shows up on
your TV screen.[11]

Clint Murchison, one of the wealthiest Texas oil producers,
told a *New York Post* correspondent that Senator McCarthy had
asked him for a producing well. Murchison has given about
$25,000 to causes sponsored by McCarthy. These included the
defeat of Senator Millard Tydings, Democrat of Maryland, and
of Senator William Benton, Democrat of Connecticut. Nevertheless Murchison says he is not too much impressed with
McCarthy. "Hell, I've got ten men in Congress who are better
thought of than McCarthy. I don't need him for influence."
Murchison spent some $100,000 in 1952 in free-lance political
campaigning.[12]

Nevertheless, Senator McCarthy is generally well regarded by
the Houston, Dallas, and Fort Worth oil and cattle barons. When
the Senator married in 1953, they sent him a $6000 Cadillac
as a wedding gift, along with a certificate from Governor Shivers
certifying that "Joe McCarthy—a real American—is now officially
a Texan."[13]

The combined incomes of the 20 richest Texas oilmen would
pay the state's entire operating cost of $350 million a year.
Fortunately for them there is no likelihood they will pay even
1 percent of it, as Texas has no income-tax law. In Houston itself,
there are estimated to be some 400 millionaires; Dallas, in its
rivalry to the Gulf Coast town, certainly would be content with
no fewer; Fort Worth and San Antonio may have to be satisfied
with a hundred or so apiece.[14]

The lives of these men range from the uncouth to the gaudy;
perhaps none has reveled more in the public eye than Glenn
McCarthy whose opening in 1949 of the Shamrock Hotel in
Houston set new records in slapstick lavishness. The postwar era
of the Texas oil millionaires has been described in many a novel
splashed with the adjective "fabulous," and none more observing
probably than Edna Ferber's *Giant*. But these people enjoy
everything—even seeing their lives portrayed in novels which
leave nothing to the imagination.[15]

Their rule of Texas is absolute, thanks to the constitution of

1876, designed in that day to provide a weak administration. The state is governed by a legislature which meets once every two years. Its members are paid $10 a day for 120 days, and $5 a day when sessions last longer than three months. As a result, the legislators for the most part are lawyers with lucrative private practice who can afford to represent their clients in Austin. A minor part is made up of University of Texas law students and other deserving young men for whom the $10 a day helps pay room and board.

The Senate, composed of 31 members, is select in its representation of the big industrial and financial interests. The House has more of the plebeians. The oil and natural gas interests give a hand to the impecunious. A "loyal" Democrat, i.e. faithful to the national ticket, can be taken care of even though his votes are wrong, if he is young. Such organizations as the Texas Mid-Continent Oil & Gas Association and the Texas Independent Producers & Royalty Owners Association are lavish hosts during legislative sessions; their ways were well lampooned by former U. S. Senator "Pappy" O'Daniel when, in one of his favorite vaudeville speeches at the forks of the creek, he used to describe their steak-and-whiskey seduction of "good old country boys" new in the legislature.

The nice thing about Texas is that there is not much hypocrisy in these relations. Generous treatment of strangers is traditional in this western country and it would be considered downright discourteous for well-heeled lobbyists not to help out the indigent. Rather typical of this casual attitude was the entirely frank admission to the writer by a young legislator of the solicitous regard shown him by the oil and gas men. They had thrown him in the way of some mighty nice leases from which he was getting a few thousand a year while going through law school. He was quite grateful and it was obvious that no thought of corruption passed through his mind; after all, the favors done him had not been conditioned on his vote on any specific measure before the legislature. With relish he recounted the details of a banquet given by one of the oil and gas associations at which he had been favored with a seat at the head table. Talk ran to a recalcitrant legislator who had aroused deep antagonism among these gentlemen. One named the figure he would toss into the next campaign to defeat the errant politician, others eagerly topped his pledge as if bidding at auction.

It is well known in Texas, as Democratic Chairman Calvert so openly stated,* that the oil and gas interests run the state, and no fuss is made about it. The press, which ranges from rather conservative to really reactionary, contents itself with deadpan reporting of affairs in the state capital. Lobbyists are seldom mentioned; their fetes for legislators rate only a paragraph if noticed at all; the business connections of those with interests in Austin are not belabored.

Nevertheless, there is in Texas a hard core of opposition to the oil interests. This is composed partly of proud Texans of varying philosophy who dislike to see their state run by Yankee corporations; some even refer to the Lone Star Republic as a Wall Street province whose enormous wealth enriches distant owners. While their state ranks first in value of petroleum reserves, it is but 34th in per capita income. The rest of the opposition comes from organized labor whose most cohesive section is the CIO oil workers union. Acquainted at first hand with the corporations, the union has labored incessantly for fifteen years to build up a progressive alliance, to break down the walls against Negroes, and to secure for the state more benefits from its natural resources.

Opposition such as this, and the need to guard the Texas Railroad Commission's crucial position, keeps the oil lobby from going flabby. Texas opposition is colorful and vigorous. After all, Maury Maverick, who contested the "Texas Regular" oil-backed group at the Democratic national convention of 1952 with a San Antonio delegation including Mexicans and Negroes, was as much a Texas phenomenon as H. R. Cullen. The oilmen on the board of the University of Texas succeeded in forcing out President Homer P. Rainey, but Rainey ran for governor in 1946 on a platform which would have been considered advanced even for a northern New Dealer, and got a third of the votes. That the Raineys will not get much more than a third is assured for the present by the poll tax, which keeps the poorer citizens, both white and black, from the voting booth.

* See page 200, above.

In Texas, the lessons of the depression have been all but wiped out in the tide of prosperity that has accompanied the tremendous growth of the oil, gas, and petrochemical industries in recent years. Along this ever-ascending plateau of wealth won easily from nature's bosom, the newly-rich are riding high, wide, and handsome, hand in hand with the oil corporations which consider Texas almost on a par with Venezuela and Arabia as a province for their enrichment.

Control of Texas means control of United States oil. With its production under rein, the production of neighboring Oklahoma and Louisiana can be curbed, and these three account for four-fifths of national production outside California. With this controlled, the price level adjusts itself and the profits roll into the coffers of the majors without regard to the risks that plague less fortunate industries.

Fortunately for the oil interests, long before petroleum was suspected to underlie the state, the legislature had devoted income from its public lands to the school fund and to nourish the University. Now that even greater good fortune seemed about to add the riches of the coastal lands to the schools, an attack on Texas's rights became an attack on her schools. For that reason, Governor Allan Shivers, from Port Arthur, the nation's biggest refinery center, girded his loins for battle on behalf of Texas's children. He went to Springfield, Illinois, to consult the Democratic standard-bearer, Adlai Stevenson. As one governor to another, Stevenson told Shivers he was for federal ownership of the offshore lands but was willing to cut the coastal states in for a slice of the pie. Shivers hurried back to Austin to ask the citizenry to inform the coming Democratic state convention of their opinion on this threat to the state's schools.

Immediately there sprang up the length and breadth of Texas organizations like Keep the Tidelands Associations, Texas Property Defense Associations, and others as ephemeral as the Gulf's May flies. The state was drenched in leaflets. Children brought them home from school, where they were spread by Parent Teachers Associations rallying to the defense of education.

The bedraggled ranks of "loyal" Democrats hardly dared speak out on the issue. Lone Star patriotism was far more important than national sovereignty in a state one of whose main humorous productions is a map showing an enormous Texas with the other 47 states grouped around straggling margins. The loyalists addressed their appeal to the state's innate Democratic prejudices and accused their opponents, the Texas "regulars," of being Republicans in disguise.

This charge stirred small indignation. The Republican state convention adopted the entire Democratic state ticket as its own.[16] The Texas regulars, reciprocating, entered a "regular" ticket with the Democratic state nominees headed by Eisenhower and Nixon. It seemed that the loyal Democratic ticket was almost a third party. Although not a single daily in the big cities spoke out for the national Democratic ticket, when the votes were counted no fewer than 970,000 Texans had remained "loyal" compared to the 1,100,000 who voted for Eisenhower.

How much money the corporations dumped into the Texas campaign will never be known. The *New York Times* reported on "reliable sources" that a million dollars was spent for Eisenhower there. The Democrats for Eisenhower said they spent $250,000 through state headquarters, but that did not include city and county funds. The state Republican committee spent $500,000, it said, of which $263,000 was sent to the national committee. In addition, the *Times* reported, wealthy individuals gave to the national committees of both parties. As for the Democratic state committee, it was practically idle throughout the campaign and a separate Stevenson organization had to be set up.[17]

Such estimates of expenditures to keep Texas safe were superficial. After all, the press could be depended on whether or not a single penny was invested in advertisements. Radio, thanks to Cullen and his associates, was theirs without further compensation. The engines of propaganda, which in venal lands must be suitably oiled, needed no such lubrication in Texas. Both political parties within the state were at the disposal of the "tidelands" interests at only the usual price.

The oil and gas lobbies, while unusually generous at election time, are always generous, and it would be unfair to count only their unusual expenses as typical of their entire contribution to the "economic ignorance" of the people.

20

Taxation—Boon to Millionaires

On THE theory that the more you take out of a well the less you have, an ingenious tax policy has been evolved to assure the production of the biggest and most blatant crop of millionaires that the nation has seen since the robber barons flourished in the late nineteenth century.

The gimmick is called "depletion allowance." The Treasury Department says it is the biggest of all loopholes in the tax laws, accounting for more than $500 million a year tax loss on oil alone. The tall stories about the "filthy rich" Texas millionaires—men whose fortunes are estimated up to a billion, mostly garnered in the past twenty years—are spun from the deep holes of depletion allowance.

When 27.5 percent can be deducted from gross income from producing wells, and all losses from dry holes can be deducted, Uncle Sam finds himself in some cases unable to pry a penny from these newest of the nouveaux riches. According to the Treasury, 10 operators in the period 1943-1947 realized incomes of more than $1 million a year each, but paid income taxes ranging from 63.5 percent to less than 1 percent. Without the magic allowance, their taxes would have ranged up to 90 percent! If depletion were eliminated and ordinary depreciation alone permitted, it was estimated by Senator Hubert H. Humphrey, Democrat of Minnesota, that the entire tax increase on those earning less than $4000 a year could have been dropped from the 1951 tax bill.[1]

The theory of depletion allowance is quite unlike that of the depreciation allowed to ordinary businesses. If a million-dollar plant has an expected life of 20 years, the owner may deduct $50,000 a year from gross income for depreciation.

But depreciation is not estimated on the cost of an oil well. If a well in which $100,000 was invested produces $500,000 worth of oil a year for 10 years and then is exhausted, the ordinary depreciation allowance would amount to $10,000 a year. But instead of allowing this kind of depreciation on the investment, the tax laws permit the investor to deduct each year 27.5 percent of the gross income from production, that is, $137,500 a year. In the 10 years, therefore, the owner would deduct $1,375,000 from his income tax on an investment of $100,000.[2]

"I know of no loophole in the tax laws so inequitable as the excessive depletion exemptions now enjoyed by oil and mining interests," said President Truman in his 1950 budget message. "A forward-looking resources program does not require that we give hundreds of millions of dollars annually in tax exemptions to a favored few at the expense of the many."

The inequity was pointed up by the example of 12 oil millionaires who paid an average income tax of only 22½ percent on their income in 1943-1947, ½ of 1 percent less than the wartime rate on the first $2000 of taxable income. In 1947, oil companies were able to deduct 13 times more through depletion allowance than they would have been permitted to do on the basis of depreciation rates allowed to most industries. The National Oil Marketers Association in 1953 estimated the government could realize more than $1 billion in revenue by allowing "true" depletion instead of a flat figure of 27.5 percent.[3]

Other mineral industries have been eager to get in on this handout, which dates only from 1926. Sulphur producers have a 23 percent allowance, coal 10 percent, and other minerals from 5 to 15 percent. Now sand, gravel, stone, clay, oyster and clam shells, and salt have been let in.

All efforts to close this loophole have been treated as an almost sacrilegious invasion of the oil industry's prerogatives. When it seemed in 1950 that the House Ways and Means Committee, under Chairman Robert Doughton, a conservative North Carolina Democrat, was about to recommend a reduction in the rate from 27.5 to 15 percent, Speaker Sam Rayburn, a Texan, leaped into the breach. "The Speaker," said Doughton, "was terribly against any change in the oil depletion allowance provision. I know he made that plain to other members of the committee. Personally, I thought that loophole ought to be closed, that it was wrong, but the others were so much for keeping it that nothing could be done."[4]

For the special type of speculator who gambles millions on wells and fields, the depletion allowance is "Open Sesame" into the modern den of the Forty Thieves. The fortunes of the H. R. Cullens, Glenn McCarthys, H. L. Hunts mount easily, in a brief span of years, to peaks which it took John D. Rockefeller half a lifetime of patient planning to achieve.

The kind of wildcatting stimulated by depletion allowances is the biggest gambling of the century. If enough is wagered, and if the gambler is in the 90 percent tax bracket, he can hardly lose. If his well turns out to be a dry hole, all costs of drilling are deductible from gross income. If a well produces, all "intangible" expenses such as the preliminary geological work and all the labor, equipment, and fuel costs of drilling, often amounting to 60 percent of all costs, are deductible. On top of this is the depletion allowance.

If the gambler's take is such that the last $100,000 of his income is subject to a tax of $90,000, and if a new well costs $100,000, then even if he merely drills a dry hole he has hardly done more than exchange a drilling bill for a tax bill. If he has $900,000 to gamble in the 90 percent tax bracket, and drills eight dry holes at $100,000 a hole, Lady Luck says his next hole will be wet. He will have lost a total of only $80,000 on the eight dry holes, and he may make a mint on the good well.[5]

To emphasize the hazards of the industry, the oil companies distributed an innocent game of chance to Congressmen. On a cardboard square a circle was divided into nine segments, eight of which were marked "dry hole," while the ninth was subdivided to show the various degrees of success in wildcatting. Most Congressmen, not being in the 90 percent taxable bracket, were properly impressed with the hazards and voted to continue the 27.5 percent depletion allowances.

But given persistence and a minimum amount of sense, the

well-heeled wildcatter is bound to win. It's simply a matter of
drilling enough holes to beat the 8 to 1 odds. It's not a game for
the little fellow, to be sure, but the biggest windfall of the
century for the man about to come across to Uncle Sam in the
80 percent and up brackets.

Some Wall Street firms operate a variety of games based on
depletion allowances. In one such, the minimum ante is $50,000.
Such ventures are based on royalties, leases, mineral rights, and
other variations. If the gambler is in the 90 percent tax bracket,
all he risks is 10 cents for every dollar he puts on the wheel. If
he loses (odds are 8 to 1 that the hole will be dry) he can
deduct his share of expenses from his tax. If he wins, he can
deduct 27.5 cents from his taxes for every dollar of gross oil
income and can also keep 10 percent of the remainder (7.25 cents)
—that is to say, what he would be allowed to retain if the income
had come from any other source—which gives him 35 cents to keep
of his income dollar, instead of the 10 cents he would have had
without benefit of oil's special indulgences. Thus every marginal
income dollar he trades for an oil income dollar gives him a 25-
cent gain. And if, instead of collecting the income, he sells out
his holdings and takes his capital gain, the tax laws let him keep
74 cents of every dollar gained.

The gambler need not know a thing about oil nor ever have
seen a well. There are "deal brokers" in New York who will take
care of him, and plenty of reputable firms who specialize in oil
and warn the small fry to stay away. In general they are interested only in those willing to spend $25,000 a year and up over
a span of time. Some $250 million a year is spent on this kind
of oil speculation, it is estimated, and only the Bureau of Internal
Revenue knows how much the government loses on it.

What is still a gamble to the outsider who stands to win only
through grace of the federal tax laws, is a sure thing to the major
oil companies. Armed with the best geophysical information and
hundreds of millions of dollars for exploration, they reap the bulk
of their profits from exactly this kind of venture. Production is
their big moneymaker,* and depletion allowance is the key to it.

Sensitive to criticism, oilmen contend that these allowances

* See page 99.

are vital to expanded oil production, which in turn is said to be badly needed for national defense. Without them, so the argument runs, wildcatting would slow down; there would be little incentive to drill in unexplored fields. The resulting scarcity of crude would drive up the price of gasoline and the consumer would be the ultimate loser. The argument conveniently overlooks the fact that the price of gasoline goes up anyway. The question remains whether exploratory drilling should be a spur to speculation rather than a planned social responsibility, the more so since petroleum is a limited natural resource.

The financial editor of the *New York Herald Tribune* commented that these allowances were "granted to those brave individuals who risked their money in the extractive industries, some privileges which do not apply to you and me and to the manufacturer of such things as tin cans and soap. As a result investors like the stocks of producers of crude oil."[6] Financial consultants refer to oil stocks as "tax-sheltered investments," an observation so common that Humble's treasurer protested that they were doing a "disservice" to the industry.[7]

Independent oil marketers take a special interest in depletion allowances, for they believe the major companies balance off losses in marketing against the extraordinary gains in production made possible by the magic 27.5 percent. The National Oil Jobbers Council has instructed its committee on economic concentration to study this angle. But the Council was warned by C. H. Arnold of the Northwest Petroleum Association that "we are engaging in wishful thinking if we believe the major companies will furnish us with figures on how they use the depletion allowance." The integrated companies, he feared, were using profits "made up through depletion, transportation, and to some extent, fast tax write-offs, which none of us have, to put us out of business. . . . If they have their way, there won't be any independent jobbers in 10 years."

21

The Dilemma of Imports

THE first important legislation of the Eisenhower regime was the payoff to the oil interests, removing the threat of federal control from offshore resources. The second big legislative issue worrying the industry was that of imports, and on this the new regime found itself painfully impaled on a dilemma.

Every proposed solution was thorny, for the industry itself was split right down the middle. Those majors mainly dependent on domestic production favored barriers against the inrush of Venezuelan and Middle Eastern crude; the independent producers of the Southwest saw their hopes for price increases blighted by the foreign flood. But Standard of New Jersey and its fellow importing majors were set against any Congressional limitation. Pleading both military needs and the danger of imperiling the nation's tenuous ties with foreign petroleum states, the big importers could call on both the State and Defense Departments for support. So far as the administration was concerned, the "foreign" majors stood in no peril whatever. As always, though, Congress was the dubious factor, the disturbing element, the sounding board for the malcontents of the industry.[1]

The strength of the "domestic" producers was indeed formidable, for they had few qualms in picking up allies. The core of their strength lay in the delegations from the oil-producing states. Flanking them were the traditional high-protection Republicans of the North, the coal interests which were losing their markets rapidly to residual oil from Venezuela, the eastern coal-hauling railroads, and the Railroad Brotherhoods and the United Mine Workers whose jobs were at stake.

The *National Petroleum News* wrung its hands in anguish at the division within the industry, and implored both sides, for reasons of higher policy, to come together. "Otherwise the oil industry is liable to be harassed beyond the capacity of the Eisenhower administration to protect it; harassed in a way to contribute to possible defeat of Eisenhower for reelection, and harassed to the extent of giving the industry still more serious problems to face four years from now at a time when it is in the weakest strategic position yet."[2]

The problem was neatly summed up in the balance between imports and domestic capacity which was "shut-in," unused. By 1955, shut-in capacity was nearing 2 million barrels a day,[3] while the volume of imports approached 1.5 million barrels. If the wells were allowed to produce, there would be no need for imports. The solution was so obvious to independent producers and the "domestic" majors that it hardly needed to be argued; they were being sacrificed by the Wall Street-State Department internationalists for the greater profits of Standard of New Jersey, Socony, Standard of California, Texaco, Gulf, and Shell. These companies bridled under the attack. Was not their Venezuelan oil almost as American as Texas or Oklahoma oil? Was it not produced, refined, and marketed by U. S. companies and thereby thoroughly Americanized?

The problem was of recent origin. Ever since Rockefeller began lighting the lamps of China, U. S. oil had been a great article of foreign trade. After Spindletop, it began moving the British Navy. Aside from a brief period in the early 1920s when crude was being imported from Mexico, the United States had always been a net exporter. But in 1948 the balance changed. The great wells of Venezuela and the Middle East began supplanting U. S. oil in foreign markets and even began invading the East Coast. In 1947, imports were 8 percent of domestic production, in 1951 they climbed to 12 percent, and in 1955 to nearly 15 percent. About half the imports were in crude and the other half in residual oil (from which the gasoline and other lighter "ends" had already been refined). Most of it came from Venezuela although the volume of Persian Gulf oil was steadily rising and Indonesian oil was flowing into California. Jersey's

Venezuelan subsidiary, Creole, accounted for a fifth of the total.

Foreign oil's gain represented a loss of $165 million a year to the coal industry, the National Coal Association claimed. In addition, the railroads were losing $94 million a year, coal miners $84 million, and railway workers $47 million, the coal people said, while taxing agencies were out some $43 million in revenue.[4]

Naturally, President Eugene Holman of Standard of New Jersey did not look kindly on limitation of imports of crude to 10 percent of domestic production. He argued national defense needs, the touchy situation in Venezuela, and the harm to fuel consumers who preferred oil to coal.[5]

The news from Venezuela was indeed disconcerting. A "wave of economic nationalism" was sweeping that country in protest against the pending bills in Congress. *El Universal* of Caracas growled: "Venezuela cannot permit its economy to be managed by U. S. congressmen." That country's National Merchants Association warned that Venezuela would not "hesitate to adopt special measures in the defense of national interests, should circumstances so demand."[6]

The ruling military junta, which did so much to enable Standard's Creole, Gulf's Mene Grande, and Shell to reap staggering profits in a country held tight under the bayonet, proved to be a sharp bargainer in holding up its own end of the deal. Watching the success of nationalization in Mexico and the situation in Iran, the junta permitted its economists to speculate in the censored press on the need for Venezuela to run its own petroleum industry. That sent tremors up the spines of the U. S. corporations. The good old days of gunboat diplomacy were gone, and there was plenty of cause to start worrying.

The situation in Texas was critical. The oil interests, both majors and independent producers, had carried the state for Eisenhower. While the "tidelands" had been thrown their way, these treasures were mainly subject to future exploitation. But the situation, month to month, was that the Texas Railroad Commission was cutting allowables.* General Thompson, chair-

* The number of producing days allowed in Texas dropped from an average of 291 in 1945-1949 to 194 in 1954. Year-by-year the figures were: 1950, 230 days; 1951, 278; 1952, 259; 1953, 236; 1954, 194; average for 1950-1954, 239 days. In May 1955, the Texas Railroad Commission set the

man of the Commission, was in a delicate position. Some of his best friends were the managers of the big importing majors; others of his best friends were independent producers fuming against the cursed imports that kept down the price of their crude. No doubt the bigger guns were on the side of the importers, but he and his fellow commissioners have to face the voters of Texas once each six years. So he, too, begged the big importers to curb themselves voluntarily.[8]

The Texas Independent Producers & Royalty Owners Association (TIPRO) was in no such docile mood. It demanded that the Texas allowables be raised to enable the state to recover some of the 400,000 barrels a day lost to foreign imports. Cutbacks in allowables had cost the state's economy a million dollars a day, TIPRO said, and there was something sadly wrong with the "market demand" statute that permitted foreigners to fatten on Texan misery.[9]

This was serious. To tamper with the sacrosanct "market demand" statute, keystone of price and production control exercised by the majors, was to strike at the very heart of the oil cartel. It amounted to downright rebellion, and it could be taken for granted that if Texas set out to increase its allowables, Oklahoma, Kansas, and Louisiana would follow suit. Then—well, either Venezuela would be shut off or the price structure would tumble. Perhaps Samson was not blind enough to pull down the pillars of the temple, but his threats sounded ominous.

Vice-president A. C. Rubel of Union Oil told the Independent Petroleum Association that "you as domestic producers are forced by the very state laws ostensibly designed for conservation purposes, to shut in your own production to make room for unneeded imports."[10] At the time, Texas wells were allowed to produce only 15-17 days of the month. The final insult, it seemed, was the arrival of a shipment of Kuwait oil in Houston in February 1954.

The Independent Petroleum Association of America (IPAA) put little faith in importers' promises to restrict the import of foreign oil. "The Congress must now accept responsibility in the public interest," it resolved. IPAA "was not organized to liquidate

---

number of producing days for the following two months at 16 days a month.[7]

the domestic petroleum industry." It called for Congressional action to limit imports to 10 percent of domestic output.[11]

Russell B. Brown, spokesman of IPAA, suspected that federal agencies, under Eisenhower as well as Truman, were dominated by Standard of New Jersey and its associates. "Too often when we find a government agent fostering destructive proposals we see the shadow of these companies at his elbow," said Brown. "We have watched with concern the ease with which officials of our State Department, the Department of Commerce and other agencies are interchangeable with officials of the importing companies."[12]

The 1952 Trade Agreement with Venezuela which cut duties on oil imports was the signal for renewed outcries from the aggrieved producers and the coal interests. The agreement ignored both of the Tariff Commission's split recommendations, one for continuing the existing duty of 10½ cents a barrel for a quota equivalent to 5 percent of U. S. refinery runs, and 21 cents a barrel on all over the quota; the other for a flat 10½ cents duty. The commission had split 3-3 on these recommendations. Neither took account of the clamor for a punitive $1.05 a barrel duty.

The Venezuelan treaty, which applies to all oil imports from countries enjoying most-favored-nation treatment, cut the duty to the legal minimum of 5¼ cents on the heavier oils and 10½ cents on higher gravity oil suitable for refining. The duties are a tax, borne either by the Venezuelan government in curtailed revenues or by U. S. consumers in a higher price level. Based on the prevailing price of oil, the new levy was a 2 percent impost. During the 1930s the comparable figure was 20 percent.[13]

As if that were not bad enough for the domestic producers, the National Security Resources Board recommended in 1952 that the duties be eliminated altogether if necessary, and was backed in this by the Mutual Security Agency. It was thought better not to seek specific approval from Congress but to by-pass that barrier by getting legislation authorizing the executive to act at its discretion. In this the Board followed the line of the President's Materials Policy (Paley) Commission.[14]

Domestic producers did not care for such ideas. When Hugh Stewart, director of the Office of Oil and Gas of the Department of the Interior, suggested that they had not been hurt yet by imports, IPAA was indignant. Counsel Russell B. Brown said that Stewart "gave the stock reply of the Texas Company." (Stewart was formerly a Texaco executive.) "When the president or other executive officer of the Texas Company opposes legislative action or seeks to influence public opinion in favor of imports, it is easy to meet him openly and publicly. His actions will be quickly identified as being in the interests of his company. When an employe of that company, placed in a responsible federal position, continues from this high perch to reflect the view of his former employer, it is time to raise the question of the soundness of his position."[15]

Canadian oil looked no better than Venezuelan to TIPRO and IPAA. They were bitter because Standard of California and other West Coast majors preferred to pipe in crude from the Alberta fields rather than from Texas. In fact the majors were accused of blocking a pipe line from west Texas into increasingly oil-hungry California.[16]

The Independent Refiners Association of America (IRAA) was also up in arms. Increasing imports of residual fuel threaten to eliminate the independent refiner, the association complained. The smaller refineries could not afford to match the price under which residual oil was dumped on the U. S. market; consequently they were forced either to install expensive equipment to split their own residual into more marketable products, or go out of business.[17]

For the big "international" companies, the low cost of their foreign crude was of course their main advantage. Their costs were closely guarded secrets, but the U. S. Department of Commerce in 1946 estimated that Arabian crude cost 30 cents a barrel, and Venezuelan 50 cents, against $1.85 for Gulf Coast crude.[18] At that time Texas crude was selling for $2.65, and that price governed the world price. In 1955 the United Nations Economic Commission for Europe put the Arabian cost of production at 35 cents a barrel.

In 1955, the Gulf Coast price was $2.90, and foreign oil had gone up proportionately. The differential in favor of Arabian and Venezuelan crude was absorbed in profits, of course, and not passed on to consumers. Domestic prices were based strictly on the Gulf base.

With the residual oil from Venezuela, the situation was different. After the gasoline and other high-value products had been refined in the big Standard of New Jersey and Shell refineries on the Dutch islands off the Venezuelan coast and sent to Latin America and Europe, the residual went to the East Coast to be sold in competition with coal.

The coal industry said the big importers deliberately rigged the price of residual oil to force coal out of the market. Residual, selling in 1950 at $1.65 a barrel, was almost a dollar cheaper than the crude from which it came. This contrasted with the price in 1949 of $3.05 for residual. The price had been slashed, said the National Coal Association, at a time when the price of gasoline and other oil products was being increased. The coal industry's spokesman in New York said: "It seems plain that this oil, much of it from South America, is being dumped at the expense not only of the anthracite and bituminous coal industries, but at the expense of independent domestic oil producers and of millions of motorists who are, in effect, subsidizing large industrial users of residual oil."[19]

National Petroleum News rushed to the defense of the importing majors. "When we look at imports or synthetic fuels or the demand for 'a national oil policy,' we find the coal crowd, including John L. Lewis. They are out to hamstring the oil industry in every way possible."[20]

The National Coal Association was flirting with the Independent Petroleum Association of America, much to the disgust of the importing majors who regarded such *mésalliances* as close to treason. On the other hand the National Oil Jobbers Council carried the war to both the coal and independent producers' groups because it hungered for the cut-price residual from Venezuela which nourished the lifeblood of many of its members. The jobbers threatened that if the coal-independent producers' alliance was able to force import cuts through Congress, then NOJC would get a Congressional inquiry into the "price and profit structure" of the crude oil producers in this country and also spur Congressmen to see "if the current depletion allowances for crude oil and coal production are excessive, and if so, to what extent."[21]

The import issue focused in 1955 on the President's foreign trade program. An amendment aimed to limit oil imports to 10 percent of domestic production. The big importing companies countered with a promise to hold imports to the 1954 level, and their promise was accepted.

The issue was critical to companies dependent on domestic production. Despite a general 1.2 percent rise in industry profits over 1953, 25 of the more important companies reported a decline in their own profits, against 16 reporting a gain. Among those gaining were all the "international" companies except Socony. The "domestic" companies blamed imports and consequent stringent limitation of domestic production for their own difficulties. Twenty-nine companies reported for 1954 a decline in their domestic production against only ten which were able to increase their output. In annual reports, no fewer than 15 companies specifically pinned the blame on imports and called for redress, preferably by Congressional action.

Ashland, a refining and marketing company, complained it had been caught in a squeeze between the competitive wholesale market and fixed prices for the crude it had to buy. Crude was stabilized, Ashland said, through severe prorationing of production aggravated by the importation of low-cost foreign crude. The little Deep Rock company in the mid-continent said "domestic companies find themselves at a distinct disadvantage in all branches of the industry without the windfall of low-cost foreign reserves."

Plymouth, with curtailed production in Texas, called for a "militant position in protection of our home market from further loss." And massive Standard of Indiana protested that while its production in Texas had been cut back 30 percent by prorationing in 1951-1954, imports had risen 35 percent. "Clearly, imports are partly supplanting—rather than supplementing—domestic production." Sun said that it had had to buy 30,000 barrels a day in the open market to make up for crude oil shut in during 1954 in its own wells. Sun's net earnings would have been $10 million higher, it claimed, if the company could have drawn oil from its own wells. In self-defense, the company was buying Middle East crude to "offset . . . part of the penalty which refiners of domestic oil currently are suffering." As if in answer to such dire deprivation, the Big Five U. S. companies in the Iranian consortium offered a 5 percent slice in Iranian production to other U. S. firms, if they would buy interests in the consortium.*

While this washing of the industry's dirty linen in public was an unedifying spectacle for Standard of New Jersey and its associates, they probably were not unduly disturbed by the threat that Congress might curb imports. Standard's Creole announced that Venezuelan production had been cut back; Standard's Humble announced its devotion to Texas production. The Jersey politburo in session at 30 Rockefeller Plaza was in full control of the situation, balancing its strategy to harmonize the needs of Creole in Venezuela and Humble in Texas. This required a good bit of tact and patience, since neither Texas nor Venezuela was exactly modest in its claims to the U. S. market. But an admirable knack for judicious compromise for the greatest benefit to Jersey was exactly why its board enjoyed such high esteem among connoisseurs of industrial government.

* See page 330.

22

Attempts at Regulation

CONGRESS, the Department of Justice, the Federal Trade Commission, federal judges ranking up from district courts to the U. S. Supreme Court itself, and the National Recovery Administration, all have tried, from time to time, to bring the rule of law into the jungle of the oil market. After fifty years of such efforts, the National Federation of Small Business could still be crying out, in 1949, for the Department of Justice to do something effective. Independent oil dealers, said the Federation, which claimed to speak for 130,000 members, "are being deprived by their suppliers of their most elemental rights as independent businessmen."[1]

THE CLAYTON ACT

The exclusive dealing contract, by which the independent jobber and retailer are tied to the major supplier, has been the main tool used to dominate the market. In 1914, the Clayton Act specifically forbade such contracts. A dealer contracting with a supplier could not be stopped from contracting also with another seller. The language seemed plain and simple, the intent obvious. But the U. S. Supreme Court in 1923, Justice McReynolds speaking, held that an exclusive dealing contract binding a lessee to use only Sinclair products in Sinclair pumps did not bar him from also buying or leasing other pumps to dispense the products of other suppliers.[2]

How true this was! Nothing barred the dealer from installing other pumps, although Sinclair thereupon would either withdraw its own equipment or charge a higher price for Sinclair products.

He was also free, if he quit Sinclair, to sign a similar lease with another major. Behind this lease, too, lay a mesh of entanglements which effectively barred him from free choice. The major extended credit, there were double leases, notes, stock purchases—an extravaganza played upon the theme of a lease by corporation lawyers. Through these devices, the mob of the market was regimented into phalanxes of uniformed dealers all responding to the price baton of the oil marshals.

NRA

The Federal Trade Commission in 1929 tried to clear out some of the underbrush in the jungle through a Hooverian code of fair practices which spelled out the conditions of marketing. This was voluntary, but not so voluntary as to escape running into legal snares in Texas where it was eyed as a tool of monopoly.

Under the National Industrial Recovery Act in 1933, this 1929 code was taken as the framework for an elaborate constitution for the industry. Price-fixing was the crux, and the little fellows were all for it to shield them from the majors. The majors were for price-fixing, too, but distrusted federal agencies for the job. If prices were to be fixed, the majors would do it. A compromise was worked out, providing for fixed margins, but not enforceable through the NRA code. Rather it was a voluntary arrangement, and those who did not care to sign were to be taken care of through a pool to remove "distress gasoline" from the market. The Department of Justice was cool to this compromise and the majors only halfhearted about it, so it was dropped. The majors proceeded to price-fixing through the more circuitous and, in the end, more effective and permanent method of controlling production.

The code of fair practices in the market concerned such engrossing problems as how much of an auto could be cleaned without charge, how big the price figures should be on signs, and fixing 2 cents as the maximum cost of a giveaway premium. As a sop to the independents, it was stated that the majors must equalize their profits in the various branches of the industry, to remove the independents' fear that the majors' losses in marketing were subsidized by profits in other branches. This proved quite unworkable, for the majors claimed that they were never able to segregate their costs.

Another rule expressly banned exclusive dealing contracts, but this was openly ignored, much to the distress of small western Pennsylvania firms specializing in lubricating oils. For 20 months, they were cut off from their markets until the code administrator got around to enforcing that rule. Even then, gasoline was exempted. As this was the main product involved, the exclusive dealing contract in effect received the imprimatur of the government, the Clayton Act to the contrary notwithstanding. It was one of the industry's major victories, for when the code went out with NIRA, exclusive dealing remained, not only as an entrenched institution, but one backhandedly sanctioned by a governmental agency.

THE SOCONY CASE

The independents bitterly wailed at this new turn in their misfortunes. Congressmen bent ear and the Department of Justice was activated. In 1936, indictments were leveled at Socony and other majors operating in the Midwest, and the case was tried in Madison, Wisconsin. Between 1931 and 1936, the Department alleged, these majors met, usually at the Blackstone in Chicago, to fix margins and terms for the hapless dealers for the ensuing year. In this collective bargaining, the dealers of course were not present. The case came up on appeal to the U. S. Supreme Court in 1940. The majors did not deny that uniform contracts were imposed upon jobbers, that uniform discounts were fixed, and that the price structure rested on gasoline prices based on Tulsa, regardless of the actual point of origin. If "distress" gasoline could be absorbed in Tulsa, it was then necessary only to control the supply there to fix the price throughout the Midwest. Socony and its confederates did not, of course, fix any particular price at Tulsa; they merely arranged the market there in such fashion that nothing but a manipulated price could result.[3]

The Supreme Court was quite indignant that such practices should flourish, the more so as they were not denied by the culprit majors. Their defense, that such practices had been approved by the Department of the Interior and the NRA, was brushed aside. The court held that federal officials lacked the power to set aside the law. Socony and its associates paid fines as penance for their sins.

It was a famous victory and gave rise to no end of learned discussions by lawyers, replete with heavy footnotes. But the dealer and jobber, with resources from a few thousand dollars to a few million, still faced the billion-dollar majors. And the majors were able to afford much the higher-priced and more respected lawyers.

In 1955 the Montana legislature was asserting that prices in that state were based on the Tulsa spot market price, plus tank car transportation to Montana, on oil produced within the state. But as the majors denied that they based their prices any more on Tulsa, it seemed clear to them, at least, that they were not violating the court's decision in the Socony case.

THE ETHYL CASE

The Department of Justice also won a victory against Ethyl Corporation in 1940. In order to maintain a closer grip on the market, Ethyl did not license its patent, but instead manufactured the fluid which takes the knock out of motors, and sold it directly to refiners. With this went conditions. The "premium" fuel must be sold at 2 cents a gallon over "regular," although the cost of the fluid was but ⅛ of a cent per gallon of gas. The dealer must also be "ethical," i.e. he must join in the conspiracy against the public by refusing to engage in price competition. The U. S. Supreme Court held that Ethyl, half owned by Standard of New Jersey, used the differential to control the price of untreated gasoline. But "premium" gasoline still sells at a 2 cents differential.[4]

The Department of Justice was after Ethyl again in 1953, in the DuPont antitrust suit. This time it wanted Ethyl divorced from DuPont (although its other half ownership by Standard of New Jersey certainly affected the market much more). DuPont and Jersey each had realized profits of $81 million from Ethyl up to 1947, when its patent expired, the Department said. By that time many motorists had become so conditioned to the virtues of

Ethyl that they continued paying the 2 cent bonus, despite testimony by Dr. G. E. Hilbert, chief of the Bureau of Agricultural and Industrial Chemistry in the Department of Agriculture, that premium gas is needed only about 5 percent of the time. Hilbert said that regular gasoline was as good as premium for ordinary light-load car operation in level territory at reasonable speeds.[5] Such information has a minus anti-knock rating; Ethyl continued to note, in the trade press, that it was its advertising in the public press that indoctrinated so many million motorists into saying "premium" at the filling station.

THE MOTHER HUBBARD SUIT

The Department of Justice in 1940 threw the book at the industry in what became known as the "Mother Hubbard" case, because it covered everything. The Department said that the American Petroleum Institute and the majors were a combination with monopolistic power, dominating each branch of the industry through size, integration, tying clauses, price-fixing, and restriction of production.[6]

But then World War II came along requiring the cooperation of the accused monopolists if victory were to be achieved. Indeed, there could not have been a war, much less a victory, if the indicted firms would not cooperate with the government which had indicted them. So the suit was put on the shelf for the duration. In 1946, it was dusted off, but neither Attorney General Tom C. Clark, of Texas, nor his successor, J. Howard McGrath, pressed it, and it died a lackadaisical death in 1951 under circumstances which in other times and other lands might well have excited more curiosity than was shown here.[7]

Perhaps it didn't matter too much, for the Mother Hubbard suit, while comprehensive in its charges, sought as a remedy injunctions that would restrain the majors from certain practices committed in certain ways. The experience of previous antitrust actions indicates the ineffectiveness of such injunctions against trade practices, which merely invite astute corporation lawyers to find other ways of accomplishing the desired end. The proposal to cure the consequences of concentration by segmenting the industry into its four divisions, as endorsed at various times by Congress, the courts, and even Presidents, was ignored in the suit.

THE STANDARD OF INDIANA CASE

Any effort to deal with a trade practice in a complex industry can get rather involved, as the so-called "Detroit case," involving Standard of Indiana, proved. The U. S. Supreme Court split 5 to 3 in 1951 on this case, which had been filed back in 1940. The Department of Justice disagreed so sharply with the Federal Trade Commission, which pressed the charges, that it refused to handle the case, and the Commission's own lawyers had to do the arguing.[8]

The case hinged on "good faith" in competition—a phrase apparently devised by lawyers to assure their own full employment. The issue was whether a major showed good faith in cutting prices to meet competition or was merely trying to ruin a competitor. In the Clayton Act, good faith was an absolute defense against charges of unfair competition. The Robinson-Patman Act of 1936 stiffened this by allowing the defendant to plead good faith, not in his original defense, but only to rebut, if necessary, some phase of the government's charges. The Federal Trade Commission charged that Standard of Indiana had lowered its price to four Indiana jobbers in order to match an offer made by a competitor. Two of these jobbers had passed the reduction on to their customers, much to the distress of the jobbers' competitors. But the Robinson-Patman Act forbade discrimination in prices charged by a supplier to its customers. Prices for similar quantities must be the same to all. Indiana replied that it had granted the price concessions in good faith to meet competition; if it could not cut prices here and there to meet such local conditions it would begin to lose sizable portions of its market.[9]

The majority in the Supreme Court held that Indiana had indeed acted in good faith and that it need prove no more, the Robinson-Patman Act to the contrary notwithstanding. The minority contended that the decision left "wide open" the question of what a seller can do in price discrimination.

THE STANDARD OF CALIFORNIA CASE

If the issues were not sufficiently befogged in the Indiana case, the opinions in the Standard of California case in 1951 offered a classic illustration of the confusion in the very meaning of monopoly, as interpreted by the dispensers of justice.

Here the Supreme Court split 5 to 4. The majority held that California's 5937 exclusive dealing contracts violated the Clayton Act by creating "just such a potential clog on competition" as the law sought to remove. Such contracts "foreclose whatever opportunity there might be for competing suppliers to attract his [the dealer's] patronage."[10]

Looking at the identical facts, four other learned justices drew the opposite conclusion. But, one and all, the justices agreed that either exclusive dealing contracts, or the absence of them, would tend to create monopoly! No wonder the public is confused.

The majority noted that California and the other majors, by such contracts, maintained their control of the markets and prevented "a late arrival from wresting away more than an insignificant portion of the market." But deprived of such contracts, the majority added, California might revert to its previous practice of owning stations outright through a subsidiary.

Exactly so, argued Justice Douglas, in the minority, and he foresaw Standard building an oil empire in the retail field. The majority decision, he said, pushes the majors into a "virulent growth of monopoly power" and "helps remake America in the image of the cartels."

Justice Jackson, also dissenting, argued that Standard could not be left at the mercy of capricious retailers, as it would then lack the incentive to carry adequate stocks.

In effect, the court's varying opinions indicated, the retailers had a choice between being captives of Standard, or employees. Such was the choice offered under free enterprise after sixty years of the Sherman Antitrust Act! Justice Douglas commented that "the economic theories which the court has read into the anti-trust laws have favored rather than discouraged monopoly. As a result of the big business philosophy underlying [cases cited], big business has become bigger and bigger. Monopoly has flourished. Cartels have increased their hold on the nation. The trusts wax strong. There is less and less place for the independent."

"Monopoly competition," he continued, "is a regime of friendly alliances, of quick and easy accommodation of prices even without the benefit of trade associations, of what Brandeis said was euphemistically called 'cooperation.' "[11]

As for Standard of California dealers, they continue much as before; some 1100 are managers of "Standard Stations," directly owned by the company; some 6000 operate Chevron stations as dealers nominally independent of the company, free indeed to switch to any other company if they so desire, but dependent on Standard for its products and good will.

THE RICHFIELD CASE

In another California case, Richfield, the Sinclair-Cities Service subsidiary on the West Coast, was enjoined from continuing its leasing tactics, either written or verbal. These leases covered stations owned by Richfield but leased to dealers, and stations owned by dealers but leased to Richfield and then leased back— the double-lease. The lower federal court had ruled that a lessee who pays his rent is master in his own premises and can handle what products he pleases. A lessee cannot also be an agent (employee). Exclusive dealing contracts were intended to "shut out all competition." The contracts covered not only oil products but also tires, batteries, and accessories (TBA). The lessees had to handle Richfield TBA although they could get more favorable terms elsewhere. A feature of the Richfield lease was the clause allowing cancellations by the company within 24 hours.[12]

The U. S. Supreme Court in 1952 upheld the lower court's decision, 7 to 0. Richfield was ordered to drop its 24-hour cancellation clause and to limit cancellations to a breach of the written contract and not to a breach of oral understanding, and the company was instructed to notify the Attorney General's office each time a lease is canceled.[13]

The lawyer for an eastern major (unwilling to be named) was interested in the Richfield decision:

I doubt [he said] that there is any substantial number of companies whose practices will be affected by it. I'm convinced that your average dealer is independent, and not coerced. The proof is right before you—you see competing products in stations.

Not with respect to gasoline, I grant you; but they're not coerced. It's just that the "split pump" looks like hell.

You know, a lot of dealers like to say they're coerced. But it's just an easy alibi. If a customer asks for a brand of oil a dealer hasn't got, the dealer just says, "My supplier won't let me carry it." If a customer gripes about the price of gasoline, the dealer says, "My supplier tells me what to charge."

It's just a way for him to get off the hook.[14]

Richfield dealers have gained a more stable contract and are free, if they choose, to have other pumps. Mostly, as before, they continue to handle the single company's products. The ordinary dealer has neither the space for a variety of pumps nor any relish for the confusion and expense entailed in caring for a number of different "islands." As for the motorist, if he prefers one brand to another, price and quality being the same, he has his choice along the highway, if not in each station.

PURCHASE OF ASSETS

In 1951 the Clayton Act was amended to forbid the purchase of assets of competing firms. This was an effort to plug a loophole in the act which allowed evasion of the ban on purchasing the stock and control of competing firms.

The *National Petroleum News* was alarmed as it contemplated the sad plight of an old man who wanted, while still alive, to sell his company. But the only purchaser big enough to swing the deal is a large corporation in the same field. The old man is just stuck with his company. He's got to compete, whether he wants to or not.[15]

This plaint took on a quite personal note when the editor and publisher of *National Petroleum News,* having weathered his allotted span of years, sold out his news enterprises lock, stock, and barrel in 1953 to the McGraw-Hill organization, the dominant firm in the business periodical industry. After a lifetime spent, as he said, in battling for the independents in oil, he gave up his own independence.

THE ATLAS SUPPLY CASE

Compete, but not "too effectively," was the moral drawn plaintively by the Standard companies in 1951 when they agreed to cease and desist from certain practices in buying tires, batteries, and accessories for their jointly-owned Atlas Supply Company. Standards of New Jersey, Indiana, Ohio, Kentucky, and California and their Atlas company were charged by the Federal Trade Commission with unfair competition because, due to their massive purchases, they got discounts of 10 to 30 percent below those available to independent tire dealers. A curious feature of this deal was that Atlas actually bought not a single tire, nor even handled one. The tire manufacturer paid Atlas an "override" on each tire ordered by an affiliated Standard company; Atlas's real contribution was to see that Standard dealers bought only through the Atlas connection. The Standard-Atlas group often shaved prices so close, complained the National Association of Independent Tire Dealers, that the tire makers had to boost their prices to the independents in order to make an overall profit. Another curious aspect of Atlas was that it adhered rigidly to Rochdale cooperative principles: its dividends were paid out to the Standard companies in accordance with purchases made and not in proportion to their investment in it.[16]

The Standards and Atlas agreed in 1951 to abide by the Federal Trade Commission order—to save themselves, as they explained, expensive and time-consuming litigation. They pointed out the difficulty of trying to abide by laws which contemplate that they must compete, but admonishes them "not to compete too effectively."

"While every buyer," commented Standard of California, "is expected to buy at the best prices obtainable, strange as it may seem, under the Robinson-Patman Act, he must be careful not to get a better price than his competitor from the same supplier."

THE WEST COAST CASES

In dropping the Mother Hubbard suit, the Department of Justice explained that it would press other suits against segments of the industry. Such were the suits against Standard of California, Richfield, and Sun, decided in 1951-1952, on exclusive dealing contracts, and the minor Mother Hubbard suit brought against the leading West Coast companies in 1950, and still pending in federal court in 1955. The Department in its West Coast suit said that pipe lines are not available to independents, that patents are available only through pools charging excessive royalties, that supplies of crude are controlled by a few companies, that prices of crude and its products are fixed, that legitimate conservation programs are being used to restrict production, and that distributors are denied supplies at prices that will permit them to compete.[17]

Ever since the first California wells began producing in the 1870s, the West Coast has been an economic province more or less independent of the rest of the country. The abundance of the California supply and the distance of the mid-continent and Gulf wells forbade any physical market connection. Standard of California is the enormously predominant producer and marketer throughout the area, but Shell was an early invader. Union and Associated gained a toehold in the region; General Petroleum became the Socony subsidiary. Richfield, the Sinclair-Cities Service unit, and the Texas Company are the other important firms.

All these are involved in the Department of Justice suit. These firms, according to the indictment, control 94 percent of crude production, 97 percent of crude trunk lines, 77 percent of gathering lines, 90 percent of gasoline refining capacity, and 86 percent of retail marketing.

The Department's interest in this setup seemed rather belated in view of the astoundingly open devices used to control production. In the rest of the oil country, rather elaborate state and interstate compact laws govern such activities, but not in California. There the leading producers, through the Conservation Committee of California Oil Producers, set quotas for wells and fields without authority of any law. The California voters rejected a "conservation" law in 1939 and so the majors proceeded to operate their own conservation. As elsewhere in the country, the majors, following a leader, post their prices in the field for crude.

A new effort to enact an "oil control" conservation law is being fought by California independents and by Union Oil, alone among the majors. While yielding to none in devotion to "true conservation," Union sees in the proposed law merely a device by the big West Coast importers, Standard of California, Texas Company, and Socony (General Petroleum), to curtail Golden State production in favor of Arabia and Indonesia.

The Pacific Coast market is rigidly controlled by the majors, except in the Los Angeles area—the seat of many independent wells and a few remaining independent refineries. The Pacific Northwest, in particular, is utterly dependent on a handful of majors for its supplies.[18]

The Department charges that the majors have bought up or control the output of the independent refineries, have refused pipe line facilities except on discriminatory terms, and raised the price of crude without raising the price of gasoline in order to squeeze the independent refiners.

In an effort to end once and for all the discrimination in the marketing of oil products, the suit asks that the majors be divorced of their marketing apparatus, that their transportation and storage facilities be made available to all, that contracts to purchase crude be limited to one year, and that all purchases of competing firms be subject to court approval.[19]

If the government should win this first marketing divorcement suit, a pattern would be set for the rest of the industry. It should be pointed out, however, that contrary to the majors' own views on the need to control marketing in order to control the entire price structure, some economists have figured that the big companies would be better off without it. They would be relieved of the costly and wasteful expenses of competitive marketing, and these burdens would be passed on to independent wholesalers and retailers. The public might even have to buy road maps and pay for the use of rest rooms!

Even the *National Petroleum News* did not share the majors' views of the catastrophic effects of divorcement. Divorcement had not ruined the meat packers or the movie makers, and there was always the example of the profitable Coca-Cola company which disdains the details of bottling and retailing its product.

The trade paper speculated on "how free the industry might

be of legislative attack and anti-monopoly suits" if marketing were separated from its other functions. The industry might be "the beneficiary of more healthy competition and profits."[20]

Such speculations did not prevent the indicted West Coast companies from preparing a vigorous defense in the divorcement suit; they preferred the advantages of legal marriage to their market, the better to service their customers.

Most of the Department of Justice suits have been aimed at objectionable trade practices. Even if the Department's victories were more notable and the suits more far-reaching, they would hardly make a dent in the control of the market by the major companies. The West Coast suit which has been pending now since 1950 aims at a more fundamental solution—the divorcement of marketing from control by the majors. If the Department wins —and there is no assurance that it may not duck the issue either by withdrawing the suit as it did in the Mother Hubbard case, or compromising it with a meager consent decree—the majors will be out of marketing on the West Coast. The end result of this may be favorable, in the long run, for the majors as it would divorce them from the losses of marketing. The most famous of all the Department's victories, the dissolution of the Standard Oil trust in 1911, made very little difference, it turned out, in the march toward monopoly.

23

Toward a National Oil Policy

THE problem of monopoly has suggested several differing courses of action:

(1) Repeal all the antitrust laws, as ineffective, insincere, or harmful, and let nature and nature's God take their course, as John D. Rockefeller, Jr., had outlined in his famous lecture on the American Beauty rose.*

(2) Let things stand as they are.

(3) Split the industry into its four branches, each independent, and further split the segments (such as Standard of New Jersey's marketing subsidiary, Esso) geographically.

(4) Set up a federal commission to guide the industry.

(5) Nationalize the industry.

DENATURING THE LAW

By the 1950s, Rockefeller's way was publicly urged only by the lunatic fringe of the industry, although privately many of the bigger majors might regard it as the more honest and forthright course. But they recoiled from the political implications, for the turbulent little fellows in production and marketing, for all their noise and nuisance, are worth their weight in gold as proof that some kind of competition really does exist. The American Petroleum Institute can boast of the 200,000 sturdy free enterprisers who inhabit the industry, even though most of them are bound tightly by exclusive dealing contracts and similar instruments.

---

* Rockefeller explained it all to a college class this way: "The American Beauty rose can be produced in the splendor and fragrance which bring cheer to its beholder only by sacrificing the early buds which grow up around it. This is not an evil tendency in business. It is merely the working-out of a law of nature and a law of God."[1]

A stealthy approach toward denaturing the antitrust laws was advocated at the 1953 meeting of the National Petroleum Association. President P. C. Spencer, of Sinclair, urged a revision and restatement of the laws, in which the controlled production and price system would be expressly affirmed and competition limited to a choice among brands. Only "unfair, predatory, fraudulent and immoral practices" should be banned outright, and the rule of reason should prevail.

The Sinclair chief urged "the needs of our industry for freedom from control to develop its full initiative and productive capacity. . . . Perhaps in no other industry is it more apparent that decontrol by Washington agencies must be replaced with self-control by the industry."[2]

Most of the majors would probably agree.

THE STATUS QUO

As a practical matter, however, they prefer to let things stand as they are. While enforcement of outdated laws by fits and starts is annoying, it is the best compromise and one tested in value through the years. The small fry, if they are vocal enough, find some precarious shelter by appeal to various government agencies.

From the point of view of these agencies, a softer enforcement is politically dangerous so long as the little fellows, the small independent producers, and the not so independent marketers, have votes and influence in their communities to be used in harassing the majors. A harder enforcement is also politically dangerous because it tends to alienate the majors and the big independent producers. Their financial support is needed to replenish the coffers of both major political parties, to advance party policies in foreign affairs, and to attain unity in national policies.

DIVORCEMENT

The radical proposal that each integrated company be split four ways into production, refining, transportation, and marketing companies, and that the larger units after such divorcement be further split geographically, has been advanced by Eugene V.

Rostow, of the Yale Law School, in his book *A National Policy for the Oil Industry*. He suggested also that it might be wise to sever foreign activities of the domestic companies, and to divorce them from the petrochemical field.[3]

All this would be attained, under the Rostow plan, by judicial fiat. He prefers court decrees because they are "surgical" and once the order is obeyed, there is no need for further regulation. No federal bureaucracy would be required to muddle in the affairs of the independent units, aside from Interstate Commerce Commission regulation of the pipe lines and their rates.

Any law for divorcement, Rostow argues, must be filled with minute prescriptions: a small refiner could not haul his products to the market; a producer could not build a refinery. In the marginal spaces of the industry between its grand divisions, corporation lawyers, it is apparent, would soon be driving a horde of exceptions which would nullify the law. As seems rather obvious, Congress would hardly enact such Draconian legislation requiring severance.

But divorcement is possible under Section 2 of the Sherman Act, which Rostow considers is not limited to such archaic definitions of monopoly as one dominant seller. He believes freedom of entry of new firms into the field to be a material distinction between competitive and monopolistic markets, and the crucial element of monopolistic power is its degree of control over price.

Rostow is enough of an optimist to believe that divorcement, in view of new trends in judicial interpretations, does not face "insuperable obstacles." But there are hurdles. The Department of Justice has first to institute the suits; after that the courts would have their say. Rostow would also kill the rule of capture in the oil fields and the so-called conservation laws in the oil states. He would substitute compulsory unitization under federal law, after the majors had been split up. The play of the market would then determine that low-cost fields would be operated as physical units within the limits of sound geologic practice, and high-cost fields would be held back. If stripper wells (the older wells under pump that produce only a few barrels a day) needed subsidies to maintain them in production, these could be given directly and would cost less than making them profitable by making other wells superprofitable.

THE ILLUSION OF REGULATION

A fourth alternative, which Rostow would avoid through his judicial hatchet, is public regulation with the aim, if not of eliminating cartelism, at least of easing its drain on the public purse and keeping avenues open for marginal operators. There is nothing very specific to speak of here, for no one has suggested ways of regulating the industry any more effective than methods already in use, and found wanting, in public utility industries.

The Twentieth Century Fund in 1946 financed an ambitious survey of cartels and monopoly under the direction of George W. Stocking and Myron W. Watkins, both of whom had won their academic spurs by studies of the oil industry. They concluded that the economy will not regulate itself in the public interest. Public regulation, on the other hand, runs up against "popular apathy, rooted in widespread economic ignorance, but a close second is the resourceful opposition of powerful vested interests." Stating the obvious fact of economic ignorance, the authors do not pursue its causes in a nation noted for its splendid educational plant, its high level of literacy, and its eager pursuit of knowledge. That economic ignorance, resulting in apathy, is but one of the methods used by the "resourceful opposition of powerful vested interests" might seem to open a fruitful avenue of inquiry. The nature of public educational and informational institutions whose end product is "economic ignorance," leaving a monopoly of economic wisdom to the operators of industry, would furnish a clue to the problem.

Experience, say Stocking and Watkins, shows that the public regulators generally are taken over by those whom they regulate. The pressure of the vested interests is greater than the elected or appointed regulators can stand. As Justice Douglas has said, "If it were not, of course, impractical, every regulatory bureau ought to be abolished after 10 years of life and some new machinery set up in its place"—certainly a desperate piece of advice.

"The entire careers of these men [the regulators] are bound up with the welfare of the specific industry subject to their jurisdiction," say Stocking and Watkins. "Many of them expect to, and do, 'graduate' into lucrative jobs with the regulated enterprises, for which their administrative experience so well qualified them. Hence the uncritical assumption that commission regulation of industry will provide effective protection of consumer interests is scarcely justified."[4]

The only practical alternative to regulation by commission, according to Stocking and Watkins, is business syndicalism of the NRA type. There is little demand for such a setup now, the authors say, but another depression, bringing problems which cannot be handled within the present structure of price and production control, will certainly recreate the pressures for another NRA.

All of this applies with special emphasis to oil, the biggest, most powerful, and tightest controlled industry of them all.

NATIONALIZATION

Nationalization of oil looms on the far horizon. Its spread from the Soviet states in 1917 to Mexico in 1938, then to other Latin American states, and to Iran in 1951, hints the future.

The ties that bind governments and their principal industries in tight community, so prevalent in most nations, have been obscured in the United States. Democratic forces have objected to the community of interests too blatantly stated; the corporations for their part have wanted no explicit alliance. They prefer that government confine itself to maintaining law and order, here and among the infidels, and mind its own business. But world tensions that arise from maintaining law and order around the globe throw corporations and government into each other's arms whether they like it or not. This is particularly true in oil, responsible as it is for some of the government's most urgent law-and-order business across the seas.

Although there is no threat of nationalization in this country bigger than a man's hand, the oil corporations have seen what they call "creeping socialism" inching its way insidiously through governmental bureaus, intent, octopus-like, in reaching out its tentacles to the corporations in cold, clammy embrace.

"Leftists and idealists will bring about nationalization of

petroleum," the *National Petroleum News* reported October 19, 1949, in summarizing speeches before the Pennsylvania Petroleum Association.

"You may say that what is happening in Europe cannot happen here," observed Vice-president W. E. Black of Esso Standard Oil of Pennsylvania. "I believe unless we acquaint the American people quickly it can happen here—it is already happening.

"Americans do not want communism or socialism, when it is labelled as such. However they can be sold the idea that a 'little' control might not be a bad idea." Those who want just a little control constitute "to my way of thinking the more dangerous group."[5]

George D. McDaniel, a Socony executive, told the same meeting that once he had not taken such talk seriously, but "I'm not scoffing any more." Referring to the threat in Congress to divorce the industry from its marketing, he said "it merely is a stepping stone to final and complete nationalization which the governmental-control advocates will push at a later date."

Even the return of the Republicans failed to reassure some. Vice-president Arthur A. Smith of the First National Bank of Dallas, addressing the Independent Petroleum Association in 1953, warned:

"There is reason to believe that although dealt a setback, the socialist trend goes steadily on, and there is little doubt but that the great basic industries have been marked for nationalization. Oil is high on the list."[6]

Actually about the only voice raised in recent years for nationalization was that of the late Benjamin C. Marsh, secretary of the People's Lobby, which battled for nationalization of all energy resources. Whether Ben Marsh was a lone survivor of the era of populism or an evangel of what was to come only the years can tell.

During Rockefeller's heyday many a fervent demand was made for the government to take over the omnipotent oil trust; agrarian, populist, and radical labor parties made that a key plank. The first resolution passed by the founding convention of the Oil Workers International Union, in 1918, called for nationalization of oil, among other key industries. Unionists apprehensive about the return of the law of the jungle to labor relations, at the end of World War I, foresaw the fate of the union in the arid years to come, if, weak and puny, it were matched against the corporations without governmental intervention.[7] With the coming of the New Deal, the union was too busy in day-to-day struggles and too hopeful of success with governmental aid to hark back to its original resolution. Today, even President Walter Reuther of the CIO, one-time socialist, does not favor national-ization, and it would be difficult now to find any person of prom-inence, in unionism, government, or elsewhere, to propose such a solution.[8]

That is not to say that it is not voiced, obliquely, in fervent warnings to the industry to mend its ways. In the concluding chapter of *Oil: Stabilization or Conservation?* Myron W. Watkins, long a leading analyst of trends in the industry, warned of the "heedlessness, suspicion and ruthless aggressiveness" of oil well operators, of the incessant drive of the majors to dominate, and thus summarized the danger:

> In no just sense can the vested interests of business enter-prise be considered paramount to these economically dis-franchised interests [labor and consumers] and thus entitled to exclusive exercise of the privilege of control. The conser-vation of a nation's supply of this irreplaceable natural resource can never be safely entrusted to the self-seeking, shortsighted stratagems of a special-interest group—such as the business men constitute. Genuine stability will come only when a scheme of industrial control is devised, as it could very readily be devised along cooperative lines, which makes the protection and promotion of these other interests, in a word, of the public interest, not merely an incidental by-product of profit making, but at least a coordinate object in the framing of policy.[9]

But even that warning cry was far from a demand for nation-alization.

Bishop G. Bromley Oxnam of the Methodist church, one-time chairman of the Federal Council of Churches, spoke of under-lying forces that were driving toward new concepts, in an address in 1947:

In the society that is passing, the driving force has been pursuit of self interest. The chief rewards have gone to the owners of the means of production. The possessors of property looked upon the state as a tool to be used by them and for them, and the underlying philosophy was materialistic.

In the society that is coming, the common good will be supreme. Reward will be based upon service to the group and greatness thus rest upon service. The necessities will be provided socially, and all socially controllable inequalities will be removed. Intelligent planning and freedom will strive for security. Rights will be balanced by duties, among them the universal obligation to work.[10]

President Roosevelt stated the issue in these words: "The power of the few to manage the economic life of the nation must be diffused among the many or be transferred to the public and its democratically responsible government."[11]

But his successor seemed to harbor no such sentiments, and President Eisenhower was at the opposite pole; he urged that the government's offshore oil lands be given away, so that the corporations would suffer no fear of federal encroachment on their rights.

The last eminent academic voice to be raised for nationalization was that of Dr. John Ise, professor of economics at the University of Kansas and author of *The United States Oil Policy*. Writing in 1929, Dr. Ise called for socialization of lands and natural resources, of which "oil should perhaps be the first." The government should always have maintained title to mineral deposits, to forest, desert, and scenic lands, to water power, harbors, coast lines, and urban lands, he contended. The landowner and speculator "are largely parasites on society."[12]

Private ownership of natural resources, he argued, has distracted men from productive work, reduced the social product, and undermined the moral stamina of the people, wasted capital and natural resources, and promoted monopoly. Such effects had stimulated "a buoyant and bombastic type of intellectual dishonesty perhaps best represented by our rampant American boosterism," he commented, thinking perhaps of the stock figure of the Texas oilman.

Private ownership of oil and gas resources has probably been attended with more unfortunate effects than has private ownership of any other natural resource. It has gone with over-production of oil, instability of the oil industry, wide fluctuations in prices of the products; with waste of oil, waste of capital, and waste of human energy; with speculation, fraud, extravagance and with marked social inequality; and with the development of monopoly conditions as the only means of escape from the intolerable conditions of private competition.

Dr. Ise pointed to the more flagrant wastes of the era before production control and to the wastes—which continue to this day—in production, marketing, and the use of an irreplaceable fuel for heating and power plants. Whether such wastes resulted in exhaustion of oil within ten years or forty, he said, was not a matter of vital argument. All oil resources still belonging to the nation should be impounded and retained for the indefinite future when privately owned lands had been exhausted. More oil lands should be acquired for the public reserve. It was too late, Dr. Ise lamented, to take over the lands now in private hands because of the exaggerated valuations placed on them. In one regard, he went part way with the oil producers: raise the price of crude. But his object was to price it out of the market so that other fuels could be used.

Since then no academician of note has publicly argued for socialization of oil. Such arguments proceed from several bases: the ethical, that oil as a natural resource belongs to all and should be appropriated by no private interests; the economic, that private ownership has led to shameful wastes, uneconomic use, and altogether exorbitant profits; the political, that domination of oil by private interests imperils democracy by corrupting the government and leaving the citizenry powerless to control its own destiny.

The arguments have been dulled, after two world wars and in the prospect of a third. To speak of the waste of oil, in face of the wastes of war, seems trivial; to dwell upon ethical or social factors now is to be in danger of criticizing the American way of life; and as for worrying about the effect of oil on democracy, that is perhaps presumptuous when oil lubricates both the democratic parties.

The prospects for nationalization would seem now to depend upon some major crisis like a breakdown in the economic system which is unlikely so long as a war economy can last; or upon some catastrophe such as collapse or defeat in a world war, an unforeseeable contingency; or upon a settlement of the international issues threatening war, which might permit once again a thoughtful approach toward the problem, free of terror and coercion.

THE MENACE OF OVERCAPACITY

The supply of crude, both domestic and foreign, that over-hangs the market poses the inescapable problem of industry-government relationship. With nearly 2 million barrels a day shut in in this country, and with the fields of Venezuela and the Persian Gulf held to a mere fraction of their potential output, the industry requires the partnership of government to throttle production in order to maintain profitability.

Overcapacity characterizes not only production but refining and marketing as well. The menace has not been overlooked by the industry itself. In 1953 the *Oil Daily* considered the problem:

> The industry is in the midst of a vast over-supply—at least a potential one that could become an economically disastrous reality almost momentarily. . . . The petroleum industry's— and the economy's—community of interest in a sane, intelligent policy of operation on the part of every member of the petroleum industry is more urgent than ever. The need for recognition of this is so compelling that it cannot be over-stated. . . . The plain, simple and cogent point is that this industry is operating in the shadow of an excess supply situation so great and so potentially devastating that it could wipe out, in short time, virtually all the asset value of even the strongest companies—if it were permitted. . . . So every oil man has a plain duty to exercise self control. If he conducts his operations for shortsighted, immediate advantage regardless of the industry that gives him sustenance and provides his livelihood, he may momentarily improve his relative position. Relative position in a self-developed dis-

aster is hardly a reasonable objective, is it? The duty as we
see it is to operate not to capture the largest possible share
of the business at whatever cost, but to obtain a reasonable
share, one that can be served and sustained under reasonable
conditions—and then to serve that business in the very best,
the most productive, the most efficient, the most remunera-
tive way possible.[13]

"Enlightened self-interest says profit-minded is survival-
minded," the *Oil Daily* warned.[14]

The *National Petroleum News* took a dimmer view than its
daily colleague. Across the years, this paper had come to discount
enlightened self-interest in the industry. The problem of excess
capacity could only be met by drastic measures. These must be
imposed either by the government or by the industry. There was
no question but that government controls "would be almost
certain to bring it—and the country—to socialism or statism."

But how could controls be set up by the industry to avert
the catastrophe? "If this already existing surplus should be released to the open market, prices in all products and all over
the country would undoubtedly break badly."

Obviously, said the trade paper, the answer lay in modifying
the judicial interpretation of the antitrust laws so that the industry "can indulge in cooperation with the government in such
restraints of trade as will meet the great problem stated at the
start of this editorial." This should be done without further
enactments by Congress, or interference from the Federal Trade
Commission or the Department of Justice. Thus there would be
no public outcry against this daring revival of business syndicalism along NIRA lines, but without any NIRA. These judicial
changes in the antitrust laws must be accompanied, the *National
Petroleum News* said, by a public relations campaign, "because
who knows just how many in office and on the bench today will
refuse to change from their thinking developed over the past
20 years?"[15]

The overhanging potential surplus, war-created, might crash
on to the market if peace came. This was the specter haunting
high reaches in the industry and leading the *National Petroleum
News* to call for radical, if quiet, action immediately.

Chairman R. G. Follis of Standard of California, the oil company most intimately associated in the Korean problem, outlined two possibilities. "As I see it, you can get two kinds of peace," he told the New York Society of Security Analysts. Under one, the nation could go on rearming and maintaining a very substantial force in the Far East "to be sure the peace in Korea did not become unglued." The effect of such a peace on the industry, he said, "will be very small because it takes surprisingly little more oil to maintain a force fighting in Korea than it does not fighting in Korea."

On the other hand, if there was a genuine settlement with the Soviets and the United States joined in a disarmament program, "the impact on the oil industry and on the whole economy would be terrific. It would be hard for me to believe that such a thing could happen."[16]

On the whole it seemed easier to continue the cold war indefinitely and take care of the industry's surplus through measures which would have the necessary degree of government approval and support. On the basis of past experience, there was little reason to assume that the government would refuse to do its part.

Part VI

The Industry Abroad

24

The Struggle for the World's Oil

PROVIDENCE with a prodigal hand stored petroleum helter-skelter around the world, under the oceans and under the deserts, in utter disregard of the needs of the industrialized nations of the twentieth century. Among the major powers, only the United States and the Soviet Union are favored with great deposits now readily available under their own soil. In the Age of Oil, the predominance of these two powers rests on underground pools, ever accessible. The leading nations of western Europe, along with Japan, China, and India, all have to seek elsewhere for the greater part of the indispensable liquid fuel. The needs of war, even more imperative than the needs of industry, lifted petroleum in the second and third decades of the century into the prime prize of civilization, the strategic treasure which, more than any other one commodity, governed the tensions which could blow the world to pieces. The uneven distribution of the great resource, in a tangled skein of conflicting sovereignties, subjected for the most part to the wills of private corporations which were themselves superstates, guaranteed the political and diplomatic inflammability of petroleum.

On the prowl for oil around the world, these great corporations applied the law of *res ferae naturae*—the rule of capture—to their prey. At one time, five-sixths of Persia was in the pocket of one British company; a U. S. corporation holds the only tangible wealth of two-thirds of Arabia; sheikdoms along the Persian Gulf from Kuwait to Oman are held in fief. Obscure despots whose realms were all but unknown suddenly vaulted into fortune by the mere signing of concessions. A king who had lived by levying tribute from pilgrims to the Moslem holy places of Mecca and Medina became within a few years one of the richest men on the face of the earth. Were the income of the Sheik of Kuwait to be divided evenly among his subjects, they would enjoy the second highest standard of living in the world. One resourceful Armenian who dreamed up a concession from the Sultan of Turkey enjoyed enormous wealth based on a mere 5 percent interest in one company.

The rise of the petroleum corporations to head the ranks of organized wealth was based on the phenomenal resources of the Middle East. Royal Dutch/Shell within sixty years became the greatest industrial corporation of all western Europe; Standard of New Jersey rose to equal position in the New World. Other companies—Anglo-Iranian, Socony-Vacuum, Gulf, Texaco, and Standard of California—were similarly catapulted into prodigious size by their successes in the application of *res ferae naturae*.

These seven Anglo-American corporations control 80 percent of the non-Soviet oil reserves of the world and produce a good half of the oil pulled to the surface each year.

The emergence of the Middle East in the past ten years has been explosive in the world's economic and political affairs. Taken together with the emergence of the Soviet Union after World War II as the predominant state in Eurasia, it has altered basically the balance of power and shattered, for the time being, the hope of One World which flickered for a time toward the end of the war.

Before World War II, the Middle East produced a mere 100 million barrels of oil a year; in 1952, the figure was 762 million— a meteoric rise within 12 years. Before World War II, the United States was producing nearly two-thirds of the world's oil; in 1952, it supplied barely more than half, and had actually become an importing nation whose East Coast would freeze in winter were it not for the liquid warmth of Venezuela and Arabia. Pessimists even went so far as to say that the United States was becoming a have-not nation so far as its domestic supply was concerned. While each U. S. well, on the average, dribbled 12 barrels a day, the Venezuelan wells gave 225 barrels a day each, and the Middle Eastern 5000. While U. S. wildcatters hoped for one

The Big Seven

Company	Assets (Millions of dollars)	Profits (Millions of dollars)	Production (Millions of barrels)	Percentage of World Production	Sales (Millions of dollars)	Reserves† (Millions of barrels)	Principal Sources
Jersey	$ 4,314	$ 585	691	13.2	$ 5,662	13.8	U. S. A., Venezuela, Arabia, Canada, Iraq, Indonesia, Peru
Royal Dutch/Shell	3,472	377	643	12.2	5,183	7.9	Venezuela, U. S. A., Borneo, Indonesia, Iraq
Socony	2,257	184	196	3.7	1,609	6.0	U. S. A., Arabia, Iraq, Qatar, Venezuela, Colombia, Canada
Gulf	1,969	183	302	5.8	1,705	10.3	Kuwait, Venezuela, U. S. A.
Texaco	1,946	226	303	5.8	1,574	6.3	U. S. A., Arabia, Bahrein, Indonesia, Canada
Standard of California	1,679	212	234	4.5	1,113	6.3	U. S. A., Arabia, Bahrein, Indonesia, Canada
Anglo-Iranian (British Petroleum)	996	67	252	4.8	—*	14.0	Iran, Iraq, Kuwait, Qatar
Total	16,633	1,834	2,621	50.0	16,846 (Incomplete)	64.6	

* Not reported.
† Reserves of U. S. companies, 42.7 billion barrels; of British companies, 21.9 billion.

(Assets, profits, production, and sales, from 1954 annual reports. Reserves, from estimates of reserves, for 1949, from Federal Trade Commission: *The International Petroleum Cartel*, p. 23, adjusted for Iranian changes.)

flowing well with each eight dry holes, there were areas in the
Middle East where a dry hole had never been encountered.
Every puncture of the earth's skin produced oil in abundance and
entire fields were sealed off.[1]

The flow of oil was matched by the flow of profits. Standard
of New Jersey, mightiest of corporations, counted its net income
at $585 million in 1954, only a third of it from U. S. subsidiaries.
Royal Dutch/Shell drew its lordly net of $377 million from Vene-
zuela, the United States, Borneo, Indonesia, Iraq, and a dozen
other lands. Anglo-Iranian, after losing the wealth of Persia,
maintained its dividends from a half share of fabulous Kuwait.
The Texas Company, Standard of California, and Gulf drew by
far the greater part of their profits from their foreign reserves;
Socony split with Jersey its income from the East Indies.

So undisputed is the power of the Big Seven in world oil that
they can adjust prices in utter defiance of the laws of supply
and demand. Throttling and temporarily abandoning the wells
of Persia, holding in tightly the output of Arabia, indulging in
further exploration only from a healthy sense of curiosity rather
than a need for output, with independent U. S. producers crying in alarm against the flood of oil washing the shores of this
country, the Big Seven were able to raise the price of crude by
25 cents a barrel in 1953. The profits, in 1952 the highest enjoyed
by this or any other industry at any time in history, continued
to mount, despite the complaints of smaller independents and
of consumers in every land.

The nineteenth century was simpler. Only John D. Rockefeller
poured oil on the waves ruled by Britannia. Until near the close
of the century, there was no other major source of petroleum
than the United States, and in the United States there was no
major source of the product except Standard. Its tankers plied the
seven seas and unloaded at ports from London to Shanghai. In
those days, it was mostly kerosene for the lamps of China and
India and lubricating oils for every nation.

But by the 1890s, Standard's world monopoly began to
crumble. In the Caucasus, the Swedish-Russian Nobels were
developing great fields. For a brief span, from 1898 to 1901,
Russia even shot ahead of the United States in production. The

European banking house of the Rothschilds, helping the Czar with his financial problems, also helped themselves to chunks of the Baku fields. No friends of Rockefeller, they saved the young Royal Dutch Petroleum Company from his embrace in 1898 and enabled its new East Indies production to skim some of the Standard markets in the Far East.[2]

The enterprising Samuel firm in London, with its company that bought and processed shells in the East Indies and hawked them as trinkets, began carrying oil for both Royal Dutch and Standard, and then ventured into exploring petroleum lands on its own. The Samuels' Shell Transport & Trading Company got into a three-way war with Royal Dutch and Standard, to the distress of the Rothschilds who, in 1902, arranged for the two European companies to live in amity. Five years later, they had merged in a 60-40 alliance with Royal Dutch as the major partner, the better to battle Standard for the world's kerosene and lubricant markets and the rapidly enlarging market for the fuel oils of Texas and Mexico to bunker both war and merchant ships.

Backed by the Foreign Office and given preferential entry into British and Dutch lands and markets, Royal Dutch/Shell rode high, wide, and handsome before World War I. Unlike Standard at that time, this combine believed in production and picked it up anywhere in the world. Standard, enjoying access to the world's premier oil fields right within the United States, saw little need to look across horizons for anything more than markets. Economic self-sufficiency in production went with political isolationism, with the result that the world became Royal Dutch/Shell's oyster.

Shell even invaded the United States in 1912, with its California Oilfields, Ltd., and its Roxana firm in the mid-continent. So rapid was its expansion that within a few years half of all Royal Dutch/Shell's world production was coming from wells in this country. Ever since, Shell has been a major U. S. producer.[3]

The British also elbowed into Uncle Sam's backyard in Mexico. The Los Angeles oil promoter, Edward L. Doheny, had staked out his Mexican Petroleum Company in 1900; four years later he struck the Pez No. 1 well, which yielded a total of 3.5 million

CHANGES IN THE WORLD OF OIL, 1880-1954

Production (millions of barrels)

Year	U. S. A.	Russia	Mexico	Venezuela	Iran	Iraq	Arabia-Kuwait	World	U. S. as percent of world
1880	26	3	—	—	—	—	—	30	87
1900	63	75	—	—	—	—	—	149	42
1920	442	25	157	—	12	—	—	688	64
1940	1,353	218	44	185	66	24	—	2,149	63
1950	1,973	266	72	546	242	50	336	3,786	52
1954	2,564	484*	85	694	22	229	695	5,244	49

* Including eastern Europe.

(Figures for 1880-1940, *Petroleum Facts and Figures*, 9th edition; figures for 1950, *Petroleum Facts and Figures*, 10th edition; figures for 1954 from Royal Dutch report for 1954.)

barrels and opened one of the most dramatic chapters in oil history. Juan Casiano No. 7 yielded 80 million barrels in its lifetime; Cerro Azul No. 4 quickly reached a production of 260,000 barrels a day before it was brought under control. The latter two wells alone met Mexican Petroleum's requirements for years.[4]

These amazing strikes, in the good old days of gushers, of millions of wasted barrels of oil, of great fires that sometimes raged until the petroleum was exhausted, of flaring gas that reddened the skies by night, immediately attracted the notice of the British. The Pearson interests followed Doheny into Mexico in 1906 and four years later brought in the most famous of all wells—Potrero del Llano No. 4, which yielded 100 million barrels before it went to salt. Shell took over the Pearson interests while Mexico was soaring to second position in world production. In 1921, Mexican output equaled 40 percent of the U. S. figure. But the foreign companies were concerned only with flush production, with "mining" the petroleum. The enormous gas pressures were wasted and salt water crept into the famed Golden Lane near Tampico. By 1930 Mexico had become a minor producer, eclipsed by fast-rising Venezuela.

If Mexico proved to be a flash in the pan in the world market, it was different with Iran. In 1901 an English adventurer, William Knox D'Arcy, wheedled a concession from the Shah covering five-sixths of his domain. Seven years later, he struck oil in the Mosque of Solomon field near the Persian Gulf and then formed the Anglo-Persian Oil Company (later Anglo-Iranian). One well, F7, produced some 30 million barrels within ten years. About this time, the British Navy was converting to oil; the First Lord of the Admiralty, Winston Churchill, believed that an assured supply was so essential that he advised his government to buy a controlling interest. With no qualms whatsoever about creeping socialism, His Majesty's government invested some £2.5 million in the venture—certainly one of the best investments history records. The government contented itself with two directors on the Anglo-Persian board, who were understood to hold only veto power on political and naval matters, but to exercise no control over ordinary commercial policy. By 1922, the center of Asian production had swung from Royal

Dutch/Shell's East Indies wells to Anglo's Persian fields. And in those days there were no Americans anywhere around the Persian Gulf.[5]

PROVED RESERVES AND PAST PRODUCTION

(Billions of Barrels)

Country	Proved Reserves, 1954	Production, 1857-1953
United States	28.9	47.8
Saudi Arabia	28.0	1.6
Kuwait	20.0	1.0
Iran	15.0	2.5
Iraq	13.0	.9
Venezuela	9.9	7.5
U. S. S. R.	9.0	7.5
Indonesia	2.4	1.5
Canada	1.9	.3
Mexico	1.7	2.7
Qatar	1.5	.08
World	135.2	79.0*

The countries listed above account for nearly 97 percent of the known world reserves.

* Rumania has also produced somewhat more than a billion barrels.

(Figures from *Petroleum Facts and Figures,* 11th edition, 1954.)

In the United States, the appalling discovery was made at the end of World War I that not only was U. S. ascendancy in the world oil market threatened, but that this country actually faced a shortage in its own domestic resources. Thanks to Standard policy and to U. S. insularity, the nation had overlooked the existence of huge deposits elsewhere. The drain on U. S. fields to fight the war, coupled with a temporary drop in domestic discoveries, was actually requiring the import of Mexican oil to supply the deficiency in the domestic market.[6]

The war had emphasized the critical importance of petroleum for victory. When the conflict hung in the balance in the winter of 1917, French Premier Clémenceau had appealed to President Wilson that oil is "as necessary as blood in the battles of tomorrow." After the war was won, thanks in part to U. S. resources, Lord Curzon was able to say that "the Allies floated to victory on a wave of oil."[7]

Oil was not only the price of victory, but its spoil. The British, the Dutch, and the French proceeded to divide the riches of Mesopotamia. Henri Bérenger, wartime oil commissioner of France and later ambassador to Washington, summed it up:

He who owns the oil will own the world, for he will rule the sea by means of the heavy oils, the air by means of the ultra refined oils, and the lands by means of petrol [gasoline] and the illuminating oils. And in addition to these he will rule his fellow men in an economic sense, by reason of the fantastic wealth he will derive from oil—the wonderful substance which is more sought after and more precious today than gold itself.[8]

Faced with these new conditions, Standard speedily revised its policy on production. It reached out for Humble in Texas and Carter in the Rockies. Then it began its own world-wide quest, backed by the State Department. It is curious to reflect now that only a quarter century ago U. S. foreign policy hinged on the battle between Standard and Royal Dutch/Shell. Notes were dispatched to London so stern that it was considered impolitic to make them public; the Secretary of the Interior, one Albert B. Fall, forbade Shell to bid on federal oil leases in this country; patriotic shareholders of Union Oil combined to prevent Shell from acquiring a dominant interest in that West Coast company; and books were written about the coming struggle for power between Britain and the United States. Ludwell Denny, in his *We Fight for Oil* (1928), wrote:

[This oil war] is significant only as part of a larger struggle for world mastery between two great economic empires. Seen alone, it seems fantastic, impossible; against the background of the wider conflict it appears tragically inevitable. There would be no serious oil war had not America suddenly grown into an empire threatening Great Britain's long commercial and naval supremacy.

In his concluding paragraph Denny counseled:

War is possible. War is probable—unless the two empires seek through mutual sacrifice to reconcile their many conflicting interests. This would involve sharing raw materials and markets, and dividing sea supremacy, without violating the rights of weaker nations. If some such miracle of diplomacy is achieved oil may cease to be an international explosive.[9]

Another world war has converted the British menace into a historical curiosity, and replaced it with the Soviet menace. Confronted now with the Soviet power and with the rise of nationalism in the Middle East, Royal Dutch/Shell and Britain are constrained to accept junior partnership with Standard and the United States, while all of them confront the new threat—the Soviets, whose petroleum resources are suspected to be larger by far than what remains of the gutted resources of the United States.

25

The Province of Venezuela

THREE-FOURTHS of all the petroleum the earth has yielded
has come from the Americas; and most of this has been wrested
from fields bordering the Gulf of Mexico and the Caribbean. In
the twentieth century, American production outside the United
States has gradually trended southward. Mexico flared in the
1910s; but as the Golden Lane ran to salt in the 1920s, Venezuela
came rapidly to the fore. The Bolívar coastal field on the eastern
shore of Lake Maracaibo became the world's biggest single
producer. Despite the sudden rise of the Arabian fields after
World War II, Venezuela in 1954 was still the major producing
country in the world outside the U. S., and its output almost
evenly matched that of Arabia and Kuwait combined. Aside
from Mexico and Venezuela, only Argentina, Canada, Colombia,
Peru, and Trinidad in the Americas produced a substantial
amount, but all together their output is still only a sixth of
Venezuela's.[1]

The eastern shore of Lake Maracaibo was Shell's pearl in the
days when Standard was not concerned about foreign production—not even in the neighboring Caribbean. After World War
I, when U. S. companies were jolted out of their complacency,
Standard of New Jersey and Socony looked eastward to the
Persian Gulf for concessions, but Standard of Indiana, always
more continental-minded, looked southward to Venezuela.
Indiana found Shell ensconced along the Maracaibo shore, so in
1922 it had to be content with what looked then like second-best
locations in the shallow waters bordering the littoral. Gulf, also
interested in Colombia, shared in the 3300-foot-wide "marine

zone" that paralleled Shell's shore concessions. As Gulf's proprietor was also Secretary of the Treasury in those days, the Mellon company had had no undue trouble in finding itself a place along-side Standard of Indiana.[2]

About this time, Mexican production began to decline sharply. Standard of New Jersey, tied up in the protracted negotiations in Iraq and troubled by the decline in its Mexican wells, decided to step into Venezuela. Its midwestern brother, Indiana, found it advisable in 1932 to transfer its Maracaibo concession to Jersey which proceeded to add submarine lands even farther out, bordering the marine zone.[3]

Standard of Indiana explained that the new duties and quotas raised against import of Venezuela oil would affect the company adversely. Indiana had no world-wide marketing apparatus to handle foreign-produced oil barred from this country; Jersey on the other hand could find outlets for Venezuelan crude in Europe and Latin America.

So rapid was the subsequent expansion of these fields that in 1937 Venezuela had supplanted Mexico as the second biggest oil country, accounting for about 40 percent of world export trade in petroleum. More than 99 percent of this was controlled by three companies—about half by Standard of New Jersey (Creole), a third by Shell, and the rest by Gulf (Mene Grande).

In the middle 1930s, rich deposits of a lighter and more valuable crude than Lake Maracaibo's were proved in eastern Venezuela in Anzóategui and neighboring states. While Gulf had pioneered in these discoveries, Standard of Jersey had to be dealt in, for political as well as industrial reasons. The outlets for the immense Venezuelan deposits presented a neat diplomatic problem for the two companies. In the 1930s, the United States in general was staggering under the blows of the depression, and the oil industry in particular from the problems engendered by the vast new east Texas field. Domestic producers were clamoring against Venezuelan imports, which they said were ruining the domestic market. They succeeded in winning a limitation on imports in the middle 1930s to 4.5 percent of domestic production, later raised to 5 percent. So the bulk of Venezuelan production had to be directed toward the European market.[4]

Already the three companies—Jersey, Shell, and Gulf—had "unitized" their Maracaibo production under a joint agreement; now Jersey took charge of the new problem presented by the eastern Venezuela fields. In 1937-1938, it was agreed that Jersey and Shell would take a one-half interest in Gulf's assets and production, and their properties were declared "pooled" concessions. Jersey paid $100 million for the half-interest in Gulf's Mene Grande company and then sold Shell a quarter-interest for $50 million. This left Mene Grande owned 50 percent by Gulf and 25 percent each by Jersey and Shell. Shell, however, was not to be Jersey's equal; disagreements were to be referred to the heads of the two companies and if they, too, disagreed, Jersey's decision was to be final.[5]

This unified control over Venezuelan production was designed to meet a complicated world situation, as well as the exigencies of Venezuela, whose ancient and bloody dictator, Juan Vicente Gomez, had died in 1935. As Gomez' semifeudal regime dissolved in the morning of Venezuela's democratic awakening, the companies needed to confront the new rulers unitedly. Moreover, the delicate matter of pushing into the United States as much Venezuelan fuel oil as the domestic producers would tolerate— roughly a third of the Venezuelan production—required a unified policy by the Big Three. In Europe, the outlets for Venezuelan oil must be meshed with those of the Middle East to the detriment of neither. Since Jersey worked with Shell and Anglo-Iranian in the Middle East, and with Shell and Gulf in Venezuela, there was little misunderstanding possible.[6]

For the companies, the proof of good production policies lies in price. For a time, Venezuelan crude was sold at Texas Gulf prices, thus assuring juicy profits; later, the prices were adjusted to a Caribbean base quite similar to Texas Gulf. When the price of crude went up 25 cents in the United States in mid-1953, Venezuela crude likewise advanced. This was in harmony with the world cartel's policy, although it could hardly be pleaded that the argument for the U. S. price increase—that of stimulating domestic production so that there would be ample reserves at home in case of war—applied to Venezuela any more than to the Middle East.

Creole, 95 percent owned, is the most splendid of Jersey's trophies. In 1954, its net was $240 million, of which $194 million was paid out in dividends. This roughly matched its payments to the Venezuelan government under the 50-50 agreement; an equal amount accounted for all its wages and expenses. As in the Middle East, it seemed that there was only one appropriate, if overworked, adjective to apply to the situation—fabulous. Never had so much money been made by so few so quickly. Assuming that Shell and Gulf together profited to the same extent, as they should under the unitized policies presided over by Creole, the total annual profit from Venezuela's crude exceeded $400 million. Nor was this all, for these profit figures referred mainly to production within Venezuela. The profits from transporting and refining most of the crude and from marketing it were reflected in the reports of other Standard subsidiaries such as Lago and Esso.[7]

Such prosperity excited the cupidity of the Venezuelans. So long as the dictator Gomez ruled, there was little trouble. Executioners and jailers silenced the critical. But after his death in 1935, Venezuela emerged from a dark century of civil war, anarchy, and military despotism. Few sadder pages can be found in history than those on Venezuela, the land which bore Bolívar, which was liberated by him from the Spaniards, and which cursed him as its "enemy" even before his death.

As parties formed after 1935, the press became inquisitive, the oil workers and others organized unions, and the country emerged into a genuine New Deal of its own. The companies were finally obliged, in 1943, to agree to share their profits 50-50 with the government. Under this arrangement, the various payments on royalties, taxes, and fees were to equal the companies' net income. Behind the companies' yielding stood the menacing growth of nationalism in Latin America as well as the world over. Mexico, but a few years before, had expelled Standard, Shell, and Gulf, together with the other foreign companies, and nationalized its oil. The expropriation aroused deep interest in all Venezuelans and ardent support among many. To be sure, the situation differed sharply inasmuch as Mexico provided its own market, whereas Venezuela consumed but 6 percent of its output and thus was dependent on the marketing outlets provided by the world cartel. Yet the example of self-reliance was exhilarating to Latin pride. Making the most of the situation, the companies for their part said humbly that the 50-50 split was their contribution to the "good neighbor" policy.[8]

After the Democratic Action party won power in Caracas with the aid of the army in 1945, the unions flourished and wanted more and more. A progressive labor law was passed which far exceeded in scope the modest Wagner Act in the United States and buttressed the new unions' efforts. Although Creole could afford to be generous (stockholders have usually gotten more in dividends than employees in wages) the implications of union strength within the government were as disquieting to ruling circles in Caracas as in Mexico City. There was plenty of money to meet wage demands, but the power of management is indivisible. In 1948 therefore, the Democratic Action government was overthrown by an army cabal; the Oil Workers Federation later was outlawed, its leaders imprisoned, and the power of the employees smashed. Creole's labor force was reduced from 20,500 in 1949 to 14,400 in 1954, although production rose 35 percent. Labor-management committees were formed in 1950, on the lines of Standard's own policy in the United States in the 1920s, to replace the threatened interference of powerful independent unions challenging management's prerogatives.[9]

More important for the companies, the threat of a labor-peasant-intellectual front that might lead to nationalization had been replaced by the old familiar pattern of army dictatorship. The junta, resting its power on the military and finding its political support in the big landowners and the rising industrialists, both government-subsidized, offered a more reliable base for the companies' immediate future.

For its part, the new junta bargained adroitly for more and more from the companies, as its reward for stabilizing Venezuela. It sent missions to the Middle East to establish contact with kindred governments in Iran, Iraq, and Arabia. In the censored press of Caracas, it permitted guarded hints that Mossadegh had some reason on his side in battling the British "imperialists," that nationalization had a good bit of merit in it, that Venezuela was being milked, even under the 50-50 deal.

There was, for example, the fact that the bulk of the country's crude was shipped to the outlying Dutch islands of Aruba and Curaçao to be refined there by Standard and Shell. There was no threat of nationalization under the Dutch, and no chance of political instability. The Americas' biggest refinery flourished on Aruba, where the Dutch frowned on unions and brought in the marines to break up the strike of Standard's employees in 1951. What concerned the junta was the offense to Venezuela's pride in seeing 80 percent of her oil refined on foreign islands which rightfully belonged to her; more important at the moment was the loss in revenues, which accrued to the benefit of the Dutch.[10]

Of underlying concern to all Venezuela was the country's utter dependence on the oil companies. Three-fourths of the country's $700 million annual budget came from oil, yet Venezuela had not the slightest control over the policies of the world cartel which adjusted production quotas to its own needs, not Venezuela's. The world recession of 1948-1949 had cut government revenues from $208 million in 1948 to $147 million a year later; by 1955, so dependent had the junta become on oil revenues and so heavy its commitments that a comparable drop in income could have meant disaster politically as well as economically.

As unreal as anything out of Hollywood is the fantastic prosperity that has descended upon Caracas, transforming it in twenty years from a dormant Latin town centering on its plaza and dreaming in its patios into a modern city whose chrome-plated suburbs reach up and down the valley high in the Andes. Should the oil run out, Arturo Uzlar-Pietri, one of Venezuela's leading economists, predicts that the stricken city, expiring among mountains of empty Frigidaires, silent Philcos, and gasless Cadillacs, would need the disaster services of International Red Cross brigades.[11]

Before oil, Venezuela fed itself, somehow. Today it produces only half the corn, half the meat, one-third of the green vegetables and grains, and half the milk it consumes. There are fewer cattle on the great llanos that sweep down to the Orinoco now than at the time of the Revolution of 1812. The entire economy has been sucked into dependence on petroleum revenues. Non-oil exports 25 years ago were valued at $20 million; today they still hover around that figure, but not a bean of coffee or cocoa would

now leave the country were it not for subsidies. The big landowners enjoy government subsidies, the parasitic consumers'
industries live by subsidy and tariff. The entire structure would
collapse like a house of cards were these props pulled out.

Prices are as high as the Andes; the bolivar is the only unit of
currency in the world, outside the Swiss franc and the Canadian
dollar, that surpasses the U. S. dollar in hardness. On imported
goods—the main purchases of the middle and upper classes—the
price equals the New York price plus transportation, plus duties,
plus carriage to Caracas, plus markups by importers, wholesalers,
and retailers. Goods produced locally sell at the sum of the New
York price, plus tariff, plus profit.

All this, of course, is merely a matter of wonderment for nine-
tenths of the people, who live outside the charmed world of oil.
Disease-ridden and hunger-wracked, their lot on their tiny
conucos on the mountainsides or in the peasants' huts of the
latifundias is much the same now as before oil was discovered.
At least 200,000 have fled the countryside for gilded Caracas
where they live under the bridges, along the gullies, or far up
the mountainside in ironically named "ranchos" built of the city's
refuse. The handsome publications of the government extolling
the glories of the capital city naturally ignore these abodes of
the forgotten.

The dangers to the country inherent in this situation are two-
fold. Even if the oil revenues were eternal and constant, they
would still support a deformed economy which lives by sucking
in revenues from the export of a natural resource and spending
them abroad on imports which, for the bulk of the population,
are fantastically unreal. But the deformed economy does not
bother the 10 percent who sit in on this modern Belshazzar's feast.
To them there is a real and imminent danger—a decline in the
world demand for Venezuelan crude, dictated either by economic
depression or by the rise of Middle East supplies cheaper than
those from Lake Maracaibo and Anzóategui.

While the price of Maracaibo and Kuwait oil is much the
same, the costs are not. If the cartel companies can make more
money selling Arabian than Venezuelan oil, they will do so—
gradually. Before World War II, Venezuela was Europe's main

supplier; today, it has yielded to the Middle East. The slack has
been taken up for the time by the growth in Latin American
markets and the steady rise in exports to the United States.
Roughly a third of the country's output goes to the United States,
a third to Europe, and a third to Latin America. But depression
can blast markets, as it has done before. And Venezuela today
has built up a costly edifice of magnificent structures, of lordly
services to its favored classes, which demand a billion bolivars
a year for nourishment. A jolt to the western world's economic
base might well topple the Venezuelan structure.

Worst of all, there is nothing the Caribbean land could do
about it. The decisions curtailing production would be made, not
in the Palace or the Capitol at Caracas, but in Rockefeller Plaza
in distant Manhattan. The junta would hear the deadly verdict on
the country's basic industry from the same radios that blared the
news in the upper class homes of Caracas. Of such are the
trappings of national sovereignty!

26

The Door Opens . . . and Closes

LIKE the cat that swallowed the canary, Britain at the end of World War I was well content. Germany, its chief European competitor, had been laid low. President Wilson's idealism would prevent him, it was hoped, from making demands on such sordid subjects as Russian and Middle Eastern oil. After all, the United States had plenty of oil. The spoils belonged to those who had bled on the oil fields of Mesopotamia and stood guard at the gateway to Persia's wealth.

Some of the British even gloated. Said Sir Edward Mackay Edgar, the petroleum banker: "The British position is impregnable. All the known oil fields, all the likely or probable oil fields, outside of the United States itself, are in British hands or under British management or control, or financed by British capital."[1]

Royal Dutch/Shell had bought out the Rothschild interests in Russia and controlled the output of the East Indies, then the principal Asian producer; with Anglo-Iranian it held the known fields of the Middle East and Burma. Shell was ensconced in Mexico and in the United States itself; along with other British firms, it was buying concessions right and left throughout Central America and in Colombia. Serious-minded American patriots warned that the British were locating concessions right up against the Panama Canal itself; the yellow press beat a venomous alarm.[2]

The Senate writhed in anguish. Senator Phelan of California sponsored a bill in 1920 to form the "U. S. Oil Corporation" whose purpose would be to pick up concessions in other lands with the help of U. S. diplomats and admirals. The defeat of the League of Nations in the Senate was due in part to the disillusionment of many who saw in the League a shield for colonial grabs under the thin veil of "mandates." These mandates clustered around the oil-soaked remnants of the old Turkish Empire.[3]

Standard of New Jersey was jolted out of its indifference to foreign concessions. It scanned distant horizons and did not disdain carrion. For such was the Nobel oil in Russia, in which Jersey picked up a 50 percent interest, although the property had already been nationalized by the Bolsheviks. Since the Nobels had been Russian subjects, Jersey couldn't even register a diplomatic protest.[4]

"The only thing needed now is an aggressive foreign policy on the part of the United States," declared Chairman A. C. Bedford of Jersey. For once the Federal Trade Commission agreed with Jersey, and recommended that "all proper diplomatic support in obtaining and operating oil-producing property" abroad be brought to bear. The test came quickly in Mesopotamia, which had been mandated to Britain under the name of Iraq.

Before World War I, British and German capitalists had bargained with the Sultan's vizier over these lands between the Tigris and Euphrates. Colby M. Chester, a retired U. S. admiral, pressed his own claims to a concession. Prudently the grand vizier withdrew these oil lands from the national domain and lodged them in the Sultan's "privy purse." In the background lurked Carlouste Sarkis Gulbenkian, an Armenian adventurer in oil with one finger in Baku and another in high finance. He had served, it was said, as an undercover man for Sir Henri Deterding, the Napoleon of Royal Dutch/Shell. After the Young Turks swept the Sultan and his vizier from power in 1909, Gulbenkian was busy laying the groundwork for what became the Turkish Petroleum Company. The German Deutsche Bank's Anatolian Railroad Company had a concession which granted the right to explore for oil in Mosul and Bagdad for 20 kilometers on either side of the right of way. This concession was merged in 1912 into a new agreement which gave the Deutsche Bank a 25 percent interest in the Turkish (later the Iraq) Petroleum Company, dominated by Royal Dutch/Shell and Anglo-Iranian, save that Gulbenkian insisted upon a 5 percent interest to cover his own efforts. But when the lights went out across Europe in

1914, the new company had not actually been able to negotiate a concession with the Turkish government.[5]

Turkish Petroleum, which had no valid concession either from old Turkey or new Iraq, emerged in 1918 as the chief trophy of the war in the Middle East. The British and the French in 1920 split the old empire between them—under League of Nations mandates, of course—Paris taking Syria and Lebanon, and London the rest. The 25 percent German interest in Turkish Petroleum was handed over to the French in exchange for pipe line rights of way through Syria and Lebanon. Standard of Jersey and Socony, angrily knocking at the closed door, were refused even the right to send exploring parties into Iraq.[6]

At this point the diplomatic pot boiled over. The State Department, in notes that waxed from indignant to explosive, demanded the "open door" in the remnants of the old Turkish Empire. The Foreign Office was polite, evasive, and dilatory. So that the impression would not get abroad in the United States that the State Department was fronting only for Standard, the Near East Development Company was organized in 1921 by seven leading majors; by 1928, five of them had dropped out. Some saw more lucrative opportunities elsewhere in the Middle East and did not choose to be bound by the restrictive limitations the partners imposed upon each other in Iraq Petroleum.[7]

Let it not be imagined that the U. S. companies were supplicants at the Court of St. James's. Despite British boasts of supremacy in world petroleum, the U. S. industry was actually producing two-thirds of the world's supplies and supplying 58 percent of all foreign requirements. While British concessions in the Eastern Hemisphere looked impressive, the fact was that either Oklahoma or California produced more oil than all of Asia combined. Anglo-American, the old Standard company in Britain, transacted more than half the business in the tight little isle itself. When it became apparent that Standard did not mean to be locked out of the Middle East, Sir Charles Greenway of Anglo-Iranian opened pourparlers in 1922 with A. C. Bedford, his opposite number in Jersey.[8]

After six years of complicated maneuvering, an agreement was reached by which Jersey and Socony took over a 23.75 percent share in Iraq (ex-Turkish) Petroleum. Three other equal shares were held by Anglo-Iranian, Royal Dutch/Shell and the Compagnie Française des Pétroles, and a 5 percent interest was handed to promoter Gulbenkian. The wealth of the Middle East, so far as the partners in Iraq Petroleum then knew, was in the hands of two British, two U. S., and one French company. All others were to keep out. No more talk was heard of the "open door."[9]

In somewhat antique language, the partnership was described as a "brotherhood of oil merchants," but the brothers were soon embroiled in a "red-line" snarl. The "red line" had been drawn around the old Turkish Empire (except Turkey itself) and the brothers were bound not to outsnatch each other in picking up concessions within the ringed area. But in 1927, while still a "brother" in the tentative partnership to be formalized a year later, Gulf got an option for a concession on the island of Bahrein in the Persian Gulf, close to the Arabian shore. The other partners insisted that this was within the red line; Gulf, on the other hand, could maintain with some historical justification that it had never been in the Turkish domain but that Persia had claimed it. In a swift lateral pass, Gulf in 1928 transferred its Bahrein option to Standard of California, which was not a "brother" in Iraq Petroleum and thus was not bound by the red-line agreement.[10] It was hardly an oversight that the British had ignored Bahrein, where they held paramount rights over the local sheik, or neighboring Arabia. Anglo's own geologists had already been over the region and had condemned it as empty of oil. Actually, at the time the Iraq Petroleum partnership was formalized in 1928, the only substantial producer in the Middle East was Iran. Exploration had proved immense reserves in the Mosul fields but production did not begin in earnest until later.

Standard of California proceeded to discover oil on Bahrein close to deep water, but it had no marketing apparatus east of Suez for the stuff. The Texas Company did. So the company with the crude and the company with the outlets got together in 1936 to form Caltex, a 50-50 partnership.[11]

Somewhat later, Standard of California made the narrow jump across the Persian Gulf from Bahrein to the El Hasa district which King Ibn Saud of Arabia had wrested from fellow Bedouin princes. Once again, Texaco was accepted into partnership with Standard of California in the new Arabian American Oil Company (Aramco).

By now it was apparent that Standard of Jersey and Socony, in their eagerness, had grabbed at the wrong prize in the Middle East. Hobbled by their red-line agreement with Iraq Petroleum, they were prevented from snatching the rich Arabian concessions. Caltex and Aramco soon proved that the oil under their concessions was as vast as Iraq's—and all theirs, not to be shared with the British, French, or M. Gulbenkian.

Jersey and Socony were covetous, and Caltex needed both the financial support of the more entrenched Standard companies and the world-wide markets open to them; but above all, it needed their moral support, their sympathetic understanding. In the explosive Middle East, it was unwise for U. S. companies not to embrace one another in mutual understanding. The Soviet menace, the rising nationalism of the Crescent nations, the covert watchfulness of the British companies who regarded them as Johnny-come-latelies on the scene—all these factors were driving the U. S. companies into each others' arms.[12]

But it was difficult to make the deal. The French and M. Gulbenkian would not tolerate Jersey and Socony, their partners in Iraq Petroleum, joining up with Caltex in Arabian American Oil, unless they, too, were permitted to share in the swag. That, after all, was the purpose of the brotherly red-line agreement. They were to share and share alike.[13]

For both the French and Gulbenkian, the issue was of crucial importance. By some quirk of Providence, no part of the world-wide French Empire had ever revealed substantial petroleum deposits; the French quarter interest in Iraq Petroleum was all they had, and it did not begin to meet the requirements of the internal French market. As for Gulbenkian, his precious 5 percent in Iraq Petroleum was the poor fellow's main source of revenue. For Anglo-Persian and Royal Dutch/Shell, the other partners, the issue was not so critical. They had Iran, Venezuela, the East Indies, and Burma from which to draw, as well as their half interest in Iraq Petroleum. So it was relatively easy for the two British and four American companies to come to an understanding, permitting the two American partners in Iraq to combine with Caltex in Arabia.

But M. Gulbenkian, he of the 5 percent, exploded when he heard of the private agreement. He cabled that "no intimidation or clever legal scheme will persuade me unless tested by court that IPC [Iraq Petroleum] can be used by majority to support their price control prevention of competition and monopolistic schemes of groups solely for their own benefit to detriment of company and minority."

Court action was the last thing the major partners cared to face. As one of the directors said, "to test our rights as we interpret them in the court implies a disclosure of the 1928 [red-line] agreement and may open a series of disclosures which, in our business interests, we might wish to avoid." The intimate relations of the world oil cartel must not be revealed.[14]

Accordingly, Gulbenkian, along with the French, was placated by substantial concessions, though they never gained entry to the treasures in Arabia. Nevertheless Mr. Five Percent was credited in some quarters with being the richest man in the world (some estimates go as high as a billion dollars), a claim that could be contested only by his fellow oil magnates, the King of Arabia, the Sheik of Kuwait, and a few Texas tycoons. It is of record that this connoisseur of oil had one of the world's finest collections of oil paintings and other priceless objets d'art.[15]

While Arabian American Oil, now owned by four U. S. partners,* pried under the desert sands to find out what it had gained, Iraq Petroleum widened its concessions in Iraq itself. To the rich Kirkuk fields it added those of Mosul and then of Basra—the latter turning out to be the richest of all Iraq fields. On the peninsula of Qatar, south of the Aramco concession, it picked up a concession estimated to contain 1.5 billion barrels of oil. From obscure sheiks along the coast of Trucial Oman more concessions were won.[16]

To simplify income tax problems with the U. S. and British governments, the brother merchants of Iraq Petroleum agreed to make as small a profit as possible. The crude was to be assigned to the partners for their disposal and the profits would go to the

* See page 283.

partner companies and not to the partnership. The Iraq government was dissatisfied with this arrangement as well as with the astonishing fact that its own oil was sold in its own country to its own people at a price based on Texas Gulf quotations. As with most oil companies in the U.S. and abroad, Iraq Petroleum was unable or unwilling to break down its costs so as to give the government an idea on which to base a fair royalty. The going price charged the partners was purely arbitrary, the company said; in addition the partners mingled their Iraq crude with Iranian and Arabian, and who was to say what cost what?[17]

In 1950, the royalty paid to Iraq was increased, but soon after that the King of Arabia won a 50-50 split on the profits from his concession, and the Iraqis felt they were still on the short end. In addition, the development of Iraq oil had been held back in favor of Iranian and Arabian production, thus cutting down the output on which the royalty was paid. After Iran nationalized her oil in 1951, a demand swelled through Iraq for similar action. The government also wanted some of its nationals on the board of directors, so as to be informed at first hand of company operations, and it wanted more Iraqis to be trained to higher positions in the company. By 1952, the 50-50 profit deal was extended to Iraq, although the government still complained that the calculations involved shortchanged it to a mere 35 percent of the true net. On the other hand the shutdown of Iranian production in 1952 required a vast increase in Iraq production so that Iraq Petroleum partners' profit was reported at $110 million in 1953. This was said to amount to a third of the selling price—a fair return, so fair indeed that the Iraqis noted that it was about 50 percent on the company's capital investment. To that, the brother merchants of Iraq Petroleum might well reply, the profit was the fruit of the risk, and the risk was high—when one surveyed the Middle Eastern scene.[18]

As for Standard of Jersey, it was estimated that it had recouped its entire investment in Iraq Petroleum by 1939.[19]

ACHNACARRY

After the State Department and Standard had pried open the door to Iraq, and Caltex had found vast deposits along the

Arabian coast, the majors of the Middle East had to reach an agreement, both on price and production. There were now such vast deposits available for the market, that if production were allowed to soar, prices would drop. The problem was by no means academic.

In this, Socony-Vacuum had an even more compelling interest, earlier, than Jersey. Socony had inherited most of the old Standard patrimony in Asia, in the 1911 dissolution decree, while Vacuum had inherited the monopoly's lucrative lubricants market that embraced every continent. Shell and Socony had fought price wars and had agreed to truces in the Eastern Hemisphere many a time. In 1926, they were cutting each other's throats in India. This grew out of the Russian situation. Shell had slapped a boycott on Russian oil, similar to the Shell-Standard boycott later put on Mexico in 1938, and the world cartel's boycott of Iran in 1951. Socony had been asked to observe the Russian boycott, and had declined. The U. S. company, having no other handy source of supply for Asian markets, needed the Bolsheviks' products even if Sir Henri Deterding labeled them "stolen." Price-cutting spread around the world, and even Shell-Standard relations in Mexico became inflamed.[20]

When Sir Henri, by 1928, had had enough of his price war, he invited Sir John Cadman of Anglo-Iranian and Walter C. Teagle of Jersey—Socony's big brother—to the grouse shooting at his Achnacarry castle in northern Scotland. It was announced that "game was a primary object of the visit," and so it was, figuratively. The quarry was the world's oil resources, and they were about to be divided among the Big Three.[21]

The grouse shooters announced at the time that "excessive competition has resulted in the tremendous overproduction of today, when over the world the shut-in production amounts to approximately 60 percent of the production actually going into consumption." They referred to the rapid expansion in Venezuela and the amazing discoveries being made in Texas and Oklahoma, as well as to the prospect that Iraq would soon be in production. In addition, Anglo's wells in Iran, the Rumanian wells belonging to Shell and others, and the Russian wells, were all expanding.

And at that time, 1928, east Texas was still to be discovered, and none realized that Arabia and Kuwait contained vast deposits.

"Certain politicians," said the nonpolitical gentlemen at Achnacarry, "with the support of a portion of the press, have endeavored to create in the public mind the opinion that the petroleum industry operates solely under a policy of greed and has itself initiated methods of wanton extravagance." The agreement the grouse shooters reached, known as the Achnacarry or "as is" agreement,* was aimed to cure any suspicion of greed and wanton extravagance by providing:

1. The status quo of 1928 was to be maintained among the Big Three in their relative position in world markets.

2. To control overproduction, existing facilities were to be made available to other producers at a price less than it would cost to create new facilities for their own exclusive use, but not less than the cost to the owner.

3. New facilities were to be added only when needed, and duplication of facilities was to end.

4. Products were to carry the same valuation at all points of origin, thus removing price competition but giving producers an advantage in markets geographically closest to them.

5. Supplies were to be drawn from the producing area nearest to the market.

6. Surplus production was to be shut in or offered in other markets at prices not less than those prevailing in such markets.[22]

These measures, it was explained, would protect the public against an increase in costs due to duplication of facilities, and thus would promote greater consumption.

This was the blueprint for the international petroleum cartel, the outline of basic principles under which the partners could profit in their brotherly exploitation of the world's oil resources. So the war between Socony and Shell came to an end, and prices were adjusted in India. The war in Mexico was also called off, with the drawing of a line separating British and U. S. spheres of influence.

Small wonder that the partners were not anxious to contest

* The terms of the agreement were made public in the trade press but seem to have escaped much attention in the public press.

the "red-line" agreement in court with Mr. Five Percent and the French; the details of the cartel arrangement would have been material evidence in such a suit. In deference to the U. S. antitrust laws, the Achnacarry agreement was stipulated not to apply to the United States. Within a year, however, in 1929, 17 U. S. companies had set up the Export Petroleum Association under the Webb-Pomerene Act,* with allocation of quotas and conformity in prices, in accordance with Achnacarry.[23]

Achnacarry's price mechanism sidestepped the U. S. antitrust laws by stating that its provisions did not apply within the United States. All the brothers agreed to price their oil at Texas Gulf quotations. As U. S. production costs were the highest in the world, this satisfied all partners. The British firms profited from the abnormal price level on their low-cost Iranian and Iraq crude, and the U. S. firms received a superprofit on their foreign production, in addition to their substantial earnings on domestic production.

* The Webb-Pomerene Act of 1918 permitted U. S. corporations in the same industry to organize joint export companies in order to promote sales of U. S. goods abroad. The act specifically exempted such export companies from the provisions of the antitrust laws.

27

The Wealth of Arabia

THE vast new fields of Arabia and Kuwait exploded upon the world oil market on top of the output of Iran and Iraq and strained to the limit the ingenuity of the Big Three of Achnacarry. Hobbled as they had been by their own confounded "red-line" agreements, they had not pioneered these new fields. The Big Three were in the embarrassing position of administering "as is" globally while looking in from the outside at deposits estimated at around 50 billion barrels.

Back in the nineteenth century, the United States had been the center of the oil world; briefly, at the turn of the century, Russia had shared the limelight. In the 1910s, Mexico had flared briefly. In Asia, the center of production had shifted slowly from the East Indies to Iran; now it was about to leap across the Persian Gulf to Araby's shores. The entire Middle East, which had produced but 6.5 percent of the output of the non-Soviet world in 1939, spurted up to nearly 20 percent in 1954 (despite the Iranian shutdown). Here was more than half the proved reserves of the non-Soviet world, compared with the United States' quarter. From 1939 to 1952, the output of the Middle East was to ascend 533 percent while Venezuelan production climbed 218 percent and the United States 81 percent.[1]

The Middle Eastern reserves were estimated at 77.5 billion barrels—and who knew how much more was concealed beneath the desert sands? At the 1953 rate of production, this would last 80 years, while the U. S. reserves would be exhausted within 12 years (barring further discoveries) and the Venezuelan in 14.6 years. And what fields! The Abqaiq field of Saudi Arabia—but one of several—exceeded in known reserves the greatest of all U. S. fields, that of east Texas. But while 26,000 wells were draining the 5 billion barrels of east Texas crude, Arabian American used only 62 in Abqaiq.[2]

For the world cartel not to control these fields would be tantamount to abandoning its hegemony. For the owners, Standard of California and the Texas Company, to defy the cartel would have been corporate foolhardiness and political imbecility. Standard of California had grabbed the new klondike on a pass from Gulf, which was bound by its red-line agreement with the other partners of Iraq Petroleum to take nothing without their approval. Gulf's option covered the concession on Bahrein Island, where Standard of California struck oil in 1932, and on the basis of which it made its deal in 1936 with Texaco to gain outlets east of Suez.[3]

The discovery must have been vexing to Anglo-Iranian, whose geologists had condemned the entire eastern shore of Arabia and its outlying islands as barren of oil. If Bahrein had oil, then it seemed likely that similar sands in the El Hasa district of Arabia, a few miles away, might also. All eyes focused on King Ibn Saud, the creator of Saudi Arabia. This potentate, chief of the fierce Wahabis, a fundamentalist Moslem sect, had been lining his royal coffers with $2 to $4 millions a year from the devout Egyptian and Indian pilgrims to the holy places of Mecca and Medina. As his nomad tribes were meager customers for world commerce, there was hardly any income from import duties; the pilgrim traffic was the King's main source of revenue. Iraq Petroleum bid for the El Hasa concession, then Standard of California upped the ante. Beside weighing the cash, Ibn Saud distrusted the British, who operated the kings of Iraq and Jordan, his hated enemies, so he favored the Standard company. He preferred a countervailing force. The price—30,000 gold pounds ($247,000)—seems trifling in the light of subsequent discoveries, but in 1933 it was the biggest sum Ibn Saud had ever seen at one time. Later the concession was enlarged to include two-thirds of Arabia—the largest concession in history.[4]

Standard of California cut in the Texas Company on its Arabian lands, too, in 1936, and in 1944 the new company was

christened Arabian American Oil Company (Aramco). After oil
was discovered in commercial quantities in 1938, a refinery was
built on the coast at Ras Tanura and a pipe line laid under the
Gulf to nourish the Caltex refinery on Bahrein. Then World War
II brought development to a temporary end.

Kind Ibn Saud was in a bad way as his oil royalties stagnated
and the war even dammed the flow of pilgrims. In distress, the
King threatened to cancel the precious concession unless he was
paid $30 millions as a sort of retainer. It was then that James A.
Moffett, one-time executive vice-president of Standard of New
Jersey and at the time head of Bahrein Petroleum and Caltex,
hurried to Washington to persuade the government to subsidize
Ibn Saud for the rest of the war. What happened, in the words
of Senator Owen Brewster, Republican of Maine, was "an amazing
picture of corporate greed when our country was in its most
bitter need."[5] The special Senate committee investigating the
national defense program reported in 1948 that the Aramco-
Caltex companies induced the government to underwrite their
Arabian venture to the tune of $99 million on a promise to sell
fuel oil to the U. S. Navy at 40 cents a barrel (the going price
was $1.05). Not wishing to be involved so directly in a subsidy
to the petroleum king, Washington entrusted him to the British
but paid the bill through lend-lease. In return, the King con-
sented to permit Aramco's airfield at Dhahran to be turned into
a U. S. military base, either to supplement or supplant the Abadan
and Suez bases.

The troubled Arabian situation caused Secretary of the Interior
Ickes, then doubling as Petroleum Administrator for War, to
propose that the United States take over a major interest in
Aramco, just as Britain had done with Anglo-Iranian in 1914.
Ickes related that first Standard of California stalled the negotiations, and then the Texas Company stalled. After Rommel had
been chased out of Africa and Caltex's prospects in Arabia
brightened, both companies balked at the Ickes deal. They
declined to sell everything or even to permit Uncle Sam to
become a junior partner, on terms which specified prices and
output; they seemed confident that the protection of the government would be given them in any event, whether the Treasury

had a financial interest in Arabia and Kuwait, or nothing but the bills of the Defense Department to pay for protecting these outlying and hazardous possessions.[6]

The upshot of it all was that, although the King was taken care of, the U. S. Navy paid $1.05 a barrel after all. The Senate committee complained that the government had paid $38.5 million too much for fuel oil. "The oil companies," it said, "have shown a singular lack of good faith, an avaricious desire for enormous profits, while at the same time they constantly sought the cloak of U. S. protection and financial assistance to preserve their vast concessions."[7]

The government couldn't even collect income taxes from the Aramco-Caltex companies, the committee added. Operating subsidiaries had been organized in Canada and the Bahamas to absorb the wartime profits without U. S. taxation; otherwise "as much as 90 percent of the earnings of the $117 millions" would have been taxable, Senator Brewster wailed. "It is a liberal education on how corporations organized under foreign flags yet seek the shelter of the American flag."

At about the same time, the House was voting to give the offshore oil lands to the states. Said Congressman Adolph J. Sabath, Democrat of Illinois: "We are spending billions of dollars for oil in Arabia that we can never get in case of war. We are endangering the peace of the world because we want to protect a few oil companies, British and American. Meanwhile, by this bill, we are giving away land containing more oil than Arabia and situated right in the United States."[8]

In 1949, the story of Aramco and the King boiled up again when James A. Moffett, by now retired from his positions as head of Bahrein Petroleum and of Caltex, sued Aramco for $6 million for services which, he said, he had rendered in obtaining relief for Aramco from Ibn Saud's importunate demands for more and more money. Moffett could hardly be fobbed off as a political foe of the companies. Son of a Rockefeller associate, he was senior vice-president of Standard of New Jersey when in 1933 he accepted appointment by President Roosevelt to the NRA Oil Advisory Committee. He claimed that Jersey fired him from his $125,000-a-year job as a result. After that, he became vice-president of Standard of California; this post he resigned to become Federal Housing Administrator. In Washington, he said, he "was really doing more work and was in a much more helpful position for the Standard Oil Company than if I had remained in the office at 30 Rockefeller Plaza." Accordingly, he asked Standard of California to reimburse him for out of pocket expenses of $100,000 he incurred while serving the government in Washington and settled in 1942 for $25,000.[9]

Moffett said he was responsible for the deal under which the British, with U. S. lend-lease funds, took care of King Ibn Saud and saved Aramco $30 million over a 5-year period. The jury awarded him $1,150,000 with back interest of some $500,000. The court, however, set aside the award, declaring that contracts involving the sale of influence by public officials were against public policy. This high moral stand aroused admiration, and also saved Standard of California $1,650,000.[10]

After the war ended, that company and Texaco proceeded to develop their vast reserves in Arabia. They needed $200 million or so to build a thousand-mile pipe line to the Mediterranean. Even more important, they needed markets far greater than those of Texaco east of Suez. So, at this point, Standard of California had to deal with its big brother, Standard of New Jersey, which had the cash and the markets. Between the two companies there had been a suspicion of coolness, illustrated perhaps by the switch of Moffett from senior vice-president of Jersey to the vice-presidency of Standard of California in charge of Arabia and Bahrein. With Moffett out of the way, the two brother companies came together. California and Texaco cut their shares in Aramco from 50 percent each to 30 percent; Jersey was awarded an equal 30 percent and Socony was cut in for the remaining 10 percent. As part of the deal, Texaco opened its marketing facilities west of Suez, in the Mediterranean, and in Europe, to Caltex—a move which strongly suggested that it had hitherto not been free to do so within the confines of the "as is" world cartel agreement.[11]

Jersey paid $76.5 million and Socony $25.5 million for their shares in Aramco, and deferred their claims on Aramco earnings for a period of years so that, in effect, their entry into the Caltex partnership cost them about $450 million. To safeguard their

minority position, Jersey-Socony insisted on the stipulation that
a two-thirds majority was needed for changes in Aramco's bylaws
and for all major transactions.

So Standard of California and Texaco profited handsomely in
sharing Arabia with the two senior Standard companies, gained
needed markets in Europe, and in addition a $102 million
guarantee on the loan to build the Trans-Arabian Pipeline
(Tapline). Perhaps as important as cash in the pipe line deal
was the united front of the four companies to get permission from
Washington to obtain the sorely needed pipe at a time when
domestic producers were clamoring desperately for such supplies.[12]

KUWAIT

Around the rim of Arabia are a score of quasi-independent
"sovereign" nationlets. At the head of each is a full-fledged sultan
or sheik who ekes out a simple existence by collecting tolls from
traffic trickling through his borders. Without these toll gates,
many of the sheiks of the Trucial Coast, Oman, Hadhramaut,
and Dhofar, would be reduced to beggary or banditry. Some
have incomes as low as $10 a month. The traveler is stopped at
makeshift customs houses and assessed duties by officials who
can hardly be distinguished from the beggars.[13]

In these sultanates and sheikdoms a British agent represents the
paramount power. Treaties have been solemnly signed between
the rulers and the British assigning control of foreign affairs to
London; on occasion the paramount power enforces law and
order directly on the rulers.

Of such is the sheikdom of Kuwait. Its main asset in the old
days was an excellent port at the head of the Persian Gulf. The
Germans eyed Kuwait as a Gulf terminus for their Berlin-to-
Bagdad railroad; thereupon the sheik proclaimed his independence of Turkey in 1899 while signing a treaty with the British
transferring effectual control of foreign affairs to them.[14]

When geologists for Anglo-Iranian condemned the eastern
shore of Arabia as oilless, they included Kuwait and the neighboring Iraq district of Basrah. After Standard of California proved
there was petroleum on Bahrein, Gulf became interested. The

Mellon firm had been euchred out of Bahrein and Arabia because it was bound by the Iraq Petroleum "red-line" agreement. So it dropped its partnership in Iraq Petroleum and laid siege to the sheikdom of Kuwait.* The British agent was agitated. Once again the State Department was called upon to pry open a closed door, as in Iraq. The fact that the U. S. ambassador at the Court of St. James in 1931 was none other than Andrew W. Mellon, chief owner of Gulf, added urgency to the State Department's insistence.[15]

As the sheik of Kuwait had been obliged to promise the British never to yield a concession without permission, he was hardly a free agent in dealing with Gulf. The British, in the form of Anglo-Iranian Oil Company, were looking over his shoulder as he negotiated, and they demanded a 50-50 share in any Gulf deal. So in 1934 Anglo was able to retrieve its initial error in condemning the region and to obtain a half share in Kuwait Oil Company. Part of the agreement provided that neither party should use the oil to "upset or injure" the other's trade or marketing position. Anglo also protected its rights in the Indian market against Gulf.[16]

The fabulous field of Burghan was discovered in Kuwait in 1938. This was the wildcatter's dream of paradise where, 'tis said, never a dry hole has been hit. In this bare patch of desert, which could be inserted into a corner of Texas, lie deposits thought to contain more than two-thirds as much crude as is left in all the United States. So immense was the threatened flood that Anglo, already amply supplied from its Iranian and Iraq wells, stipulated that Kuwait production should be kept down; if Gulf needed crude in that region, it could tap Anglo's oil from Iran on a cost basis. While Gulf did not much care for the terms, it had little choice but to accept, being in effect a junior partner in British-controlled territory.[17]

* Gulf was one of the seven companies in Near East Development, formed in 1921 to contest for an interest in Iraq Petroleum. It dropped out when the Iraq Petroleum Company partnership was formed in 1928, but already had become interested, in 1927, in gaining a concession in Kuwait. As membership in the Iraq Petroleum Company, with its "red-line" agreement, would have forbidden Gulf to take up a Kuwait concession without the company's permission, Gulf preferred to drop its Iraq Petroleum partnership and maintain a free hand along the Persian Gulf.

But the wheel was to turn against Anglo in Iran in 1951-1952. Anglo's misfortune became Gulf's fortune. From 6 million barrels in 1946, Kuwait production shot up to 273 million in 1952, more than Iran had ever produced in one year. In 1953, Kuwait actually surpassed Arabia.[18]

While Anglo desperately needed the Kuwait output, Gulf was embarrassed by its sudden affluence. Its wells in the United States and Venezuela sufficed for domestic and export needs. So Gulf made a deal for Shell to buy 175,000 barrels a day of its Kuwait production for a period until 1969, calling for some eighth of the sheikdom's estimated reserves.

The Gulf-Shell agreement bound the two companies not to cut prices or snatch markets from each other. This was riveted by the proviso that Gulf sold to Shell at no fixed price but rather shared 50-50 in Shell's profits on Kuwait oil.[19]

The arrangement assured to Gulf an outlet, and to Shell a supply, thus freeing Shell of its previous dependence on its quarter share of Iraq Petroleum and its Indonesian wells to provide for Eastern Hemisphere markets. Part of its own share not taken by Shell, Gulf sold to Socony and Atlantic, and in 1950 some 40,000 barrels a day were being shipped to the East Coast.[20]

Before its Iranian troubles, Anglo also had its problems in disposing of Kuwait crude. Soon after the Gulf-Shell dicker, Standard of New Jersey and Socony agreed to take 1.3 billion barrels from Anglo over a 20-year period. All three companies joined to project a Middle East pipe line linking the fields of Burghan and Iran to the Mediterranean. In this, the Standard companies once again had something more precious than gold to offer—the pipe, which could be procured in the required quantity only from the United States, where it was in short supply.

Through this network of deals, Anglo, Shell, Standard of New Jersey, Socony, and Gulf were thus bound together as brothers, one for all and all for one. This was reinforced on the one end by the Anglo-Shell-Jersey-Socony partnership in Iraq Petroleum, and on the other by the Jersey-Socony-Texaco-California partnership in Aramco. Jersey clearly was the kingpin of the whole setup.[21]

As Anglo's oil was to be sold to Jersey-Socony on a cost-plus basis, the brothers were faced by the problems of accounting. Anglo had not the slightest intention of divulging its costs; Jersey not the slightest of accepting Anglo's version. Who was going to audit the books? After a good bit of haggling, the issue was compromised by arranging for semi-independent auditors.

Standard's share of Kuwait was to be marketed only west of Suez, so as not to interfere with Anglo's Eastern markets. If the Standard firms devoted more than 5 percent of their "off-take" to Eastern markets, they were to be charged market prices and not cost-plus.[22]

THE NEUTRAL ZONE

Among the political oddities of the score of "sovereign" sheikdoms and sultanates on the rim of Arabia, none is more curious than the two neutral zones separating the realms of the King of Arabia and the Sheik of Kuwait from that of the King of Iraq. Wandering Bedouins are little concerned with notions of sovereignty and care not where they seek water and forage for their camels and sheep. It was to quell the animosities of the desert lords, and to provide buffer zones where the nomads could pitch their tents without concern for flags, that the two neutral zones were set up.

The zone to the south of Kuwait interested Ralph K. Davies, former Standard of California official and Harold L. Ickes's right bower in the Petroleum Administration for War. There was a good bit of talk in Congress about a few selfish oil companies hogging the resources of the Middle East; it seemed a good idea to the State Department that the little fellows be offered a corner to dig in. This, it was hoped, would take some of the heat off the Department, which demagogues charged cared only for Standard.[23]

So the American Independent Oil Company (Aminoil) was organized in 1947 by Davies. Phillips Petroleum took 34 percent; Hancock 15; Signal 15; Ashland 12; J. S. Abercrombie 6; Deep Rock 3; Sunray 3; Lario (Globe) 2 percent. Davies kept 8 percent for his trouble.

In 1948 Davies got a concession from the Sheik of Kuwait

covering his share of the neutral zone; in 1949 Pacific Western, Paul Getty's Los Angeles firm, got a similar concession from the King of Arabia, and the two companies joined in exploration. But unfortunately for the small fry, the bargain counter days in Arabian concessions had ended. While Standard of California had picked up Bahrein and Saudi Arabia for piddling sums, the desert monarchs by 1948 had a better idea of the wealth beneath their sands. Aminoil had to pay $7.5 million cash to the Sheik along with a minimum royalty advance of $625,000 a year, whether a drop of oil was ever found or not. With this went 15 percent of the profits, if any, and a million-dollar yacht. A year later the Getty interests of Pacific Western had to pay the King of Arabia, by now a sharp bargainer, $9.5 million for a similar concession and a million dollars a year advance royalty, oil or no oil, and if any was found, 25 percent of the profits.[24]

After several dusters, oil was struck in 1953 at Wafra No. 4, with a yield of 3500 barrels a day of fair gravity crude. By 1955, 14 wells were producing 30,000 barrels a day and reserves were estimated at 350 million barrels. The strikes were far from phenomenal, considering that the companies had spent $30 million on development. There was some question as to whether the neutral zone wells were an extension of the great Burghan field of Kuwait or isolated pockets. As things stood, the small independents were, as usual, taking the skimmed product while the cream went to the big companies. In the meantime a hot fight had broken out in the inner ranks of Aminoil between the Phillips Petroleum group and President Davies for control of the firm, and was up for adjudication in 1955 in the California courts.[25]

28

Politics of Oil in the Middle East

FOR centuries the peoples of the Middle East lay locked in decadent feudalism, living and dying without notice from the West. Curious travelers returned from these lands, distant in time as well as space, with Arabian tales to while away an evening. Only merchantmen of the sea and the caravan routes traversed their coasts and arid wastes. All non-Moslems were barred from the sacred cities.

The discovery of vast deposits of petroleum catapulted the Middle East into the center of world tensions. The West eyed the Middle East with singleminded fascination—how much wealth could be extracted, and how fast? The prize was the greatest untapped treasure on the entire globe.

One United States firm—Standard of California—alone got $645 million in profits from its Asian holdings in the years 1948-1954. In the one year 1954, profits were $117 million on an investment of $13 million. Dividends in the seven-year period for this one company were $337 million. At the same time, California's equity in Asia, built on undistributed earnings, rose to $385 million. For each dollar invested, California had acquired an equity of $29.61.

In nearby Kuwait, Gulf reported earnings of $82 million in 1952, and this presumably was half the total, for Anglo was a 50-50 partner.

Standard of New Jersey's Venezuelan subsidiary, Creole, long the world's leading producer, was elbowed out of first place in 1952-1953 by Aramco. It was hard to determine primacy, as both Aramco and Kuwait were producing at around 900,000 barrels a day for a time. In 1954, Aramco produced 348 million barrels, and Kuwait 301 million. On this it was estimated that the total profit was nearly $300 million, and that an equal amount went into the purses of the King of Arabia and the Sheik of Kuwait. Thus the corporations and the rulers of these medieval lands kept roughly half of what was shelled out by the consumers of Europe and the United States.

The corporations had no choice but to be generous to their feudal hosts. They were strangers in strange lands, halfway around the globe from home. The days of gunboat diplomacy, when British cruisers in the Persian Gulf could wring terms from the Shah, were gone forever. Anglo-Iranian had played that game, and was no longer Iranian.* The Arab-Moslem peoples of the Middle East, as they awoke from their centuries-old sleep, smarted at the indignities that had been heaped upon them by the West, and developed a strident nationalistic fervor. And, even more frightening to the oil companies, over the rim of the Caucasus stood the Soviets, watching carefully the record being written on the desert sands. Thus the 50-50 split in profits represented, not generosity, but necessity.

Anglo, faced with an even more menacing threat in Iran, had preferred to try to bull it through. It was not that Scottish managing directors were more inconsiderate than Standard's, but that Britain, frightfully wounded in two world wars, felt that she could not give up an extra ha'penny of income so bitterly needed to assuage austerity at home. Iraq Petroleum, under British control, felt the same. So it was left to Standard, again, to take a harder look at the cards and to decide that generosity is the better part of wisdom. In 1950, the 50-50 deal was extended by Aramco to the King of Arabia, and shortly afterward Kuwait Oil followed suit, perhaps by Gulf's prodding rather than Anglo's. Iraq Petroleum haltingly conceded the 50-50 split, after Iran, Iraq's next-door neighbor, had seized its own oil away from Anglo.[1]

So it was that King Ibn Saud's treasurer, who used to dole out gold coins from a bag on his belt, was accounting, by 1952, for royalties of $140 to $170 millions.[2]

* See pages 324 ff.

And still the grasping King was dissatisfied. Like Midas, all he touched turned to gold; the man who once knew hunger at the head of marauding Wahabi tribesmen now ordered fleets of Cadillacs for his harem, the windows so devised that his favorites might look out, but none might look in. He was demanding that more oil be produced, so more royalties might pour in; he had become expert in accountancy and was demanding income calculations that would increase his net; he commanded Aramco to shift its headquarters from Rockefeller Plaza to Dhahran, the air-conditioned desert oil town; he wanted not only 50-50 on profits but 50-50 on the Aramco board of directors; like Venezuela, he hankered after an artificial rate of exchange to relieve him from accepting part of his income in soft sterling; he wanted other portions of his realm in the Aramco concession explored quickly so that more crude could rush up through the sands to his greater financial glory; he wanted a hard-cash guarantee that in case war shut down production, he could continue to live in the style to which he had become accustomed.[3]

The style was Oriental in magnificence for Abd al-Aziz ibn Abd al-Rahman Al Faisal Al Sa'ud, who headed a puritanical kingdom. His plane was a flying palace with a revolving throne, an elevator to the cabin so that the aging monarch might not have to climb a plebeian gangway, and a bedroom-sitting room with private bath. His $250,000 air-conditioned trailer, in which he moved about his realm, was adorned with golden throne, kitchen, and deep-freezer. The fleet of Cadillacs followed respectfully. His brother, the Emir Abdullah, boasted a new 30-room palace and 88-room harem costing more than a million dollars.[4]

As in the story books, the King was monarch of all he surveyed—literally. The name of his domain is Saudi Arabia, to emphasize its personal ownership by Ibn Saud. His word, and the light of the Koran, was the law. He ruled through ministers, but so new are the problems created by sudden wealth and so few among his subjects those who could cope with them that he was obliged to turn to Syria and other Arab countries for many of his Cabinet members. In his own land, 95 percent of his people were illiterate.[5]

Justice in Saudi Arabia is rough and ready. The death sentence is executed by flaying; for minor offenses hands may be cut off and other mutilations inflicted. The British Anti-Slavery Committee estimates there may be as many as 750,000 slaves in Arabia. Wealthy pilgrims use their extra servants as travelers' checks in Mecca.[6]

In this land of the Arabian Nights, no labor organization whatsoever is permitted. Unions of course are illegal, but so are workers' social clubs or any formal coming together of employees for any purpose. The rule is common to Arabia, Kuwait, and Bahrein, so far as oil workers are concerned.

It was therefore totally unexpected when, in October 1953, 13,000 of Aramco's 15,000 Arabian employees struck—apparently all but the supervisory and clerical force. More than a hundred were jailed for presuming to organize a union in violation of the law. Martial law was immediately declared. The strikers were said to be demanding wage increases.[7]

The uprising, accompanied by riots, it was reported by Associated Press and United Press, presented a problem that not even the foreign-born ministers of the desert despot had foreseen. Strikes and riots were commonplace in turbulent Teheran and in Bagdad, but the simple Bedouins were presumed to be incapable of such unrest. Revolution might tear at the vitals of regimes based on teeming cities and villages festering in filth and disease, but not in this desert realm, which knew no cities in the modern sense, and no proletariat and peasantry massed in millions.

The strike was all the more notable because Aramco, basing itself on the best Standard of New Jersey employee paternalism, had spent millions on housing for its Arab workers. Aramco had even been generous—as in its 50-50 deal with the King—by lifting the wages of its employees from 27 cents a day in 1940 to a minimum of $1.35 in 1952. And still these people—less than a generation from the camels—were not appreciative. The Soviets, armed with their Marxian doctrines, must have watched this development with more than usual attention, although not even Aramco charged that the strike was incited by Russian agents.[8]

If the strike was shocking to Ibn Saud, it must have been discouraging to Aramco. Standard of New Jersey policies, dominant in Aramco, are the best policies that can be devised by realistic, intelligent men seeking high profit prudently. And yet the worm was in the Arabian apple, despite the most favorable environment foreign capital is ever likely to find in an imperfect world.

Aramco had sedulously avoided the sahib mentality of the British in Iran. Its first men bowed low before the King, attentive to his every wish. Did he want a railroad to cross the desert from the Persian Gulf to his capital at Riyadh? Aramco engineers undertook the task, even though a motor road might have been just as good for the scant needs of the royal hamlet. Would his nomads like to have water for their flocks along the Tapline? Water wells were drilled and troughs provided, at some distance from the pipe line stations. Aramco issues no financial report, but its annual Report of Operations to the Saudi Arab Government is one of the handsomest publications in English or Arabic. The English starts from the front, the Arabic from the back, with identical text and pictures, both prefaced by photos of His Majesty. American bonhomie, however insincere, replaces British arrogance, however sincere; ostensible respect, disdain.[9]

The fact was that the cupidity of the King was matched by materialistic desires of his subjects, employees of Aramco, for better working conditions. Because illiterate men cannot function efficiently or safely in an oil field or refinery, Aramco had to open its own schools. But with literacy, there may also come enlightenment. If Arabs at last can read, they may not confine themselves to literature approved by the company and the King. Ideas are generated, and windows open upon the world. The camel-tender, little different now from his ancestor in Mohammed's time, suddenly becomes a twentieth-century industrial worker; the King, who once battened off pilgrims, becomes one of the wealthiest men in the world. Arabia, long walled off from the modern world, is suddenly plunged into it. Where formerly Aramco had only the distant threat of the Soviets to consider, now it must cope with the King's avarice and his subjects' rebelliousness. So if Aramco's stay in the Middle East may be short, by most historical standards, all the more reason to recoup itself as handsomely as possible while it can.

After the death of the aged patriarch of Arabia on November

9, 1953, new forces became visible to western eyes. Advisors reported to be hostile to the United States clustered about his son, the new King Saud. Perhaps he was not amused by criticisms in U. S. newspapers of "royal profligacy," of gleaming neon-lighted palaces on the desert, of oil largesse tossed to 10,000 persons in the royal retinue on whom a sixth of Saudian revenues were spent. The U. S. attitude toward Israel had never pleased the leaders of the most fundamentalist of Moslem sects; now U. S. aid to Iraq, headed by a hated Hashemite monarch, disturbed the new Arabian ruler. While he was willing to accept Pentagon help in modernizing his army and in planning a navy and air force, King Saud in 1954 curtly ordered the United States to withdraw its Foreign Operations Administration unit even before its appropriation of $1.6 million had been spent. The United Nations technical aid teams, on the other hand, were permitted to remain.[10]

Aramco twitched uneasily, despite the smiling assurance of an Arabian minister that his King had no thought, at the time, of nationalizing oil. More to the point, the King had thought of creating a Saudian merchant marine, and how better to begin than by having a fleet of tankers? Saud had hardly been on his throne three months when news leaked out that he had negotiated an agreement with Aristotle Socrates Onassis, the tanker magnate, to create the Saudi Arabian Maritime Company. The government was to get a shilling and a half (approximately 20 cents) for every ton of oil moved. Much to the astonishment of Aramco, the agreement provided that after 1953 the U. S. company could move its own oil only in whatever bottoms it then owned. It would not be permitted to replace its existing tankers, and as they went out of use, Onassis' ships would gradually take over the lucrative business.[11]

The implications were explosive. Onassis, born in Greece, citizen of Argentina, legal resident of Uruguay, with offices in Paris and Monte Carlo, had sparked an idea that might inflame the greedy in Caracas and Jakarta, Bagdad and Bogotá. The State Department and Foreign Office felt as aggrieved as did Aramco. If Onassis's tankers carried 60 percent of Arabian production, the King would get another $50 million a year in royalties; by the same token Aramco would eventually lose the profits amassed from carrying its own oil.[12]

The State Department protested to Saudi Arabia against the "monopolistic" contract. The Arabians could reply *"tu quoque"* and point to the U. S. law providing that 50 percent of U.S. aid to foreign countries must be carried in U. S. bottoms. Why shouldn't some Arabian oil be carried in bottoms nominally Arabian although in fact Onassisian? A State Department official explained that if the oil tanker deal could go through, there was nothing to keep other countries with a major export—bananas, iron ore, manganese—from doing the same.[13]

Aramco was not without its own defenses. Its owners were also partners in the new Iranian setup; if the valves were to be opened wide on Iranian wells, the need for Arabian crude would dwindle, along with royalties to King Saud. Not that Aramco passed quickly to threats. After all, the global oil situation was too parlous, the flames of nationalism were licking too high, the Soviets were too watchful, to permit any but the most nimble parrying with the Arabian despot.*

THE SHEIKDOM OF KUWAIT

If the court of the Arabian King presents a bizarre spectacle as gold from oil rushes into it, that of Kuwait is out of this world. The money flooding in upon King Saud, if spread equally among his 6,500,000 subjects, would give them an annual income of only $23 apiece; but the royalties paid the Sheik of Kuwait, spread equally among his 200,000 subjects, would assure every man, woman, and child an annual income of $750. Actually the average annual income in 1951 was around $50. The Kuwaitis, potentially within grasp of one of the highest income levels in the world, were in reality among the poorest in any civilized land.[14]

In this tiny corner, wedged in so diplomatically by the British between Arabia and Iraq, lies the seaport town of Kuwait, backed by the desert which boasts not even a single oasis. But under the sands lies the Burghan field, the richest concentration of oil

* On the initiative of King Saud, the dispute was turned over in the spring of 1955 to arbitrators for Aramco and Saudi Arabia.

known in the world—more than Iran or Iraq and more than half
the reserves known to underlie the entire continental United
States.

Such wealth is embarrassing. The British agent in charge of
the Sheik's affairs is at his wit's end to know what to do with the
golden flood, short of air-conditioning the entire sheikdom. The
Sheik himself has run out of ideas; there is a limit to the number
of 90-foot statues from Paris that can be placed in the lobby
of his new palace; and anyway, such statues absorb less than a
day's income.[15]

Of course something *could* be done with the money. Nearly a
million refugees from Israel are rotting in desert camps. Illiteracy
in Kuwait is nearly 100 percent; 90 percent of the people have
tuberculosis. The Sheik has built a water distillation plant to
avoid the need of importing the brackish water of the Shatt-al-
Arab from Iraq in tankers, but the people are said not to like the
flat taste of pure water, and so some of the Shatt-al-Arab's
dubious liquid is added for taste.[16]

A third of the Sheik's revenues, said to total around $140 mil-
lion a year, is devoted to public uses, which include modernization of the ancient city and its port. A third goes into his privy
purse and the other third he invests in foreign securities against
the day when the golconda of oil will be exhausted.[17]

As in Arabia, the Sheik rules with despotic power, the sole
maker and administrator of the laws. Murderers are flogged daily
until dead; women criminals are sewn up in sacks and stoned
to death in the public square. No unions or clubs are tolerated.[18]

THE SHEIKDOM OF BAHREIN

Out in the Persian Gulf, the Sheik of Bahrein enjoys an income
of nearly $10,000 a day. Of this, he keeps some $2500 for his own
expenses and with the rest runs the public services. Bahrein enjoys a reputation along the Gulf as a model land. Most houses
have running water and plumbing, and schools have been encouraged. Rather cannily, the Sheik does not permit Caltex to
provide the usual social amenities for its employees; that is his
prerogative. In that way the police can keep a closer check on
such subversive proclivities among the Bahreinis as forming

unions or clubs, which are *verboten* as elsewhere along the Gulf.[19]

Minor sheiks also share in the rich harvest. On the peninsula of Qatar, south of Aramco's concession, the Sheik enjoys an income of more than $11 million a year from Iraq Petroleum. Farther along lies the Trucial Coast, where an uneasy truce between the British and the king of Arabia is punctuated by armed raids. The paramount power sees that the sovereign sheiklets along this barren coast are armed to meet the Saudi soldiers. Dark suspicions are entertained that the Arabian claims there are not so much to sand and nomads as to oil which Aramco would like to have.[20]

ALONG THE PERSIAN GULF

Over the entire region along the Persian Gulf, from Iran to Qatar, hangs a leaden curtain of suspicion, fear, and hatred. Even if there were no oil, the situation would be precarious. Iran is only the most violent example. Ibn Saud's Arabia was won by himself with fire and sword. The Sheiks along the Gulf are creations, for the most part, of the British Navy, nourished either by subventions or oil royalties. The history of Iraq, which runs back only thirty years or so, is one of government by bribery, assassination, and intrigue. Instability is inherent in all these synthetic regimes.

Overlaid on instability are flaming hatreds—hatred of the British for their domination, growing hatred of the United States as an accomplice, hatred of Israel as an intruder on Arab lands and expeller of nearly a million refugees, hatred of Communism on religious as well as political grounds. While the hatreds are common to all these lands, there is little cement in them to bind them to a common purpose, or strength to make them effective, as was shown in the war against Israel.

Under this powder keg there lies oil worth a hundred billion dollars. All this is owned by hated foreigners who hope, at current rates of profit, to pocket some $25 billion from the Middle East. As the price for relative stability, these companies are willing to pay an equal sum—$25 billions—to their local political caretakers.

But the very development of the oil resources in turn creates new problems. A violent strike hits Aramco's operations in union-less Arabia; the head of the Kuwait police is reported to have attempted to seize power from his Sheik to avail himself of the fabulous revenues of state; in Iraq, political convulsion is en-demic; in Iran, the British were even driven out for a time. The creation of a working class, the inescapable spread of literacy, the existence of vast sums of easy money in the hands of the rulers and their hangers-on make any equilibrium unstable. And so the U. S.-British companies are following the only policy tenable—to make as much as possible as quickly as possible before they are engulfed in the deluge.

29

The Pricing of Oil

WHILE the Iranians were complaining that Anglo-Iranian Oil gave the British Navy a subsidy on its fuel oil costs by special price concession which lowered the payments due Teheran, the British government during World War II had a different story, one strikingly similar to that stated by a U. S. Senate committee. To His Majesty's ministers, it seemed odd that while Britain was fighting for its life, Anglo-Iranian should be billing bunker fuel at Texas Gulf prices, plus transportation from Houston to Abadan, for supplies produced in Iran and loaded at Abadan. Under great pressure upon the point of "unconscionable" price, Anglo and Caltex agreed to name the Persian Gulf as a basing point for their oil. The price was still "as if" loaded in Texas, but the enormous tanker charge from the Mexican Gulf to the Persian Gulf was eliminated. His Majesty's government, despite the presence of two directors of its own on Anglo's board, was still unable to find out what it actually cost to produce the fuel.[1]

After the war, Persian Gulf crude was posted at $2.22, which placed it on a parity with Texas and Venezuela. Later, in 1948, when a Caribbean base price was substituted for the Texas Gulf, and Aramco's Tanura refinery was also made a basing point, the price of Middle East crude went down to $2.03.[2]

When the Marshall Plan went into effect in Europe in 1948, the administrators were astonished to find that Middle East oil was being delivered in New York at a lower price than in Britain and France. The majors said this was temporary and marginal; the European Cooperation Administration (ECA), which was footing the European bills, protested. As a gesture in public rela-

tions, the price of oil to ECA was cut 15 cents, to $1.88. The
exact basis for this reduction was as mysterious as the production cost.[3]

In 1949, the "as is" companies decided to make New York
instead of London the equalizing point in the price of crude,
whatever its source. The price of Arabian crude was then set
at $1.75 in 1950, and maintained at that figure until 1953. On this
basis, Middle East oil was "competitive," i.e. could be delivered,
tanker rates included, at the same cost as Venezuelan and Texan
crude, on the Atlantic coast of the Americas all the way from
New York to Buenos Aires.[4]

The price of U. S. crude was boosted 25 cents to $2.90 a
barrel on June 15, 1953, in order, it was said, to stimulate exploration and production of domestic supplies for defense needs.
This posed a neat problem for the importing companies. Socony,
Gulf, Texaco, and Standard of California each were importing
50,000 to 70,000 barrels a day of Middle Eastern crude.[5] The
question was, how could they justify a price increase for
Venezuelan and Middle Eastern crude at a time when domestic
supplies were close to record levels, when entire fields in the
Middle East, including Iran's, were shut in, and a substantial
part of Venezuela's output as well? How explain to consumers a
price increase when profits for 1953 already promised to run well
above 1952's record level?

On the other hand, how was it possible *not* to increase world
prices? The "as is" principles of Achnacarry dictated a common
world price level for crude, wherever produced, otherwise the
reason for the existence of the cartel would vanish and competition would rear its ugly head among regions, if not among companies.[6]

This dilemma was readily solved; after all, it was only the consumers who would suffer by price increases; and they were
ineffective politically, it seemed, both in the United States and in
Europe, the main consuming centers. Creole, Jersey's subsidiary,
posted 10-30-cent increases for Venezuelan crude on June 23,
1953, a week after the U. S. increase. On July 8, Gulf upped
the price of Kuwait crude by 25 cents. Anglo fell in line July
16, for both Kuwait and Iraq. As "defense" could hardly be

pleaded as an excuse, the cartel companies wasted no time on apologies. The less said, the better.

PRODUCTION AND EARNINGS OF BIG SEVEN COMPANIES
OUTSIDE THE UNITED STATES

Company	1939	1954	1954	1954
	Production (Millions of barrels)		Net Income (Millions of dollars)	Profit per barrel
Jersey	163	527	452	85 cents
Shell	150	486	285	59
Texaco	8	141	121	85
Socony	14	101	83	82
Gulf	12	202	121	60
Standard of California	6	119	117	99
Anglo-Iranian	85	225	68	30

(1939 figures from U. S. Tariff Commission report on Petroleum, 1946; figures for 1954 are from annual reports of companies, except that the figures for the two British companies are for the year 1953.)

The National Oil Marketers Association estimated the cost to U. S. consumers at $1 billion; the National Grange said it would cost the nation's farmers an extra $100 million; the armed forces estimated its share at $50 million; the airlines, $12 million.

Consumers might have hoped, though, when Aramco finished its mighty pipe line to the Mediterranean, that they would benefit. Not only were pipe line costs lower, but the Suez Canal tolls were eliminated. Tanker costs from the Persian Gulf to the eastern Mediterranean were estimated at 45½ cents a barrel, against pipe line costs of 18 cents. But the rate posted at Sidon, Lebanon, turned out to be the equivalent, after all, of the Ras Tanura base price plus tankerage around Arabia and through Suez. Aramco said it could not charge otherwise. Only 40 percent of the crude was moving by pipe; was the company therefore to sell 40 percent of its crude at a lower price?[7]

However consumers fared, the companies did very well. Aramco cleared 91 cents a barrel in 1948, 95 cents in 1949, and 85 cents in 1950. That was about double the cost of production. The profit statements[8] showed these figures:

Company	1950	1951	1953
	(Millions of dollars)		
Arabian American	$115.0	$159.9	$180.0
Caltex-Bahrein	50.6	98.4	115.0
Gulf (Kuwait)	22.0	32.0	76.0
Jersey-Socony (Standard-Vacuum)	38.6	43.0	41.0

The breakdown on Middle East earnings in 1953 by company was:

Standard of California	$117.5 million
Texas Company	117.5
Standard of New Jersey	65.5
Gulf	76.0
Socony	35.5

While Congress was busying itself investigating the rise in gasoline prices consequent on the increase in crude, the Europeans could do little more than complain. With some asperity, Dr. Paul H. Frankel, an English petroleum economist, said that "if the Americans wish to protect their industry, they should do it at their border and not at the source, as it were, in other people's countries." He insisted that the European market required a different price structure from that dictated by the defense needs of the United States for stimulated domestic production. The Continent requires more residual and fuel oils and less gasoline than the United States.

The Mutual Security Administration estimated that the 25-cent boost would cost Europe an extra $122 million a year, and would increase the already serious dollar drain. The London *Economist* countered that the cost would be $130 million in local currencies and $50 million in dollars.

Such complaints overlooked the fact that big U. S. companies were domestic as well as foreign producers. There wouldn't be much sense in Standard's Creole selling Venezuelan crude in the United States at $2.65 while Standard's Humble tried to sell Texas crude at $2.90. The same observation applied to Middle Eastern crude. Nevertheless there were bugs in the oil. The Soviets and the Rumanians took advantage of the price rise to enter the French and Argentine markets; Venezuelan production fell in 1953 for the first time in history; the shot in the arm given U. S.

production resulted in growing inventories, in spreading price wars, in sharply reduced allowables in the producing states. The aching malaise in world markets caused by prices out of all relation to production costs gave point to the Egyptian query as to "whether petroleum consumers throughout the world are not being held to ransom under a price structure based on the high cost of production of oil in the United States."[9] The cost of protecting the free world's stake in the Middle East was bearing heavily on consumers everywhere, not least in the United States.

After the Federal Trade Commission's report on the international petroleum cartel had directed attention once more to the curious pricing system in the Middle East, the Department of Justice on August 22, 1952, filed suit to recover some $67 million from Standard of New Jersey, Caltex, and Socony.* This was the overcharge, said the Department, on oil products sold to the European Cooperation Administration and the Mutual Security Agency from May 1949 to June 1952 for the Marshall Plan countries.[10]

In June 1951, MSA had halted the financing of Arabian oil shipments, complaining of the "exorbitant" prices being charged in Europe while similar products were being dumped in New York at lower prices.

From April 1948 through April 1952, petroleum products had accounted for $1,389,600,000 of the $13 billion spent for European economic aid by the U. S. government.[11]

Back in June of 1948, Senator Joseph C. O'Mahoney, Democrat of Wyoming, had protested to Standard of Jersey that ECA was paying "phantom freight." The Senator said that Arabian oil delivered to Haifa in Palestine was charged on the basis of Texas Gulf prices plus tankerage from Houston to Haifa. This, he said, doubled the price.[12]

The *Chicago Tribune* sniffed suspiciously at the entire ECA layout, which it viewed as a Wall Street conspiracy. The Rockefellers were behind it, Colonel Robert R. McCormick charged,

* In its annual report for 1954, Standard of New Jersey noted in regard to the suit against it for $52 million that "the ultimate liability will not be materially important in relation to the total assets of the [Standard] companies."

and now Standard Oil was profiting. President Eugene Holman of Jersey replied indignantly. Defending its charges, the *Tribune* responded:

> The editorial pointed out that members of the Rockefeller family played an important part in putting over the Marshall Plan from which the Rockefeller companies are profiting. They worked thru an organization called the Committee for the Marshall Plan to Aid European Recovery. Winthrop W. Aldrich, brother-in-law of John D. Rockefeller Jr., and Nelson A. Rockefeller, the son of John D. Jr., were active members of that committee.
>
> Mr. Holman objects to our statement that John D. Jr. is the boss of the Standard Oil companies. The point can be argued but it need not detain us. No one is likely to deny that the Rockefeller family and various allied interests have large holdings in the securities of these companies and therefore a large interest in their prosperity. What we showed was that some Rockefellers, like a good many other men of great wealth who live in and about New York City, have obtained a handsome return on the money they invested in Marshall Plan propaganda. Nothing that Mr. Holman has to say in his letter contradicts that conclusion.[13]

Early in 1949, ECA called in a panel of experts to look into the price of Arabian oil. But it was not until late in 1950 that ECA got around to ordering a cut of 50 cents a barrel. Caltex refused to be a party to undermining the "competitive" price and declined to accept more ECA orders.[14]

After the Department of Justice had filed its overcharge suit, in August 1952, MSA asked it to look into similar cases affecting Kuwait oil handled by Gulf, Socony, and Atlantic.[15]

Domestic producers and refiners had their own complaints against the European recovery plan. New refineries in Britain and on the Continent, financed partly by ECA-MSA funds, meant that U. S. refiners independent of the cartel would find no more markets there. Worse yet, there was a threat that the new refineries would soon saturate their markets and send their overflow, estimated by 1954 to be 100,000 barrels a day, to the U. S. Atlantic seaboard. These refineries would, of course, operate on

Middle East and Venezuelan crude. Before World War II, the Americas supplied 44.4 percent of the European demand; by 1954, the percentage would be down to a mere 12.5, with the Middle East supplying the rest. Another potential market for U. S. crude and refined products had been eliminated, and that partly through U. S. government funds put into European refineries.[16]

In France, as well, there was grumbling. Independents had accounted for 20 percent of imports there before the war. Now the seven "as is" companies supplied all French needs at one price and in a single deal. There was no "chiseling" and no opportunity for independents to pick up job lots here and there around the world to ease the pressure on France.[17]

Not only was the international brotherhood of oil merchants subjected to flank attacks from the independent U. S. producers, but the brothers themselves were held together only by the bonds of pelf. When it turned out that this pelf was not common gold but, for the British brothers, a sterling affair, and for the U. S. brothers, a dollar affair, the ties frayed.

The situation becomes vexatious when markets shrink in the face of the overabundance of petroleum. Then it is that the junior partners of the cartel, Royal Dutch/Shell and Anglo-Iranian, become restive and seek to gain advantage from Britain's old supremacy around the globe. Such a situation developed as an aftermath of the world recession of 1947-1948 when the British government closed a sterling deal with Argentina to supply 160,000 barrels a day, mainly from Anglo and Shell sources in the Middle East. This elbowed U. S. dollar oil* from the Plate River. What made U. S. producers even more restive was that the oil destined for the Argentines was being processed in British refineries erected with the help of Marshall Plan funds.[18]

* "Dollar oil" is that produced in countries whose currency is adjusted to the U. S. dollar, as Venezuela; "sterling oil" comes from countries in the sterling bloc, such as Iraq and Iran. Immediately following World War II, when the United States was at times almost the sole supplier of equipment for oil fields, the British companies were obliged to buy much U. S. equipment with dollars. This affected "sterling" oil with a "dollar" interest, i.e. the costs of production had to be valued partly in each currency. Also, in countries such as Kuwait, where a company is jointly owned by U. S. and British interests, the oil produced has a mixed dollar-sterling content.

In Sweden, about the same time, the lack of dollars led to an increase in sterling imports. In this the British firms had the enthusiastic support of their government, so much so that as one oil executive put it, "you cannot determine where the British Foreign Office stopped and the British oil corporations took over."[19] But on this occasion the State Department under Dean Acheson, instead of backing up U. S. companies, actually aided the British by handing over ECA dollars to them.

While some U. S. and Venezuela production was being shut in, the Middle East was booming, and two-thirds of it was sterling oil. Nearly all the Iranian and Iraq production as well as Qatar's was sterling, and three-fourths of Kuwait's, to boot. The only dollar oil was Aramco's, Bahrein's, and the fourth of Kuwait that Gulf merchandised.[20]

The U. S. companies were uneasy. Yet overall U. S. imperial policy called for bucking up the British and their fragile sterling, even if it cost U. S. taxpayers dollars to build British refineries. At this juncture in 1949, Shell got a $250 million loan from U. S. insurance companies to expand its facilities around the world. Charges on the loan were to be met by importing 50,000 to 75,000 barrels a day of Shell Venezuelan oil into the U. S. At about the same time, the British devalued the pound, resulting in a 30 percent cut in the price of British oil. President Walter S. Hallanan of the National Petroleum Council derided the assistance being given the British by various U. S. interests. They were, he said, "out-Britishing the British." The time had come, he added, "to give some consideration to America and Americans."[21]

Late in 1949, the British placed an "embargo" on dollar oil. The Japanese were even informed that they could not use their sterling balance to buy U. S. oil unless that sterling was used later by the U. S. companies to buy Japanese goods for export to sterling areas. Caltex and Standard-Vacuum, hurt in their Oriental markets, protested vigorously.[22]

The British began cutting their imports of Venezuelan dollar oil, even though it came from Shell production. The State Department protested, but the National Petroleum Council claimed the protest was no more than a mere "regret." Senator Connally went so far as to term the embargo "an act of hostility to our economy."[23]

The British proposed that U. S. companies assign their concessions to British corporations and submit to British control and taxes in return for relaxing sterling restrictions and permitting the sale of some dollar oil in Britain itself. While the bargaining proceeded, the United States froze funds assigned for financing the expansion of British refineries. An agreement was reached in 1950 to cut imports of dollar oil in Britain from 13 million tons a year to nine million and to adjust the dollar-sterling content of Iraq oil. The Jersey-Socony interests agreed that their share of Iraq Petroleum's oil sold in sterling areas would be paid for in sterling to be used in the sterling area for durable goods and local necessities. On sales outside the sterling area, they would pay the British 75 percent of the cost price in sterling and 25 percent in dollars.[24]

Early in 1951, a further agreement was reached by Jersey-Socony by which the U. S. companies were to reduce the "dollar content" of their Iraq oil to the British level. Before the embargo, U. S. companies were selling three-fourths of their oil in the sterling area for dollars; by 1951, this had been cut to 40 percent and by 1954 it was to be only 30 percent. By then it was estimated the British would have saved $250 million. This was achieved by bringing sterling oil to Britain in non-dollar tankers, taking sterling for much of the U. S. companies' needs in the Middle East, and buying sterling oil for sale outside the sterling area. Jersey began building tankers in Britain with its sterling funds, expanding its refineries there with sterling, and ordering British equipment. This of course cut out U. S. shipbuilders, oil-field supply, and refinery equipment suppliers—a further blow to U. S. industry.[25]

Socony prepared to build a $30 million refinery at Coryton in England while the great Jersey Fawley refinery on Southampton Water, the largest in Europe, cost £37.5 million ($105 million). This one plant supplies a fourth of Britain's needs. This shining target for atomic war caused property values in the New Forest, a favorite spot for retired people, to tumble an average of a thousand pounds for each holding.[26]

The amazing "dollar content" of British oil confounded British economists. It was estimated that Europe had spent $700 million on dollar oil in 1950—mostly Arabian and Venezuelan, but even Iraq oil had a high dollar content because so much equipment had been purchased in the United States. At the heart of the mystery, reported the *New York Times* from Geneva, "are the internal accounts of the great international oil companies." Even the British government was unable to do more than guess about its own Anglo-Iranian, in which it was a majority stockholder. In Anglo, the dollar and the pound were so interlocked as to baffle outside accountants, who in any event had little more than the barren annual statements of the company to go by.[27]

These statements revealed that in 1953 Royal Dutch/Shell did quite well, with a net income of £130.4 million ($365 million), which gave it second ranking among the world's oil companies next to Standard of Jersey. The gross income was £1701 million ($4763 million).

Shell production for 1953 averaged 1.3 million barrels a day, compared to Jersey's 1.8 million; and Shell's refinery runs were 1.7 million barrels a day compared with Jersey's 1.9 million.[28]

Anglo-Iranian, sheared of its Iranian production, nevertheless did quite well too. Its net income was $68 million in 1953, only a slight drop from 1952.

Not only did these profits inure mainly to the benefit of British stockholders, but the Shell-Anglo imports from the Middle East into Britain were estimated by Standard of New Jersey to have saved that country some $400 million otherwise spent on dollar oil from Venezuela. Jersey estimated that its own Fawley refinery, operating on sterling, would save Britain $100 million a year in dollars. In addition Britain became able to export $150 million a year in oil products, which otherwise might have come from American sources.

Such figures, publicized in Jersey's *Lamp,* expressed the cordial brotherhood of John Bull and Uncle Sam, and of the members of that exclusive club, the world oil cartel. They made sour reading for independent oil producers and refiners in the United States and were scheduled for wider reproduction in Congressional hearings. While the glossy pages of Jersey's *Lamp* probably reached a group much more influential in world affairs than the dull newsprint pages of the *Congressional Record,* it was some comfort for the independent producers and refiners to reflect that at least their protests were printed, even if not widely read or deeply weighed.[29]

THE WESTERN EUROPEAN OIL REPORT

The issue of oil pricing flared into the open again in 1955 when the United Nations' Economic Commission for Europe published a report on the subject.[30] The Commission objected to the inordinate costs for western European consumers resulting from hitching the price of Middle Eastern oil to that of the United States. There was little basically new in the ECE report; the Federal Trade Commission report on The International Petroleum Cartel, in 1952, had explored the situation carefully.

Labor members rose in the House of Commons to denounce the "unlawful racket" and to assail the cartel as chief contender for the title of "Public Enemy No. 1."[31] "There is now no longer any free market price in oil, anywhere in the world," wailed the *New Statesman and Nation.* "Europe is being bled by needlessly high monopolistic oil prices. It is estimated that if countries other than the U. S. were allowed to purchase oil at its real economic price, there would be a saving of $400m. annually in the 'rest of the world's' dollar expenditure."[32]

Nor was there anything new in the circumstances surrounding the publication of the ECE report. In the United States it had taken the persistent demand of Senator Hennings, Democrat of Missouri, and others to persuade President Truman to release an expurgated version of the Federal Trade Commission report on the cartel. The oil companies declaimed that its publication gave aid and comfort to the Kremlin. The *Oil Forum* surmised that "one is justified in wondering if there were any communist-inclined officials in the Federal Trade Commission responsible for the 'Secret' international Oil Industry report. Now, belatedly, that the report is being made public it might be well to play safe, and have the FBI investigate every man who participated in its preparation and writing."[33]

It was obvious, in Geneva, reported the *Wall Street Journal,* that powerful oil industry and State Department officials were equally opposed to the release of the ECE report. The London *New Statesman and Nation* queried whether Secretary-General Hammarskjold of the United Nations had bottled up the report.[34] Exactly as in Washington with the FTC report, copies of the ECE report "leaked" to the press and so, belatedly, it became necessary to release it officially. But the State Department protested, stating that it "appears to suggest the desirability of governmental or intergovernmental controls over oil prices. This would be contrary to U. S. Government policy."[35] According to the *New York Times* Geneva correspondent, the State Department complained to ECE that "there is too much ammunition in it [the report] for people interested in finding new sticks with which to beat the United States for supposedly exerting a baleful influence on the European economy in the interest of 'monopolies.' "[36] Chairman R. G. Follis of Standard of California echoed the comment by saying that "the philosophy of the report is contrary to the policies and interests of the United States."[37] The British government let it be known that it, too, agreed with the position of the State Department and the United States oil companies.[38]

As for the industry, it complained privately that there was "no explicit recognition in the ECE report that the pricing of crude oil in the Middle East is overwhelmingly a political problem, not an economic one. The companies pay what they have to pay to keep the governments of the area contented enough to let the companies continue to take the oil out."[39]

There was something to the industry's complaint. The ECE report said that 70 cents had to be paid the King on every barrel of Arabian oil. Obviously the companies could accept no less as their profit, so that there was a total take of $1.40 on each barrel of oil sold to western Europe. The report put the cost of production at 35 cents a barrel.[40]

The situation called for superlative adjectives, but these did western European consumers little good. They could comfort themselves by reading the ECE report, as some Americans had in reading the FTC report, but neither the British, the Dutch, the French, nor the United States governments was likely to run counter to the imperial interests of the Big Seven who composed the international oil cartel.

Part VII

The Future of Oil

30

Mexico, Beacon of Hope

In THE free world straddled by the international oil cartel, the small but steady light of Petróleos Mexicanos shines as a beacon of hope for the oil-rich but poverty-stricken lands of Latin America and the Middle East.

When Mexico expropriated Standard Oil, Shell, and several smaller foreign companies in 1938, and declared its economic as well as political independence, it was freely predicted that within a year at most the foolhardy nation would come crawling on its knees, imploring the monopoly to return. The "monkeys" in Mexico were said to lack the "know-how" to manage one of the most complex of all industries.

But the story of how Petróleos Mexicanos (Pemex) produced Mexican oil for the Mexican people has turned out to be one of the most dramatic of present-day epics. Because it is not cut to the pattern of *Saturday Evening Post* tales of free enterprise, it is little known in our country. But down in Texas and Oklahoma, oilmen who look in occasionally on the industry across the Rio Grande admit ruefully that Pemex is "doing a job."

In 1938, when President Lázaro Cárdenas cut the Gordian knot that had tangled the nation's politics and economics for a generation, he was denounced by reactionaries on both sides of the border as a "Communist" or at best a foolish visionary who knew little of the hard realities. Fighting a wage award, the oil companies had defied the oil workers' union, a federal arbitration board, and the nation's supreme court; then they insulted Cárdenas to his face, confident that he would give in at the last moment. What alternative had he? The government had not planned nationalization and had no apparatus to take over the industry. Nationalization indeed was the final desperate act of a nation trying to preserve its dignity and independence from the lords of Rockefeller Center.

Behind nationalization in 1938 were twenty years of crude exploitation of the nation's natural resource for the benefit of foreign capitalists, of brazen contempt for the government and people, of studied defiance of Mexico's constitution, laws, and efforts to impose taxation, of continued interference in internal politics, of incessant bribery and subornation of federal and state officials, of subsidies for armed uprisings and maintenance of "white guard" armies in the oil regions.

The match which touched off the explosion was the refusal of the companies to meet a difference of $1.7 million a year between their final offer to the union and the government's award. While the companies said the federal wage award would bankrupt them, it was evident that they really feared something else—the intervention of a Latin American government in the private imperium of petroleum. Shell and Standard had always imposed their own terms and did not propose to allow governmental intervention in their affairs. To do so would be to set a precedent: contemptible little governments might presume to tell the world cartel under what terms it could operate, what wages it must pay, what taxes. Eventually, who knew, New York, London, and Amsterdam might have to deal on terms of equality with Mexico City, Caracas, and Teheran!

Certainly Mexico would not dare to stand up to the final test. Venezuelan production, then growing rapidly, was the club which was to be used to beat down President Cárdenas. The cartel did not need Mexican oil. It could abandon Mexico for a time, seal off the country's exports, condemn it to economic strangulation, and when Cárdenas had fallen by his own folly, the cartel might kindly reconsider and take over again.

Rarely has a government faced a more hopeless dilemma. For years Standard (Huasteca) and Shell (Aguila) had been gutting the Golden Lane, leaving the world's once-premier oil field a premature victim to inrushing salt water. The refineries had degenerated into rust buckets during a prolonged quarrel with the government over taxes. The pipe lines led, naturally enough, to the seaports so that the nation's oil could be sped abroad.

Although Shell's Aguila claimed it was strictly a Mexican corporation with only "technical" ties to the mother company, the Chamberlain government in Britain was quick to denounce expropriation as confiscation. Soft with Hitler and Mussolini, the Tories were tough with little Mexico. The State Department reacted as sharply as the Foreign Office to this challenge to the United States-British-Dutch world cartel.

It was true that Mexico had no corps of oil experts; Standard and Shell had seen to that. The companies' own technicians decamped after expropriation, leaving their houses to caretakers, confident they would be back within a month or two.

The bulk of Mexican production had been exported, but now the world markets were cut off. Shell and Standard informed all and sundry that, as Mexico's oil belonged to them, possible purchasers were buying "stolen" goods. The companies had thoughtfully dispatched nearly all tank cars to the United States and had withdrawn all tankers.

About the only people who knew anything about oil, obviously, were the oil workers. So they took over. Drillers and stillmen became superintendents and moved into front positions in Pemex. From the union's ranks came devoted servants of the people, and that Pemex survived at all in its early years is largely because of their efforts, backed to the hilt by President Cárdenas.

The keys to nationalization of oil thus lay in the hands of President Cárdenas and the organized oil workers. Cárdenas, counterpart of Roosevelt, was the great radical president of 1934-1940. He fostered the growth of the Mexican Federation of Labor (CTM), under the leadership of Vicente Lombardo Toledano, and of the peasants' unions. During the expropriation crisis, most of the bourgeoisie contented itself with sniping at Cárdenas; the Church prayed for his downfall; some generals hoped he would overreach himself, and at least one was ready to take foreign gold to lead a revolt. Behind the unflinching President stood the organized workers and peasants, most of the intelligentsia, and a group of small business men and industrialists who sought the rise of a truly national industry free of foreign control.

Gradually and haltingly Mexican production got under way. But there was the big problem of how to make tetraethyl. Ethyl Corporation, creature of Standard Oil and General Motors, had a 100 percent monopoly and thought it could guarantee the "knock" in Mexican gasoline by refusing to license Pemex. Engineers were sent to the United States to see what they could find out independently. Finally, when a tetraethyl unit was set up in Mexico City, Shell's top man laughed and said he would drink every drop of ethyl the Mexicans could make. Although explosions and poisoning killed several of the experimenters and maimed others for life, within a few years Pemex was producing the fluid— though at a cost twelve times that of Ethyl's. When the corporation realized that the Mexicans were not only producing the liquid but might also be on the way to breaking the world-wide monopoly, a deal was made and Pemex was licensed.

The outbreak of World War II eased the pressure of the boycott. Sinclair, then the maverick of United States oil, opened negotiations. Claims for $32 million were whittled down to $8 million and the price Sinclair was willing to pay for new oil jacked up. Cities Service was next to settle. The deals, in effect, provided that the expropriated properties were to be paid for in a few years through the proceeds from some of the production— a kind of bootstrap operation utterly distasteful to Standard Oil and Shell which wanted immediate payment on the barrelhead. Mexico at all times had disowned the idea of confiscation and had said it was willing to pay a fair sum within a reasonable period.

What with nationalization and President Cárdenas's refusal to knuckle under to the cartel, it became obvious to the Roosevelt regime that the old gringo-greaser relationships had outlived their time. The north wind had been unable to blow down Mexican resistance; perhaps the sun could soften it. The sympathetic Josephus Daniels as United States Ambassador to Mexico managed to wind up Standard Oil negotiations for compensation. Later, Shell came grudgingly to a settlement. Mexico was at last free from outside pressures and mistress in her own house when it came to oil and its development through Pemex.

Despite bungling, sabotage, and the disruption caused by World War II, Pemex survived its early years and then began to burgeon under the direction of Antonio J. Bermudez. This millionaire had made his fortune distilling whiskey in Chihuahua near the United States border; as mayor of Ciudad Juarez, across from El Paso, he had made a national reputation by cleaning up the town; later he was elected a senator. He is that rare bird in Mexican politics, a man who got rich before he became a politician. Miguel Alemán, when he was elected president in 1946, chose Bermudez to head up Pemex.

It was as if the government, conscious of its defects, had erected a fence around Petróleos Mexicanos. Graft, bureaucracy, and inefficiency might flourish elsewhere, but Pemex was so vital to the nation's future that such luxuries could not be tolerated there.

March 18 is celebrated in the oil regions and Mexico City as Expropriation Day. On this anniversary of economic independence, a gala is held at the Palace of Fine Arts attended by the president and his retinue. The dress circle is reserved for the diplomatic corps; United States and British envoys join with those from Venezuela and Iran to hear the director of Pemex give his annual report on the state of the industry. Preceding that, there are two hours of music, singing, dancing, bands, and orchestras.

Over a national radio and TV hookup, Director Bermudez reports to his stockholders—the twenty-five million people of Mexico. In public squares of the cities and in villages in remote mountains where Spanish is still an alien tongue, Bermudez's voice is heard in a businesslike report on progress. Summarized, it is like this:

Year	Production (Barrels)	Reserves (Barrels)	Wells Drilled	Income (Pesos)	Taxes (Pesos)
1939	42,000,000	835,000,000	32	243,600,000	66,402,000
1947	56,000,000	1,058,000,000	64	759,000,000	253,000,000
1951	78,000,000	1,424,000,000	268	1,838,000,000	473,000,000

Year	Workers	Wages and Salaries (Pesos)	Social Benefits (Pesos)	Wages and Benefits (Total, Pesos)
1939	17,600	80,682,000	17,066,000	97,748,000
1947	28,822	206,469,000	43,190,000	249,659,000
1951	31,911	273,660,000	147,811,000	421,471,000

Although production has nearly doubled since 1938, it is still somewhat less than half of the 1921-1922 figure, when the Golden Lane was the world's premier producer outside the United States. The newer Poza Rica field is now the mainstay of Mexican production, and other fields are being brought in constantly to give the lie to Standard Oil's claim in 1942 that only the Americans and British know how to discover oil. Not a single field was discovered in 1932-1936, and only one from 1938 to 1946, but 31 have been brought in since then.

The fruits of nationalization are seen more clearly in the amazing rise in consumption. In the old days, most of the oil flowed out through Tampico and Tuxpan across the seas. Of 193 million barrels produced in 1921, 172 million were exported. In 1954, of 85 million barrels, only 22 million were exported. Much of the export is to pay Shell for its Aguila properties, the rest to finance the importation of costly equipment. Where once Mexico's petroleum served foreign needs and lined foreign pockets, today it powers the land, and its revenues nourish the nation.

In 1956 Pemex plans to drill 750 wells. Compared with 1939, the rise is impressive; contrasted with the United States program for drilling 40,000 wells, it is negligible. This is the sorest point in the Pemex picture. The country lacks both the money and the skilled crews for a bigger program, and has turned to foreign contractors, mostly Americans, to supplement its program. This gives rise to reports that Mexico has "sold out" its dream of nationalization. The contracts call for payment of 15-18 percent of the oil produced to the contractor for 25 years, plus 50 percent of production until his expenses of drilling are compensated. If he drills a dry hole, the expense is all his. Title to all oil rests with Pemex.

The major American companies have contemptuously rejected the terms; only some small firms and adventurers have chosen to take a chance on such a gamble. Whatever may be the prospect of the government's "selling out," the present contracts certainly offer no bargains.

Pemex, which once seemed dismally headed for bankruptcy, now turns nearly 500 million pesos a year into the government's treasury in various taxes. The peso is equal to about eight cents.

The foreign firms in 1936, before expropriation, paid 44 million pesos—and screamed confiscation even then. Today Pemex helps to pay for great dams and irrigation projects and for the industrialization of the country.

"Mexolina," the 70-octane gasoline, at eighteen cents a gallon, and "Super-Mex," the 80-octane at 23 cents, are today the cheapest gasolines sold anywhere in the world except Venezuela. In the old days Mexicans paid more for gasoline produced in their own country than United States consumers paid for the very same product, imported on the Gulf Coast. While it would be tempting to Pemex to improve its financial showing by increasing prices at least to the United States level, it has been guided steadily toward the goal expressed in its slogan, *Al Servicio de la Patria.*

Director Bermudez, in his 1952 report to the nation, told of refineries modernized and new ones built, of pipe lines enlarged and new ones laid, and particularly of the ambitious program of piping natural gas to Mexico City, Monterrey, and other cities. This gas the foreign firms had flared uselessly to the sky—a frightful loss running perhaps into the billions of dollars. But Standard and Shell cared not a fig for the industrialization of Mexico. Today the gas is prolonging the life of the fields through repressurizing wells, and is used increasingly for industrial and domestic purposes.

Distribution is Pemex's weakest link. The railroads don't help much. They were laid out for foreigners to get minerals out of the country, and so there is no truly national network. Even Tampico, the oil center, has no direct rail link with the capital, and the northwestern states are still supplied from California.

While Pemex distributes much of its own production, private enterprise has a big foot in the door, through thousands of service stations, large and small, good and bad. Here political influence works and ugly stories float around.

"Super-Mex," comparable to United States regular, is rarely available except in the metropolis; kerosene, important as illuminant and fuel in the villages, is in chronic short supply. The pressure for export to earn dollars and the enormous growth in domestic demand leave little margin of supply. It was to break out of this strait jacket of inadequate production-consumption that Pemex hoped back in 1949 to raise a big loan north of the border. At the time, a United States House committee, concerned with the problem of increasing available oil supplies for use in cold and hot wars, recommended that Mexican production be tapped. It seemed that two needs were about to meet, and Bermudez submitted plans calling for investment of $200 million in helping Pemex increase production. Nearly everybody in Washington beamed on the handsome Pemex director. But not the State Department; there, in what one Mexican authority on oil has called the "untouchable fortress" of Standard Oil, there was only advice, not sympathy. Mexico must abandon "socialism" in oil; must permit Standard and other United States majors to return; must rejoin the free world to the profit of the international oil cartel. Mexico declined the golden chains.

Referring to this incident in his 1952 report, Bermudez boasted that Pemex by its own efforts had achieved the program submitted to United States politicians and financiers, and was still master in its own house. But the need for greater production still remains, and it is a fact that neither Pemex nor the American contractors are able to meet it; therein lies the danger that some future Mexican government may capitulate if pressure is strong enough and its own course becomes irresolute.

Wages and working conditions are far above the level common to most Mexicans. While their purchasing power is probably no greater now than before expropriation, oil workers enjoy more humane working conditions and their social benefits are superior to those wrung from the foreign companies. The union contract, a 246-page document covering all non-confidential employees, is well enforced and improved from time to time. The latest provision is for double pay for the month-long vacations, to enable workers' families really to enjoy their free time. Pemex deducts 10 percent of wages for a savings fund, to which it adds 20 percent, thereby enabling many to buy homes, radios, refrigerators and, in the higher brackets, even automobiles. So preferred is the status of oil workers that they now constitute a closed corporation within the body social; and new jobs are restricted to the sons of oil workers. The creation of such a labor aristocracy is not without its dangers in alienating this sector from the gnawing problems that affect most of the Mexican people.

The Mexican government claims to be based on a tripartite alliance of workers, peasants, and small business, one of the "revolutionary institutions" to which politicians pay lip service. Behind this façade operate the officials who retire as millionaires with great landed estates and generous slices of stock in the mixed-capital companies fostered by *Nacional Financiera*.

Many a conscientious union man and intellectual supports the Party of Revolutionary Institutions as the lesser of two evils, as their counterparts in this country support Democrats against Republicans. They point to the alternative, always lurking in the political shadows—a militarist, Catholic, reactionary government which would make short shrift of the elaborate social and labor legislation which safeguards many Mexicans.

"Democracy," an industrialist who is also something of an intellectual and writer told me recently,

> is the luxury of rich nations. Poor countries such as Mexico, whose people are still illiterate, disease-ridden and poverty-stricken, must seek other forms of government if they are not to fly to pieces and become the prey for capitalist agglomerations such as Standard Oil and Shell. The government, corrupt as it is, is still strongly nationalist and works in a general way for the welfare of the people. Corruption is the price we pay for independence; a businesslike government would long ago have made Pemex into a "mixed" company with Standard and Shell money and we would be back to the days before 1938, but in the grip of an even more powerful force —our native bourgeoisie firmly locked in embrace with Wall Street. I support the government but work all the time for the extension of the Pemex idea into other industries. Our pride in Mexicanism and our success in Pemex are the guarantees that we may yet evolve into true socialism. We have no other future worthy of the name.

His pride in Pemex is well founded, and generally shared throughout the nation. Even the Pemex superintendents, not at all sunk in bureaucracy, beam with enthusiasm as they describe their plans for expanding their plants. The rust buckets they inherited are being scrapped for new equipment; the modern units shine with loving care. Nor is it all spit and polish. Latin humanism pervades even a refinery; in the Ciudad Madero refinery broad avenues are being laid out, tree-bordered, and adorned with lawns, to moderate somewhat the nauseous atmosphere inescapable in refineries, and to relieve the eye.

The restaurant of the Eighteenth of March refinery in Mexico City, of latest modernist design, is managed by one of the country's ablest restaurateurs. He took the job as a patriotic assignment, for he is already rich from his swanky establishments in the City and Acapulco. The restaurant reflects the social concern of an enterprise "in the service of the nation." The ultramodern architecture, the Monel metal glistening within the kitchen and along the service counters, the pleasant tables, might be considered "waste" in a United States refinery, but in the Eighteenth of March refinery it is all part of a deliberate effort to change the wretched dietary habits of workers, to introduce milk and salads, vitamins and balance, and to open a new vista on an important aspect of life—that of eating, in a nation many of whose inhabitants from centuries of malnutrition have lost even their appetite for food.

In the back is a special room for the technical staff, but it is now used only for visitors. The technical staff said it wasn't democratic to segregate themselves, and anyway they like the main dining room—it's a pleasant place.

In a country strongly animated by nationalism and proud of its achievements under the Revolution, Pemex is not likely to be sold out to the world oil cartel. The success of Pemex has reversed centuries of pessimism and defeatism. The perennial croakers, usually identified with the servitors of foreign capital or worshipers of the dead past, have been refuted by the achievements of the nationalized oil industry.

How long Pemex can persist as a quasi-socialist enterprise in a country that is assiduously building up a grande and petite bourgeoisie and fostering a farming class as well as the landed *hacendados,* is the problem that worries many a Mexican radical. For some, Pemex is the prelude to further nationalization; they would even end the foreign exploitation of lead and silver. But this is not part of the government's program. The concentration of wealth and luxury within Mexico City, where the beggars must step lively to keep from being run down by the Cadillacs, presages an era of Coolidge-Hooverism.

Pemex's own growth points the need for a big expansion in the iron and steel industry to supply oil field and refinery equipment. For the most part, Mexico is dependent on United States firms for the highly elaborate machinery needed in drilling and refining. Until Pemex is able to draw on national resources for most of its equipment, it will continue to be subject to the pressure of United States boycotts and embargoes, a none too subtle warning to the Mexican government that it must tread warily in world affairs if its oil industry is not to be choked.

But among the treacherous crosscurrents in Mexican political life, Pemex shines out as a beacon to the people, proving their capacity and urging them on to greater conquests. To other countries Pemex is proof that there is an alternative to domination by Standard, Shell, and Anglo-Iranian.

31

The Threat from Iran

IRAN long lay outside the orbit of the U. S. companies in the Middle East. Sinclair and Standard had scouted the country after World War I, but British hostility to invasion of their own chosen garden and Iran's fear of offending its northern neighbor by giving concessions along the Caspian stopped U. S. penetration.[1]

The disaster which overtook Anglo-Iranian in March of 1951, when its properties were nationalized, was a bolt from the blue. Prophets had predicted that the Soviets might invade Iran, or the country itself might slip into Communism. But it was not expected that a government run by feudal landlords would chase the British out.

Governor Dewey of New York had looked into a glass darkly but a month before nationalization, and saw this vision: "Will we move into war if the Red Czar invades Iran? If not, will we let him take all of Iran's oil and then take Iraq and Israel and then perhaps march down into Saudi Arabia? Will we allow that crucial oil supply to fall into Russia's hands? Nobody knows. It is a vacuum and dictators move into vacuums."[2]

Into at least a part of this particular vacuum the Iranians moved, under Prime Minister Mossadegh. The British had offered too little too long, and when they finally conceded the 50-50 deal in effect in the rest of the Middle East, the pot had boiled over.

In the meantime the U. S. companies in the Middle East had profited hugely from Anglo's discomfiture. Aramco increased production from 200 to 300 million barrels a year in Arabia, and Kuwait shot up from 128 million to 273 million, to fill the Iranian vacuum. Perhaps Jersey did not grieve too much at the body blow dealt their British colleague; on the other hand, the very real vacuum created within Iran by the shutting down of its production and the closing of the Abadan refinery, biggest in the world, created a constant threat to the cartel. By mid-1953, Iran was beginning to export small lots to the have-not nations, such as Italy and Japan, at cut prices. In May 1953, four shipments of 42,000 tons to customers not impressed by the world oil cartel's boycott on Iran were storm signals.[3] In August, the Iranian army overthrew Mossadegh; the new Prime Minister Zahedi, who had been arrested by the British during the war for his Nazi connections, announced that Iran would "dump" no more oil.[4] The cartel was relieved and proceeded to the reconquest of Anglo's lost domain. Winston Churchill, who in 1913 as First Lord of the Admiralty had caused the British government to buy a majority interest in Anglo, clearly did not choose, as Prime Minister, to preside over the dissolution of his favored firm.

Confident in the confusion, Anglo declined to write off its Iranian assets in its annual reports; stockholders also got comfort from reflecting that while gross profits declined $33 million from 1951 to 1952, the net was off only $3 million.[5]

The British steadfastness in refusing to concede defeat contrasted with the panicky reaction in the U. S. State and Defense Departments to Iran's nationalization law. The Pentagon felt sure that the Soviets would strike with the shutdown of the Abadan refinery, the main source of aviation gasoline in the Eastern Hemisphere. "Avgas" was in short supply even for the Korean war; the outbreak of a world war in 1951, according to U. S. strategists, would have found the Air Force crippled from the start. If the Soviets meant war, Abadan was their signal. But they didn't move.

The State Department offered Mossadegh various compromises whose net result was to increase British suspicions of U. S. intentions and, on the other hand, to inflame Iranian sentiment against the United States as accomplices of the British. While the State Department feared that Iran would slip quickly into Communism, the Foreign Office stood firm that Mossadegh should be taught a lesson. If one were to negotiate with a nationalizer in Iran, what might not happen in Iraq, Kuwait, and Arabia?

Both confidently expected Mossadegh's early fall through internal bankruptcy. In this they echoed similar prophesies of the downfall of President Cárdenas in Mexico after he expropriated the foreign companies in 1938. But the Iranians, who for centuries had lived at or below the subsistence level, noticed hardly any change in their hunger when the oil wells shut down.[6]

Figures supplied by the Iranian government indicate that at no time did royalties exceed 15 percent of its revenues, and in 1950 they were 12 percent. This was but 4 percent of the national income. From 1911 to 1920, Teheran claimed, there had been no royalties at all; from 1921 to 1930, about $60 million; from 1931 to 1941, about $125 million, mostly spent for military equipment later used by the British and the Russians without compensation; and about $250 million from 1941 to 1950.

On the other hand, according to the Iranians, Anglo had recovered its initial investment of $100 million some twenty-five to thirty years ago, and its gross profits since then had been 25 times the original capital. What galled the Iranians most was that Anglo in 1950 paid $142 million in taxes to the British government, and only $45 million in royalties to the Iranian. And, to make matters worse, 56 percent of the dividends also went to the British Exchequer.

Gross operating income since 1914 was estimated by the Iranians at $5 billion, of which the British Admiralty had realized $500 million in cheaper bunker fuel; the Exchequer $1.5 billion in taxes; the shareholders $350 million in dividends; the company $2.7 billion for depreciation and expansion. There was no doubt whatsoever that in 1951 Iran was getting 18 cents a barrel on its oil, while Bahrein got 35 cents, Saudi Arabia 56, and Iraq 60.[7]

The Iranians had other grievances. Nearly all the gas from their wells was flared to the sky, although Teheran and other cities could have used it. Gasoline sold at 40 cents a gallon. Wages were said to be only a quarter those paid to comparable Venezuelan workers. Anglo had been reticent in training Iranians to take over operating posts either at Abadan or in the fields. The housing at Abadan, after forty years, was abominable.

Small wonder that Ayatollah Hashani, religious leader and president of the Majlis, told a delegation of the International Confederation of Free Trade Unions that "Iran can live without oil, and so far as I personally am concerned, I would just as soon destroy the refinery at Abadan and forget that it ever existed."[8]

Such sentiments, considered "mad" by the State Department and the Foreign Office, revealed the depth of the wound to the Iranian spirit after forty years of intimate knowledge of Anglo. Palace revolutions might follow each other in Teheran, but no faction, it seemed, would ever again be able to come to terms with Anglo.

As far back as 1946, Hussein Ala, then Ambassador to Washington and later Prime Minister, regarded as friendly to the Western powers, had warned that a new deal was needed in oil:

> It would seem that the best method of safeguarding the political and economic interests of Iran, and, at the same time, enabling the world to benefit from our rich deposits would be to pool all the oil of Persia, including the area controlled by the Anglo-Iranian Oil Company, and set up an international corporation in which Iranian, American, British, Soviet, French, and Dutch companies could have shares. The management might be entrusted for a term of years to the technical experts of a country not a neighbor of Iran. The whole matter might be referred for study to the Economic and Social Council of the United Nations. A special committee of the United Nations is dealing with the atomic bomb; why should not oil, which is just as explosive, be a matter of concern to our world organization?[9]

The proposal, in modified form, came again in 1951 from the International Cooperative Petroleum Alliance. It told President Truman that Iran's right to nationalize production and refining should be recognized while Anglo could continue to transport and market Iran's oil products. The two parties should join in a long-term contract with an international petroleum cooperative on whose board would sit three Iranians, three Britishers,

and three members from consuming countries. Patronage refunds, on Rochdale principles, would guarantee savings to consumers. Howard Cowden, of Consumers Cooperative Association,
the biggest U. S. oil co-op, as spokesman for the world body,
was referred to George C. McGhee, Assistant Secretary of State
specializing in Middle East affairs. He told McGhee that Mossadegh would accept the plan if the State Department would
approve it.

"That cooperative proposition is completely out of the question," McGhee was quoted as replying. "If Iran wants to settle
this controversy, she will have to deal with Anglo-Iranian or
Royal Dutch/Shell."

"Why, that is exactly what the international oil cartel is demanding," Cowden said. "Mossadegh couldn't agree to anything
like that. Surely you know that. It would be suicide for him to
do so. Anglo-Iranian and Royal Dutch/Shell are the two companies that Iran is fighting and has kicked out of the country."

"Nevertheless," said McGhee, "that is the situation and that is
what we are insisting on."

"Do you mean the State Department is doing that?"

McGhee nodded affirmatively.[10]

Elmer Patman, the Superior Oil Company lobbyist and critic
of the oil cartel, was indignant. During the "panic" caused by
the Iranian shutdown, he said, Texas was implored to raise its
allowable. But as soon as the international supply committees
had been set up by the Big Seven, the crisis as suddenly passed.
This, he said, led to the question whether "we will maintain
any vestige of a competitive free enterprise economy in the
petroleum industry at home or abroad." The "as is" companies,
he surmised, were dictating U. S. foreign policy.

"Does this," he asked, "in effect make the President and the
Senate followers instead of architects of our foreign policy in
the field of international oil? . . . Is it safe for the United States
to permit its Foreign Service to be used as an arm of an international business in an effort to hold down the nationalistic
designs of strategic allies?"[11]

It was ironic, Patman added, that as soon as the antitrust
laws had been abrogated in setting up the international supply

committees with Department of Justice approval, the industry devoted itself to its annual Oil Progress Week to prove that it is competitive, progressive, and operated in the public interest, and that prices are determined by economic laws of supply and demand.

THE IRANIAN CONSORTIUM

The mounting sales of Iranian "stolen oil" to Italy and Japan at bargain prices precipitated Mossadegh's fall in August 1953, and his replacement by Zahedi. By Labor Day, Secretary of State Dulles had assigned Herbert Hoover, Jr., to the task of clearing away the Iranian debris. That it took him more than a year was a tribute to the stubbornness of Anglo-Iranian in holding out for the best terms it could get from the U. S. Big Five and its brother company, Royal Dutch/Shell, and to the potency of the nationalization fervor that persisted in Iran despite Mossadegh's removal.[12]

Hoover marshaled the U. S. Big Five—Standard of New Jersey, Socony, Standard of California, Texaco, and Gulf—into a united front that apparently remained solid throughout the exhausting negotiations. They presented the "consortium" plan to their British confreres: the U. S. companies were to share 50-50 with Anglo in Iran's riches. Distasteful as this division may have been, Anglo was obliged eventually to yield. The U. S. Big Five came out with 40 percent, split into 8 percent segments; Anglo got 40 percent; Shell, 14 percent; and the French wangled 6 percent against an original assignment of 5 percent. The British could console themselves that they still held a majority interest; the U. S. firms probably speculated on the rivalry between Anglo and Shell and the dissatisfaction of the French interest to maintain a dominant position.[13]

The consortium's property was calculated to be worth $1 billion. The other companies, in effect, paid Anglo-Iranian $600 million to share in its claims, of which 15 percent was to be in cash within 18 months, and the balance at 10 cents a barrel. Based on production levels stipulated in the agreement, Anglo's profits in 1957 would be $89.7 million from its Iranian properties;

Shell's $26.6 million; for each of the five U. S. companies, $15.2 million; and for the French, $11.5 million.

Later it was revealed that the U. S. Big Five had each agreed to set aside one-eighth of their interest in a pool for such other U. S. companies as wanted to enter the consortium. The pool's share was 5 percent in the consortium. Nine companies were reported to be interested in taking up shares costing $1 million each and entitling each to 1 million barrels of oil a year when output reached the stipulated 1957 level. With the profit estimated at 85 cents a barrel, the $1 million investment by each of the 12 companies would return an $850,000 profit annually—not a bad bargain in these days.

Among the companies reported to be negotiating for entry into the consortium were Atlantic, Richfield, Standard of Ohio, Tide Water Associated, and the two firms interested in the Kuwait-Arabian neutral zone, American Independent and Pacific Western. It was interesting that other big U. S. firms such as Standard of Indiana, Phillips, Union, Sun, Continental, and Pure —most of which had been wailing about the menace of imported oil—were not reported to be seeking entry.

Sitting in judgment on applications for junior membership in the consortium was Price Waterhouse, accountants for Standard of New Jersey, Standard of California, Gulf, and Shell, all senior members of the consortium. The application of the International Cooperative Petroleum Association for a share was turned down. It did not qualify as a U. S. company, Price Waterhouse decided.[14]

In his negotiations with the Westerners, Premier Zahedi retained as his technical adviser Torkild Rieber, whose too outspoken fondness for Adolf Hitler had led to his retirement as chairman of the Texas Company in 1940. As for his own country, Zahedi decided to bypass his own hand-picked Majlis, even though the Constitution demanded parliamentary approval for any agreement on oil.[15]

At this point, the consortium balked. Zahedi's position was precarious enough; the companies insisted on more than his personal signature to any pact, and reluctantly he agreed to obtain Majlis approval. The Constitution forbade giving over

Iranian oil to outsiders. This was solved by a formula by which the consortium set up two companies to act "on behalf of" the Iranian government in production and refining. Zahedi's original notion that the consortium would confine itself to marketing the oil, and lend the Iranian national oil company "advisers," soon vanished. Then he pleaded that the consortium go through the motions of acting through some such intermediary as the International Bank for Reconstruction and Development, but the British insisted upon direct control of the wells and refinery. Voices in Teheran became bitter. "We are not the Mau Mau or British Guianans to be treated like imperialist slaves," protested a Zahedi newspaper.[16]

The final formula, declared Howard W. Page of Standard of New Jersey, was "just as effective" as ownership. Duly ratified, October 21, 1954, in the Majlis, by 113 to 5, it provided for consortium control for 40 years.[17]

A plaintive note was sounded by the Independent Refiners Association of America. IRAA claimed that the same companies which caused all the import woes in the United States were now banded together, with approval of the State and Justice Departments, in a new cartel that would only perpetuate the independent refiners' problems. The State Department, the refiners said, gave no heed either to the flood of imported oil or to equality of opportunity for independents to get at foreign oil. That was an exaggeration, for Secretary Dulles forwarded their protest to Hoover for appropriate action.[18]

The consortium had more pressing troubles. As they negotiated among themselves and with Zahedi, they were conscious that all the time the rulers of Arabia, Iraq, Venezuela, and other petroleum territories were peering over their shoulders, scrutinizing each clause. There must be no intimation that Iran, having nationalized oil, was getting a better deal in any regard. Iran got the 50-50 division on profits common to the other countries; its production was to rise gradually over a three-year period; and there was no loophole through which an Onassis could make a tanker deal. The consortium hoped that it had proved that no country had anything to gain through nationalization, that none could hope to market oil except through the facilities of the cartel.[19]

In recognition of his services, Hoover was made Under-Secretary of State, without ever having announced publicly his views on foreign issues, either to the Senate Foreign Relations Committee or to the press. But then, "open diplomacy" had never been a watchword for the oil companies.[20]

32

The Need for International Control

"TELL me," said Secretary Harold L. Ickes, the Petroleum Administrator for War, early in 1944, "the sort of agreement that the United Nations will reach with respect to the world's petroleum resources when the war is over, and I will undertake to analyze the durability of the peace that is to come."[1]

After the war Benjamin C. Marsh, the last of the Populists in Washington, was talking to Bernard Baruch, who had been explaining that allocation of raw materials among the Allies had been essential for winning the war. "Then," asked Marsh, "why don't we continue such controls to facilitate reconstruction?" "Because private owners won't permit it," the elder statesman replied. Would war follow the failure to allocate the world's raw materials equitably, Baruch was asked. "Probably," was his answer.[2]

Who was to inherit the free world was never in question, really. Some experts of the War Production Board had asked that the new international organization arising from the ashes of war be empowered to administer the world's stock of raw materials. The British Labor Party had sponsored a similar plan. But both the Foreign Operations Committee of Ickes' own PAW, staffed by the major companies, and the Petroleum Industry War Council, the industry's direct agent, entered a firm veto. They formulated a document, *A Foreign Oil Policy for the United States,* based on the thesis that "oil development can best be handled by private enterprise." That guided Washington.

To end, once and for all, the fearful triangular struggle over the world's premier oil resources in the Middle East, the Inter-

national Cooperative Alliance in 1947 proposed to international-
ize the industry there. The plan was designed to assuage the
conflict between the Soviet and non-Soviet nations over these
treasures, to assure the peoples of the Middle East a lasting
benefit from their riches, rather than a guarantee of annihilation
through war, and to afford lower prices to consumers everywhere.

The cooperators, who said they spoke for 85 million member-
families in 39 countries, presented their plan on July 19, 1947,
to the Economic and Social Council of the United Nations. They
proposed, in brief, a UN Oil Authority to take over the administration of the Middle East deposits to provide equal access to
all nations and buyers, in accordance with the terms of the
Atlantic Charter. "The plan," reported the *New York Times*, "is
expected to meet stiff opposition from American and British
petroleum interests that now control most of the oil extracted
from the Middle East."[3]

The Middle East, the Cooperative Alliance said, is a relatively
compact area well suited to become a laboratory for the management of an irreplaceable natural resource. The monopoliza-
tion of these resources in large part by the nationals of only
two countries made it imperative that the UN Economic and
Social Council center its efforts first and exclusively on this area.
"The future of the United Nations itself may well hinge on how
Middle East oil problems are approached and handled."

The cooperators laid down what they considered the basic
principles to be applied.

> Equal access to natural resources, as set out in the Atlantic
> Declaration, must be considered an irrevocable condition of
> economic construction, of rebuilding free interchange of
> goods among nations, and of the maintenance of peace. . . .
> International rivalry over raw material resources, either on
> the part of predatory private monopolists or on the part of
> imperialistic governments, or both, lead to an unbalance in
> economic affairs, inevitable conflicts and the jeopardizing of
> peace, such as we have witnessed recently, for example, in
> the struggle for control of oil resources in the Middle
> East. . . .

The center of gravity of the petroleum industry is shifting already to the Middle East, and oil deposits in that
strategic area are now a bone of contention among the
nations, great and small, and are, therefore, one of the greatest potential threats to world peace. . . .

From the consumers' viewpoint it is absolutely necessary
that raw materials should be made available to humanity
on equal terms. No valid reason can be constructed for regarding every raw material as the monopoly of the state
within whose boundaries it happens to exist, or can be produced. On the contrary, raw materials should be the first
thing after armaments to be placed under the control of the
United Nations; and the model for their exploitation should
be the principles applied within the Cooperative Movement,
viz: equal conditions for all, and the right of every enterprise using raw materials to buy as much as it considers it
can utilize.

The cooperators minced no words in describing existing
controls:

[The five big U. S. oil companies] tend to take on the status
of industrial super-governments when dealing with the small
states of the Middle East. They guide, if not formulate, foreign policy on oil, and, as matters now stand, tend to by-pass
the United Nations. And yet, because national security is tied
in with adequate oil resources, these nationals, for all practical purposes, have back of them the United States government itself. They are inextricably bound up together, and
nothing would demonstrate that fact better than for some
third power to threaten to interfere with the Saudi Arabia
oil concession.

These marriages between oil nationals, on the one hand,
and small sovereign states of the Middle East, on the other,
are uneasy, unnatural alliances. There usually is suspicion
and distrust on the part of the grantor of such concessions,
and usually a fear of impending doom on the part of nationals with huge sums invested.

The Cooperative Alliance directed attention to the revised
draft of the U. S.-British oil treaty, then pending, which stipulated at great length that neither the U. S. government nor the
United Nations would have power to interfere with Middle

East concessions or in relations between the corporations and the governments there (an amazing surrender of sovereign rights):

These reservations argue more eloquently than anything that can be written on the subject that the nationals of these two countries, having acquired these vast land areas, underlying which are the bulk of the earth's petroleum resources, are determined to keep their hold upon it, come what may. This attitude not only violates the spirit of the Atlantic Declaration but is, at the same time, a devitalizing force which may, in time, render the United Nations organization as impotent as the League of Nations proved to be. The salvation of the United Nations and the peace of the world can come only if the organization is able to face and handle the great economic empires, the real super-states of the modern world. No government has ever been able to control the oil combine in the general interest. We fervently hope the United Nations can do so. That is the supreme test it is facing at the moment.

"The point is," the cooperators emphasized, "that the great oil companies, sitting astride the principal oil reservoirs of the world, are something like public utilities—they're vested with a public interest." The companies' reservoirs grow more valuable "as more and more nations tend toward the 'have not' status, and that includes the United States, among others."

The cooperative plan for international control sought a conference of the Middle Eastern nations to vest the United Nations Petroleum Commission with these powers:

1. To see that oil concessionaires there operate in the public interest.

2. To plan and enforce oil conservation measures.

3. To provide equal access to oil supplies, assuring all nations, large or small, the right to buy oil on an equal footing.

4. To assure all types of purchasers—governments, co-ops, or private corporations—access to oil on a basis of equality.

5. To prohibit price discriminations in favor of particular governments or purchasers and to assure that all can buy in adequate quantities.

6. To serve as a tribunal to adjudicate any oil disputes that may arise. Complaints could be brought by member governments, oil field franchise or leaseholders, or purchasers.

The cooperators had a most self-interested stake in their proposal for a UN Oil Authority. The International Cooperative Petroleum Association, they said,

[is] the only commercial organization in the field working for lower prices to consumers in every country. Because of that fact, every effort will be made to stop it. And with 90 percent of the world's oil resources now lodged in a handful of British and American nationals, and with no international policeman on the beat, ICPA can look forward to living dangerously, even though it may be backed by the resources of many powerful cooperative wholesales.

Something more than moral suasion will be required before Middle East oil companies will supply a cooperative competitor out of the great oil reserves there. If the Swedish cooperative oil wholesales, for example, are to build a refinery in Sweden and import the crude oil on which to operate it, can they depend on getting crude oil at the market from a producer in the Middle East who is a distributor of refined products as well in Sweden? If not, in spite of the fact that an ample supply of crude oil is available, to what agency with authority can the cooperative turn for a review of the circumstances and for possible action?

For instance, the Consumers Cooperative Association, largest of the U. S. co-ops, had asked four refiners to quote prices on tanker loads of gasoline from the Middle East. Three of the four expressed "regret" and the fourth said it did no marketing in the Middle East.

The cooperative proposal won the endorsement of the World Federation of Trade Unions, at that time the single world-wide labor federation. "There is a risk," said the WFTU, "of the struggle for oil disturbing world peace, the more so as the possession and processing of this basic raw material is increasingly becoming the prerogative of a few nations and of a few private monopolist companies."[4]

But when the proposal came to a vote in the Economic and

Social Council on August 12, 1947, it was befriended only by Norway and Colombia. Eight members, including the Soviet states, abstained; eight, including the United States, Britain, and the Netherlands, voted against. At the Santiago, Chile, meeting of 1951, the proposal, too hot to handle, was dropped for good and all.

Far more threatening to the cartel powers was the omen in the UN's economic and financial committee on December 11, 1952. This committee approved a proposal by Iran and Bolivia in favor of the right of nationalization, and only the United States voted opposition. It was a stiff shock to investment capital. A U. S. amendment asserting the rights of foreign nationals in their investments was voted down 27 to 15. Among the countries voting against the U. S. amendment were Argentina, Brazil, Colombia, Egypt, Ethiopia, Indonesia, Iran, Iraq, Mexico, and Saudi Arabia—all countries with more or less substantial oil resources. Burma, Peru, and Venezuela abstained.[5]

The vote seemed to answer the decision of U. S. diplomats in Latin America, convened in Rio de Janeiro in November 1948. Then it had been agreed that no U. S. governmental loans would be made to any Latin American country for national oil development. If any oil were to be developed, Standard and its confreres were to do the developing.

Back in 1923 Nicholas Davenport in his book *The Oil Trusts and Anglo-American Relations* had asked: "When will the oil wealth of the world be regarded as a trust for humanity to be exploited for the benefit of the human race—with a first charge on local field revenues for the benefit of the backward peoples living over the oil? To ask such simple questions today will no doubt bring a laugh to sophisticated politicians."

The laugh, in 1953, was by no means so hearty, but the grasp upon the oil wealth was tighter than ever, and the determination to keep it at any cost more rigid. If a few prophets within the industry warned of doom to come, they were not heeded by the powers of Achnacarry. In a Christmas editorial in 1951, Keith Fanshier, editor of the *Oil Daily*, had tried to introduce a Christian idea into the business. He wrote:

For petroleum, let's consider the implications of a durable, honest and universal peace just as practically as you wish. If you wish to consider solely the materialistic question, the issue is: Would real peace reduce the world's petroleum consuming potential, compared with something like a condition of unending semi-war?

If your answer is yes, you are saying that a program of virtually planned waste through permitting nations to war upon each other, to keep the world in slavery to the idea of war preparation, would outconsume petroleum in contrast with a program of genuine prosperity based on productive utilization of the world's forces to create better, richer lives for its people.

Personally, we believe that if the people of the world were freed of the fearsome burden of recurrent wars and the need to prepare against them, there would be—after some early moderate adjustment period—such a surge of productive activity let loose in the world devoted to giving effect to the ways of peaceful life as to dwarf needs of any war or war-preparation economy. . . .

Whether it is possible to expect a test or demonstration of this conviction soon—is something else. Of this we may be excused if we remain somewhat dubious, under present world conditions. Yet it will have to come.

But meanwhile it is unfair and inaccurate to label petroleum as a war industry. It is in effect a slander upon the good name of a great and increasingly important element of the nation's and the world's life. Petroleum has no stake in war's preservation as an institution of man's so-called civilization. True, petroleum has enabled this nation and its allies to overturn their enemies in recent time, only through its use.

We believe petroleum more truly can be termed a peace industry. . . .

The world's statesmen have not yet begun to utilize the power in a drop of oil to force evil out of men's plans and devisings, and to force good to take its place. It can extinguish, rather than fan, the flames of ambitious designings against the good of peoples.[6]

These pious observations could be echoed by the peoples of the world. The International Cooperative Alliance, representing organized masses of consumers gouged by the unnatural level of "as is" petroleum prices, would have applauded the *Oil Daily*. So would the members of the world labor movement, divided and irresolute though they stood in the miasmas of the cold war. Most of the delegates to the United Nations would have eagerly voted into being a World Oil Authority, were it not for the certain veto of the two powers which owned most of the world's oil resources.

Stronger for the time than people or ideas, the Achnacarry corporations ruled. But for them, also, was appropriate the saying: "After us, the deluge."

Acknowledgments

The editors of *Monthly Review* expressed an early interest in The Empire of Oil. When it became obvious that commercial publishers were not interested in the manuscript, the editors generously renewed their offer to undertake publication. I am especially indebted to Paul M. Sweezy for general revision of the manuscript, and to many, in the industry and out, who have contributed valuable suggestions and criticisms.

References

SHORTENED REFERENCES

Denny: *We Fight for Oil,* by Ludwell Denny (Knopf, 1928).

Fanning: *American Oil Operations Abroad,* by Leonard M. Fanning (McGraw-Hill, 1947).

Fischer: *Oil Imperialism,* by Louis Fischer (International Publishers, 1926).

IPC: *International Petroleum Cartel,* Staff Report to the Federal Trade Commission submitted to the Subcommittee on Monopoly of the Select Committee on Small Business, United States Senate, 82nd Congress, 2nd Session, 1952.

Kemnitzer: *Rebirth of Monopoly,* by William J. Kemnitzer (Harper, 1938).

The Lamp, quarterly publication of Standard Oil of New Jersey.

Leeston: *Magic Oil,* by Alfred M. Leeston (Juan Pablos Books, 1951).

Lenczowski: *The Middle East in World Affairs,* by George Lenczowski (Cornell University Press, 1952).

Mikesell and Chenery: *Arabian Oil,* by Raymond F. Mikesell and Hollis B. Chenery (University of North Carolina Press, 1949).

NPN: *National Petroleum News,* weekly until November 1954, monthly thereafter.

New Sources of Petroleum: Investigation of Petroleum Resources (New Sources of Petroleum in the United States), Hearings Before a Special Committee Investigating Petroleum Resources, United States Senate, 79th Congress, 1st Session (O'Mahoney Hearings), 1946.

Petroleum Facts and Figures: (American Petroleum Institute: Ninth Edition, 1950; Tenth Edition, 1952; Eleventh Edition, 1954.)

Platt: *40 Great Years—The Story of Oil's Competition,* by Warren C. Platt (National Petroleum News, 1949).

Ross: *The Evolution of the Oil Industry,* by Victor Ross (Doubleday Page, 1920).

Rostow: *A National Policy for the Oil Industry,* by Eugene V. Rostow (Yale University Press, 1948).

Spingarn: Press Release, Office of Commissioner Stephen J. Spingarn, Federal Trade Commission, September 10, 1953.

Stocking: *The Oil Industry and the Competitive System,* by George Ward Stocking (Houghton Mifflin, 1925).

Stocking and Watkins: *Monopoly and Free Enterprise,* by George Ward Stocking and Myron W. Watkins (The Twentieth Century Fund, 1951).

TNEC *Hearings:* Investigation of Concentration of Economic Power: Hearings Before the Temporary National Economic Committee, 76th Congress, 2nd Session, 1940. Various parts.

Thompson: *Since Spindletop: A Human Story of Gulf's First Half-Century,* by Craig Thompson (Gulf Oil, 1951).

Watkins: *Oil: Stabilization or Conservation?* by Myron W. Watkins (Harper, 1937).
World Geography of Petroleum: edited by Wallace E. Pratt and Dorothy Good, for the American Geographical Society (Princeton University Press, 1950).

CHAPTER 1

1. *U. S. News & World Report,* April 1, 1955, based on U. S. Department of Commerce figures.

CHAPTER 2

Scholars have yet to write a general history of the oil industry. The beginnings of the industry in western Pennsylvania are described in *The Evolution of the Oil Industry,* by Victor Ross (Doubleday Page, 1920). *Wealth Against Commonwealth,* by Henry Demarest Lloyd (Harper, 1894) is the classic description of the rise of Standard Oil. Rockefeller's role is stated, pro and con, in *John D. Rockefeller: Robber Baron or Industrial Statesman?* edited by Earl Latham (D. C. Heath, 1949). *The Oil Industry and the Competitive System,* by George Ward Stocking (Houghton Mifflin, 1925), gives an overall picture of the industry until after World War I. The rise of the non-Standard majors after the Spindletop discovery in 1901 is told in *Mellon's Millions,* by Harvey O'Connor (John Day, 1933) and in *Since Spindletop: A Human Story of Gulf's First Half-Century,* by Craig Thompson (Gulf Oil, 1951). The period since 1910 is discussed in *40 Great Years —The Story of Oil's Competition,* by Warren C. Platt, a reprint from *National Petroleum News,* 1949. The period of the 1930s is reflected in the extensive *Hearings of the Temporary National Economic Committee,* 76th Congress, 2nd Session, 1940. *TNEC Monograph 39, Control of the Petroleum Industry by Major Oil Companies,* by Roy C. Cook, is a summary of the hearings.

1. *Petroleum Facts and Figures,* Ninth Edition, 1950, pp. 145-149.
2. Same, p. 82.
3. *TNEC Hearings,* Part 14, p. 7595.

CHAPTER 3

Statistical information is drawn largely from the annual reports of the companies. The internal structure of Standard of New Jersey has been described at length in *Fortune* magazine, October and November 1951. The extent of Rockefeller control in the various Standard companies is indicated in lists of the 100 largest stockholders of various oil companies, *TNEC Hearings,* Part 14-A, pp. 8003-8042, and p. 7713.

Platt, already cited, Thompson, already cited, *The Texaco Story: The First Fifty Years, 1902-1952,* by Marquis James (Texaco, 1953), and various company publications describe the development of individual companies. Standard of New Jersey publishes *The Lamp* four times a year; *The Humble Way* is published every other month by Humble Oil & Refining; most of the majors have similar house organs for employees and stockholders.

The *International Oil Worker,* Oil Workers International Union, CIO,

Denver, published bi-weekly, frequently carried articles on the various companies. Since the merger with another union, the paper is now *Union News of the Oil, Chemical and Atomic Workers International Union.*

Financial Analysis of 30 Oil Companies for 1950, by Frederick G. Coqueron and Joseph E. Pogue (Chase National Bank, Petroleum Department, 1951). Also succeeding annual editions for 1951, 1952, 1953, 1954.

Financial Analysis of 38 Oil Companies, 1939-1951, by E. E. Phelps (Oil Workers International Union, Denver, Research and Education Department, 1952).

Financial Facts About 24 Oil Companies, 1951 (Oil Workers International Union, Research and Education Department, Denver, 1952).

Capital Formation in the Petroleum Industry, by Frederick G. Coqueron and Joseph E. Pogue (Chase National Bank, Petroleum Department, 1952).

The Case for Wage Increases in Oil and Allied Industries, to be presented before the Wage Stabilization Board, Oil Workers International Union (1952).

1. Federal Trade Commission report, *New York Times,* September 13, 1951.

2. *Fortune,* October 1951.

3. *Life,* January 23, 1950, from *TNEC Hearings.*

4. *Forbes,* June 1, 1951.

5. *13th Annual Report of Stockholder Activities at Corporation Meetings, 1952* (published by Lewis D. Gilbert and John J. Gilbert, 1165 Park Avenue, New York City).

6. *New York Times,* May 29, 1952.

7. *Investigation of the National Defense Program by a Special Committee,* U. S. Senate, 77th Congress, 1st Session, 1942 (The Truman Committee), pp. 4561-4584; *Patents for Hitler,* by Guenther Reimann (Victor Gollancz, 1945), pp. 55 ff.

8. *America's 60 Families,* by Ferdinand Lundberg (Vanguard Press, 1937), p. 208.

9. *Oil Forum,* June 1952.

10. See Thompson and O'Connor, already cited.

11. Fanning, pp. 58-59.

12. *Oil Daily,* December 22, 1952.

13. *Petroleum Outlook,* July 1953, p. 75.

14. *International Oil Worker,* December 24, 1951; May 19, 1952.

15. NPN, April 11, 1951.

16. NPN, October 7, 1953.

17. *World Government News,* January 1949.

CHAPTER 4

Occurrence of petroleum underground is discussed in *World Geography of Petroleum,* edited by Wallace E. Pratt and Dorothy Good, published for the American Geographical Society (Princeton University Press, 1950), and in *Petroleum* (American Petroleum Institute, 1949).

The legal problem of ownership is treated in *Legal History of Conservation of Oil and Gas* (American Bar Association, Mineral Law Section, 1939), and in *Oil for Today . . . and for Tomorrow* (Interstate Oil Compact Commission, Oklahoma City, 1953).

Early drilling is reviewed in Ross, already cited. *The Oil Industry and the Competitive System*, by George Ward Stocking (Houghton Mifflin, 1925), discusses drilling problems of the 1920s, and, at pp. 140-210, production methods in vogue then. *National Petroleum Convention* (Venezuelan Ministry of Mines and Hydrocarbons, 1951) details current production techniques.

1. *TNEC Hearings*, Part 17, p. 9581.
2. Rostow, pp. 16-18, 45; Watkins, pp. 38-39.
3. Fanning, pp. 17-18.
4. *Petroleum in the United States and Possessions*, by R. Arnold and W. J. Kemnitzer (Harper, 1931).
5. *The Lamp*, June 1951.
6. Stocking, p. 171.
7. Rostow, p. 41.
8. *TNEC Hearings*, Part 17, p. 9529.
9. *TNEC Hearings*, Part 17, pp. 9512-9556.
10. *The Independent Petroleum Company*, Hearings Before a Special Committee Investigating Petroleum Resources, U. S. Senate, 79th Congress, 2nd Session, 1946 (O'Mahoney Hearings), p. 93.
11. *Hot Oil*, by Samuel N. Pettengill (Economic Forum, 1936), p. 232.
12. Pettengill, p. 73.
13. Stocking, pp. 174 ff.
14. Stocking, pp. 177-179.
15. *TNEC Hearings*, Part 17, p. 9513.
16. *TNEC Hearings*, Part 14, p. 7597.
17. *TNEC Hearings*, Part 17, p. 9603.
18. *Annals*, American Academy of Political and Social Science, May 1920, p. 132.

CHAPTER 5

Lease and royalty procedures are examined in *New Sources of Petroleum in the United States*, Hearings Before a Special Committee Investigating Petroleum Resources, U. S. Senate, 79th Congress, 1st Session, 1946 (O'Mahoney Hearings).

1. *New York Times*, January 22, 1950.
2. *Texas Oil and Gas* (Texas Mid-Continent Oil & Gas Association, 1951).
3. *New York Times*, January 22, 1950.
4. *TNEC Monograph 39*, pp. 11-13.
5. *TNEC Hearings*, Part 15, pp. 8568-8583.
6. *Barron's*, November 12, 1951; *New York Times*, October 14, 1952.
7. *U. S. News & World Report*, July 20, 1951.
8. *New York Times*, September 21, 1952.
9. Stocking, pp. 276-302.
10. *New York Times*, November 18, 1951.
11. *New Sources of Petroleum*, pp. 411-440.
12. Same, pp. 441-445.
13. Same, p. 429.

CHAPTER 6

The problems of "conservation" were the main concern of the TNEC Hearings. Below are listed the testimony and statements of many of the leading witnesses covering not only production, but refining, transportation, and marketing.

TNEC Hearings, Part 14:

Testimony of Dr. Joseph E. Pogue, vice-president of the Chase National Bank, pp. 7112-7143; The Economics of Conservation and Proration in the Petroleum Industry, pp. 7435-7457, and Economics of the Petroleum Industry, pp. 7457-7491, both by Dr. Pogue.

Testimony of President J. Howard Pew of Sun Oil, pp. 7163-7265.

Testimony of Marion M. Travis, of Southport Petroleum, pp. 7265-7291.

Testimony of John B. Dailey, owner of oil lands in the Old Ocean field, Texas, pp. 7291-7305; his statement, pp. 7520-7551.

Testimony of Louis J. Walsh, vice-president of the Eastern States Petroleum Company, an independent refiner, pp. 7333-7461; his statement, pp. 7573-7591.

Testimony of Karl A. Crowley, independent oil attorney of Fort Worth, Texas, pp. 7361-7387; his statement, pp. 7591-7661.

Testimony of E. DeGolyer, petroleum geologist, pp. 7389-7423; his statement, pp. 7662-7675.

Testimony of John E. Shatford, independent producer and refiner, pp. 8147-8205; his statement, pp. 8517-8568.

Testimony of Ernest O. Thompson of the Texas Railroad Commission, pp. 8206-8249.

TNEC Hearings, Part 15:

Testimony of Eugene L. Orvis, attorney and traffic manager, pp. 8309-8323.

Testimony of Dr. Robert E. Wilson, president of Pan American Petroleum & Transport Company, pp. 8323-8390; his statement, pp. 8619-8670.

TNEC Hearings, Part 16:

Testimony of Paul E. Hadlick, secretary, National Oil Marketers Association, pp. 8837-8891; his statement, pp. 9151-9170.

Oil for Today . . . and for Tomorrow, Interstate Oil Compact Commission (Oklahoma City, 1953), deals generally with the subject of conservation.

1. The majors' argument for conservation is given in *Petroleum* (American Petroleum Institute, 1949), pp. 97-112.

2. Watkins, pp. 30-39.

3. Same, pp. 40-52.

4. Kemnitzer, pp. 122-151; Rostow, pp. 19-22.

5. *TNEC Hearings,* Part 14, p. 7292.

6. Kemnitzer, pp. 96-121; Watkins, pp. 53-55; Rostow, pp. 27-30.

7. Watkins, pp. 56-119.

8. Rostow, pp. 40-41.

9. *Oil Daily,* March 11, 1953; *New York Times,* March 26, 1952.

10. *The Interstate Oil Compact: Its Background and Development,* by Wilfred Dunbar Webb, Ph.D. thesis (University of Texas, 1940).

11. *Oil Daily,* February 2, July 24, 1953.

12. *Interstate Oil and Gas Compact:* Hearings Before the Committee on

Interstate and Foreign Commerce, 82nd Congress, 1st Session, 1951; also, *New York Times,* June 12, August 22, 1951.
13. Rostow, pp. 29-33; Kemnitzer, pp. 60-77.
14. Rostow, pp. 34-36.
15. Watkins, pp. 247-256; Rostow, pp. 35-38.
16. Stocking and Watkins, pp. 389-392.
17. *Oil Daily,* April 27, October 23, 1952.
18. *Oil Forum,* November 1953.
19. *Oil Daily,* December 16, 1951.
20. *State Regulation of Oil and Gas Industry in Texas,* by Robert Lucas Conrod, thesis (University of Texas, 1931).
21. *Administrative Control of Petroleum Production in Texas,* by York Young Willborn, Ph.D. thesis (University of Texas, 1943).
22. NPN, May 11, 1949.

CHAPTER 7

Petroleum Productive Capacity: A Report on Present and Future Supplies of Oil and Gas (National Petroleum Council, 1952).

New Sources of Petroleum in the United States, Hearings Before a Special Committee Investigating Petroleum Resources, U. S. Senate, 79th Congress, 1st Session (O'Mahoney Hearings), 1945: particularly, testimony of J. Edgar Pew, vice-president of Sun Oil, pp. 4-47; of E. L. DeGolyer, petroleum geologist, pp. 54-58, 275-281; the statement of Michael W. Straus, Assistant Secretary of the Interior, pp. 317-324.

Annals, American Academy of Political and Social Science, May 1952, devoted to conservation: particularly, "The Fuel Complex: A Projection," by George A. Lamb, pp. 42-54; "Adequacy of Our Mineral Fuels," by Robert E. Hardwicke, oil attorney, pp. 55-72; "International Fuel Economy," by Eugene Ayres, of Gulf Research and Development Company, pp. 73-78.

World Geography of Petroleum, edited by Wallace E. Pratt and Dorothy Good, published for the American Geographical Society (Princeton University Press, 1950); particularly, the section on resources and reserves, pp. 152-158, "The Major Areas of Discovered and Prospective Oil," by Eugene Stebinger, pp. 325-329, "The Availability of Petroleum—Today and Tomorrow," by Kirtley F. Mather, pp. 333-343.
1. *New Sources of Petroleum,* pp. 7-8, quoting both Requa and Pogue.
2. *Oil Daily,* March 16, 1955.
3. *Petroleum Outlook,* April 1955.
4. *New York Times,* August 23, 1949.
5. *New Sources of Petroleum,* p. 50.
6. NPN, November 12, 1952.
7. *Oil Daily,* April 15, 1953.
8. *Energy Resources—The Wealth of the World,* by Eugene Ayres and Charles A. Scarlott (McGraw-Hill, 1952).
9. *Annals,* American Academy of Political and Social Science, May 1952, pp. 42-54.
10. NPN, November 15, 1950.
11. *New York Times,* November 11, 1951.
12. *New York Times,* September 18, 1949, November 19, 1950; *New York*

Herald Tribune, February 1, 1949; *U. S. News & World Report*, February 11, 1955.

13. *U. S. News & World Report*, February 25, 1949.

14. NPN, October 28, 1953; *New York Times*, June 16, 1952; *Petroleum Productive Capacity*, cited above; A. C. Rubel, vice president of Union Oil, in *Journal of Petroleum Technology*, February 1954, pp. 9-19.

15. *Fortune*, November 1951.

16. NPN, October 3, 1951.

17. *Oil Daily*, January 21, 1953.

18. NPN, November 14, 1951.

CHAPTER 8

Rostow's *A National Policy for the Oil Industry*, pp. 57-66, reviews efforts at federal control and regulation of the pipe lines. *Petroleum* (American Petroleum Institute, 1949), pp. 59-68, discusses transportation. *Petroleum Facts and Figures* (American Petroleum Institute, 1954 edition), pp. 181-226, gives a statistical outline of transportation. The Interstate Commerce Commission, Bureau of Transport Economics and Statistics, publishes annually *Statistics of Oil Pipe Line Companies*. Kemnitzer's *Rebirth of Monopoly*, pp. 78-95, and Stocking, *The Oil Industry and the Competitive System*, pp. 211-237, discuss pipe line control by the majors.

TNEC Hearings, Part 14:
Testimony of Dr. John Ise, University of Kansas, pp. 7105-7107; testimony and statement of J. Howard Pew of Sun Oil, pp. 7178-7180, 7199-7204, 7249-7257, 7261-7265; testimony of Louis J. Walsh, vice-president of Eastern States Petroleum Company, pp. 7338-7343; testimony of Karl A. Crowley, pp. 7376-7378, 7385-7387.

TNEC Hearings, Part 14A:
Economic data on transportation, pp. 7719-7731.

TNEC Hearings, Part 15:
Testimony of Fayette B. Dow, American Petroleum Institute, pp. 8262-8308.

TNEC Hearings, Part 17:
Testimony of William S. Farish, president of Standard of New Jersey, pp. 9715-9717, 9730-9736, 9753-9762.

TNEC Monograph 39, Control of the Petroleum Industry by Major Oil Companies, pp. 19-28, 37-39.

1. Oil field lingo is recorded in *The Petroleum Dictionary*, by Lalia Phipps Boone (University of Oklahoma Press, 1952). A roughneck is a member of the drilling crew; a gear jammer, a truck driver; a boll weevil, a green hand; a tool pusher, the boss in charge of rig builders and drillers.

2. *TNEC Monograph 39*, p. 25.

3. *TNEC Monograph 39*, p. 22.

CHAPTER 9

TNEC Hearings, Part 15: statement of Dr. Robert E. Wilson, president of Pan American Refining & Transport Company, pp. 8619-8670.

The Independent Petroleum Company: Hearings Before a Special Committee Investigating Petroleum Resources, U. S. Senate, 79th Congress, 2nd Session, 1946: testimony of Fayette B. Dow, representing the National Petroleum Association and Western Refiners Association, pp. 176-178, 187-208.

Watkins, pp. 152-168, deals with the NRA period; *Petroleum* (American Petroleum Institute, 1949), pp. 69-82, discusses refinery processes; *Petroleum Facts and Figures* (American Petroleum Institute, 1954 edition), pp. 155-180, gives a statistical review.

Rostow, pp. 67-69; "Vertical Integration Re-examined," by Eugene V. Rostow and Arthur S. Sachs (*Yale Law Journal*, 1952), pp. 856-914.

Kemnitzer, pp. 152-164, reviews the plight of east Texas refiners under proration.

1. *New York Times,* February 2, November 23, 1952; *New York Herald Tribune,* October 21, 1951.
2. *Oil Daily,* March 6, 1953.
3. *New York Times,* November 6, 1949.
4. *Cooperative Consumer,* September 30, 1953.

CHAPTER 10

Stocking, pp. 83-114, reviews the market and price situation up to 1925; Watkins, pp. 169-193, and Kemnitzer, pp. 180-203, in the 1930s. Rostow, pp. 70-87, reviews the court decisions involved. "Leadership and Conflict in the Pricing of Gasoline," by Joel B. Dirlam and Alfred E. Kahn (*Yale Law Journal,* 1952), pp. 818-855, examines the current situation.

Petroleum (American Petroleum Institute, 1949), pp. 83-96, describes the current marketing setup; *Petroleum Facts and Figures* (American Petroleum Institute, 1954 edition), pp. 227-244, provides a statistical summary.

TNEC Hearings, Part 14:
Testimony of Marion M. Travis of Southport Petroleum Company, pp. 7265-7291.

TNEC Hearings, Part 15:
Testimony of spokesmen for Pennsylvania independent producers, pp. 8458-8485; testimony of Sidney A. Swensrud, vice-president of Standard of Ohio, pp. 8391-8456, his statement, pp. 8671-8718; testimony of Paul E. Hadlick, secretary of National Oil Marketers Association, pp. 8837-8891, his statement, pp. 9151-9170.

TNEC Hearings, Part 16:
Testimony of A. W. Hewett, president, and L. A. Hartley, secretary, Petroleum Retailers Association, pp. 9023-9066; testimony of Henry A. Crouthamel, executive secretary of the Maryland Association of Petroleum Retailers, pp. 8934-8950, his statement, pp. 9211-9219; testimony of George B. Ingram, president of the New Deal Oil Company, of Canton, Ohio, pp. 8951-8987, his statement, pp. 9219-9244; testimony of James A. Horton, Chief Examiner, Federal Trade Commission, pp. 9127-9147, his statement, pp. 9347-9367.

Also, *TNEC Monograph 39,* pp. 41-50.
1. *Economics for Consumers,* by Leland J. Gordon (American Book Company, 1944), p. 390.
2. *Oil Daily,* December 16, 1951.

3. *New York Times,* March 6, 1953.
4. *New York Herald Tribune,* December 17, 1948.
5. *New York Times,* January 24, 1949.
6. *New York Times,* January 3, 1950.
7. NPN, May 25, 1949.
8. NPN, June 7, 14, 1950.
9. Associated Press dispatch in Lubbock, Texas, *Avalanche,* April 9, 1949.
10. *New York Times,* July 1, 1949.
11. NPN, August 6, 1952.
12. *Oil Daily,* October 16, 1953.

CHAPTER 11

TNEC Hearings, Part 14:
Testimony of Marion M. Travis, Southport Petroleum Company, pp. 7265-7291.
TNEC Hearings, Part 16:
Testimony of Paul E. Hadlick, secretary of the National Oil Marketers Association, pp. 8837-8891, his statement, pp. 9151-9170; testimony of B. W. Ruark, general manager, Motor and Equipment Wholesalers Association, pp. 8920-8933, his statement, pp. 9196-9204; testimony of Henry A. Crouthamel, executive secretary, Maryland Association of Petroleum Retailers, pp. 8934-8950, his statement, pp. 9205-9219; testimony of A. W. Hewett, president, and L. A. Hartley, secretary, Petroleum Retailers Association, pp. 9023-9066, their statement, pp. 9305-9310.
TNEC Hearings, Part 17:
Testimony of Wilmer R. Schuh, chairman, National Association of Petroleum Retailers, pp. 9429-9507.
Oil Supply and Distribution Problems: A Final Report of the Special Committee to Study Problems of American Small Business, U. S. Senate, 80th Congress, 1st Session (Wherry Committee), 1949.
1. NPN, April 6, 1949.
2. NPN, June 6, 1951.
3. NPN, December 26, 1951, February 27, 1952.
4. NPN, January 30, March 26, 1952; *Oil Daily,* April 1, 1952.
5. NPN, January 19, 1950.
6. NPN, October 18, 1950.
7. NPN, October 17, 1951.
8. NPN, October 17, 1951.
9. NPN, July 4, 1951.
10. NPN, January 23, 1952.
11. NPN, November 8, 1950.
12. NPN, May 24, 1950.
13. NPN, May 24, 1950.
14. NPN, November 8, 1950.
15. NPN, November 1, 1950.
16. NPN, October 25, 1950.
17. NPN, January 9, 1952.
18. NPN, January 26, 1949.
19. NPN, January 23, 1952.

20. NPN, February 5, 1951.
21. NPN, November 21, 1951.
22. NPN, January 5, 1949.
23. NPN, January 26, March 2, February 16, 1949.
24. NPN, September 20, 27, 1950.
25. NPN, May 4, 1949.
26. *New York Times,* November 9, 1949.
27. NPN, February 27, 1952.
28. NPN, April 30, 1952.
29. NPN, April 16, 1952.
30. NPN, March 1955.

CHAPTER 12

1. NPN, August 23, 1950.
2. Press release, Governor's office, Trenton, N. J., June 14, 1951.
3. NPN, June 20, 1951.
4. NPN, December 12, 1951.
5. *Providence Journal,* July 10, 1951.
6. *Providence Journal,* June 19, 1951.
7. NPN, January 14, 1953.
8. NPN, December 24, 1952.
9. NPN, March 15, 1950.
10. NPN, July 5, 1950.
11. NPN, January 21, 1953.
12. NPN, January 14, 1953.
13. NPN, December 5, 1951.
14. NPN, March 2, 1949, August 23, 1950.
15. NPN, January 23, 1952.
16. *The Gasoline Retailer,* March 16, 1955.

CHAPTER 13

1. NPN, May 31, October 25, 1950.
2. NPN, October 5, November 8, 1950, May 16, 1951.
3. *New York Times,* February 4, 1949.
4. *Harper's,* January 1953.
5. *Oil Forum,* January 1952.
6. *Oil Forum,* December 1951.
7. *U. S. News & World Report,* March 9, 1951.
8. NPN, June 14, 1950.
9. *New York Times,* October 7, 1951, February 10, 1952.
10. *New York Herald Tribune,* January 2, 1952.
11. *Fortune,* September 1950.
12. NPN, December 5, 1951.
13. American Broadcasting Company, news release, November 14, 1951.
14. *Sponsor,* February 11, 1952.
15. *Sponsor,* May 19, 1952.
16. NPN, November 29, 1950; *New York Times,* October 8, 1950.
17. NPN, November 2, 1949.

18. *Fortune,* December 1952; *New York Times,* October 12, 1952, February 12, 1953; *U. S. News & World Report,* August 24, 1951; *The Five Per Cent,* by Beardsley Ruml and Theodore Geiger (National Planning Association, 1951).
19. *The Lamp,* March 1953.
20. Austin, Texas, *American,* March 21, 1949.
21. *Saturday Review,* April 19, 1952.
22. *New York Times,* May 18, 1951; NPN, September 26, October 17, 1951.
23. NPN, September 26, 1951.
24. *New York Times,* October 20, 1949.
25. *Providence Journal,* November 28, 1948.
26. *Saturday Review,* February 12, 19, 1955.
27. NPN, March 3, 1954; *New York Times,* June 18, 1954.
28. *New York Times,* January 6, 1953.
29. NPN, February 2, October 12, 1949.
30. NPN, February 24, July 14, 1954; *New York Times,* February 15, 1954; *The Growth of Integrated Oil Companies,* by John G. McLean and Robert William Haigh, Harvard Graduate School of Business Administration (Harvard University Press, 1953).
31. *Saturday Review,* August 27, 1949.
32. NPN, October 4, 1950.
33. NPN, September 3, 1952; *Oil Daily,* November 10, 1952.
34. NPN, September 17, 1952.

CHAPTER 14

1. *Oil Daily,* April 19, 1954; NPN, April 21, 1954.
2. *New York Times,* April 18, 1954; *Oil Daily,* April 19, 1954.
3. NPN, July 7, 1954.
4. NPN, November 1, 1950.
5. NPN, November 1, 1950.
6. *Oil Daily,* June 5, 1953.
7. *Oil Daily,* January 27, 1953.
8. *Oil Daily,* April 28, 1953.
9. NPN, April 13, 1949.
10. NPN, April 5, 1951.
11. NPN, January 28, 1953.
12. NPN, October 11, 1950.
13. NPN, April 13, 1949.
14. *Providence Journal,* July 20, 1952.
15. NPN, September 17, 1952.
16. *Oil Daily,* February 12, 1953.
17. NPN, October 15, 1952.
18. NPN, August 10, 1949.

CHAPTER 15

The development of the oil cooperatives is described in *Petroleum Operations of Farmers Cooperatives,* by Warren Mather (U. S. Department of Agriculture, Farm Credit Administration, May 1951). *Petroleum Coopera-*

tives 1953-1954 (Cooperative League of the U. S. A., 1955) summarizes recent trends.
1. NPN, March 19, 1952.
2. NPN, August 8, 1951.
3. *New Republic,* September 10, 1951.
4. *Cooperative Consumer,* January 31, 1952.
5. *How Can We Save the Nation from an Oil Monopoly?* by Howard A. Cowden (Consumers Cooperative Association, 1949).
6. NPN, January 12, February 2, 1949.

CHAPTER 16

The growth of the union is described in *The History of the Oil Workers International Union,* by Harvey O'Connor, published by the union (Denver, 1950).
1. NPN, December 26, 1951, May 14, 1952.
2. *Fortune,* October 1951.
3. NPN, February 24, 1954.

CHAPTER 17

1. *Oil Daily,* May 26, 1953.
2. *International Oil Worker,* November 3, 1952.
3. *Oil Daily,* November 10, 1953; NPN, November 18, 1953.
4. *Oil Daily,* December 13, 1951.
5. NPN, June 14, 1950.
6. NPN, November 1, 1950.
7. NPN, April 15, 1953.
8. NPN, September 16, 1953.
9. NPN, February 18, 1953.
10. NPN, November 15, 1950.
11. *New York Times,* October 9, 1951.
12. NPN, August 30, 1950.

CHAPTER 18

National Petroleum Council, Membership Lists, Articles of Organization, Documents of Establishment, Exchange of Correspondence between Attorney General and the Secretary of the Interior, January 20, 1953, published by the Council.
A description of offshore oil lands is given in *World Geography of Petroleum,* pp. 319-324. "Oil for the Lamps of Learning" was the subject of a speech by Senator Lister Hill in the U. S. Senate, published in 1951.
1. NPN, November 9, 1949.
2. NPN, November 23, 1949.
3. NPN, October 4, 1950, January 31, 1951; *Oil Daily,* December 8, 1952.
4. *Oil Daily,* June 25, 1952.
5. NPN, August 30, 1950.
6. NPN, October 31, 1951.

7. *New York Herald Tribune,* January 9, 1948.
8. Secretary of the Interior, *Annual Report,* 1948.
9. *New York Times,* September 24, 1948.
10. *Oil and National Policy,* by Joseph E. Pogue (Chase National Bank, 1948).
11. *A National Oil Policy for the United States: A Report of the National Petroleum Council,* 1949.
12. NPN, August 29, 1951.
13. NPN, May 23, 1951.
14. *New York Times,* October 27, 1949.
15. Wesley C. Clark in *Annals,* American Academy of Political and Social Science, March 1952.
16. *New York Times,* February 4, 1952.
17. Thomas L. Stokes in *Providence Journal,* August 29, 1948; *New Republic,* November 1, 1948.
18. *New York Herald Tribune,* July 14, 1948.
19. Fort Worth, Texas, *Labor News,* October 14, 1948.
20. *New York Times,* December 22, 1948.
21. *New York Times,* January 24, 1949.
22. *New Republic,* March 27, 1950.
23. *New Republic,* May 22, October 2, 1950.
24. NPN, June 7, 1950.
25. *American Political Science Review,* March 1951.
26. *New York Times,* September 17, 1950.
27. *New Republic,* March 26, 1951.
28. *New York Times,* July 31, 1951.
29. *Oil Daily,* January 23, 1952; *New York Times,* February 10, 1952.
30. *New York Times,* March 26, 1952.
31. *New York Times,* May 18, 1952.
32. *New York Times,* June 7, 1953.
33. *New York Times,* October 14, 1952.
34. *New York Times,* March 5, 6, 1952.
35. NPN, November 12, 1952.
36. *Providence Journal,* March 1, 1953.
37. *Oil Daily,* December 23, 1952.
38. NPN, January 28, 1953.
39. *New York Times,* January 17, 1953.
40. *New York Times,* March 12, 18, 25, April 1, 2, 1953.
41. *New York Times,* April 21, 23, 25, 26, May 1, 1953.
42. *New York Times,* May 6, 1953.
43. *New York Times,* March 16, 1954.
44. *Harper's,* February 1953.

CHAPTER 19

1. *International Oil Worker,* March 10, 1947.
2. *Production of Crude Petroleum in Texas: A Statistical Analysis,* by Melvin M. Webber, Ph.D. thesis (University of Texas, 1948).
3. *Hugh Roy Cullen: A Story of American Opportunity,* by Ed Kilman and Theon Wright (Prentice-Hall, 1954).

4. *New York Times,* November 21, 1953.
5. *Nation,* November 3, 1951.
6. *New Republic,* June 25, 1951; *Nation,* June 30, 1951.
7. *New Republic,* October 6, 1951; *Nation,* November 3, 1951.
8. Fort Worth, Texas, *Labor News,* January 31, 1952.
9. *U. S. News & World Report,* March 4, 1955.
10. Fort Worth, Texas, *Labor News,* June 18, 1953.
11. *Providence Journal,* September 20, 1953.
12. *Nation,* August 22, 1953.
13. *New York Times,* October 22, 1953.
14. Chapter on Texas by Hart Stilwell in *Our Sovereign States,* edited by Robert S. Allen (Vanguard Press, 1949); *New York Times,* March 8, 1953.
15. *New York Times,* February 26, April 8, 1952; NPN, February 13, 1952.
16. *New York Times,* October 5, 1952.
17. *New York Times,* December 1, 1952.

CHAPTER 20

1. *New York Times,* February 9, 1950, March 2, 1952.
2. *Tax Loop Holes,* by Senator Hubert H. Humphrey (Public Affairs Institute, 1952).
3. *New York Times,* September 23, 1953.
4. *New Republic,* June 12, 1950.
5. *Fortune,* April 1953.
6. *New York Herald Tribune,* September 24, 1951.
7. *Oil Daily,* April 21, 1954.

CHAPTER 21

Foreign Oil and Imports (American Petroleum Institute, 1953) gives the majors' point of view on the problem. "The Imports Controversy: Its Pros and Cons" was published as a special survey in *National Petroleum News,* March 18, 1953.
1. *Oil Daily,* May 5, 1953.
2. NPN, November 19, 1952.
3. *New York Times,* May 23, 1954.
4. *Providence Journal,* November 22, 1953.
5. *New York Times,* April 16, 1953.
6. *Oil Daily,* April 30, 1953.
7. Texas Pacific Coal & Oil Company, Annual Report for 1954.
8. *Oil Daily,* May 5, 1953.
9. *Oil Daily,* November 10, 1952, May 5, 1953.
10. *Oil Daily,* May 5, 1954.
11. *Oil Daily,* March 18, 1953.
12. *Oil Daily,* January 7, 23, 1953.
13. *New York Times,* February 28, 1954.
14. *Oil Daily,* June 24, 1952; *New York Times,* June 24, 1952; *Oil Daily,* December 23, 1952.
15. NPN, February 22, 1950.

16. *New York Herald Tribune,* March 1, 1953.
17. *Oil Daily,* March 12, 1953.
18. Mikesell and Chenery, p. 19.
19. *New York Times,* May 23, 1950; *Oil Daily,* January 9, 1953.
20. NPN, March 21, 1951.
21. *Oil Daily,* March 6, 1953; NPN, April 1, 1953.

CHAPTER 22

Rostow, pp. 70-89, reviews judicial decisions on many of the cases cited; Watkins, pp. 72-193, reviews the NRA period.
1. NPN, January 12, 1949.
2. Federal Trade Commission *vs.* Sinclair Refining Company, 261 U. S. 463 (1923).
3. United States *vs.* Socony-Vacuum Oil Company, 310 U. S. 150 (1940); Stocking and Watkins, pp. 284-288.
4. Ethyl Gasoline Corporation *vs.* United States, 309 U. S. 436 (1940); Stocking and Watkins, pp. 472-473.
5. NPN, May 25, 1949.
6. United States *vs.* American Petroleum Institute, Civil Action No. 8523 (D. C., 1940).
7. *New York Times,* June 7, 1951; NPN, June 13, 1951.
8. In re Standard Oil Company, 41 F.T.C. 263, 173 Fed. 2nd 210 (1951); *New York Times,* November 8, 1949, June 6, 1950; NPN, February 16, 1949.
9. *Christian Science Monitor,* April 24, 1950; *New Republic,* January 29, June 2, 1951; *New York Times,* January 9, 1951; NPN, January 10, 17, 1951.
10. United States *vs.* Standard Oil Company, 78 Fed. Supp. 850 (1948), 337 U.S. 293 (1949).
11. *Platt's Oilgram,* News Supplement, June 13, 1949; NPN, June 15, 1949.
12. NPN, May 16, 23, June 13, July 11, 1951.
13. NPN, April 23, 1952.
14. NPN, July 11, 1951.
15. NPN, December 5, 1951.
16. *New York Times,* July 25, 1950; NPN, July 5, 26, 1950.
17. *New York Times,* June 7, 1951.
18. "Vertical Integration Re-examined," by Eugene V. Rostow and Arthur S. Sachs (*Yale Law Journal,* 1952), pp. 904-905.
19. NPN, December 31, 1952.
20. NPN, May 23, 1951.

CHAPTER 23

TNEC Monograph 38: A Study of the Construction and Enforcement of Federal Antitrust Laws, by Milton Handler (1941), and Watkins, pp. 247-256, deal with aspects of law enforcement. *Toward Nationalization of Industry,* by Harry W. Laidler (League for Industrial Democracy, 1949), pp. 13-16, touches on oil nationalization.
1. *Social Darwinism in American Thought,* by Richard Hofstadter (University of Pennsylvania Press, 1944), p. 31.

2. NPN, April 22, 1953.
3. Rostow, pp. 119-148.
4. Stocking and Watkins, p. 522.
5. NPN, October 19, 1949.
6. *Oil Daily,* April 29, 1953.
7. *History of the Oil Workers International Union,* by Harvey O'Connor, published by the union (Denver, 1950), p. 15.
8. *U. S. News & World Report,* April 6, 1951.
9. Watkins, p. 256.
10. Address by Bishop Oxnam at Ecumenical Methodist Conference, Springfield, Mass., September 26, 1947.
11. Quoted by Alpheus T. Mason in *American Political Science Review,* June 1950, p. 330.
12. *Our Vanishing Oil Resources,* by Dr. John Ise (League for Industrial Democracy, 1929).
13. *Oil Daily,* January 28, 1953.
14. *Oil Daily,* February 13, 1953.
15. NPN, April 22, 1953.
16. *Wall Street Journal,* April 1, 1953.

CHAPTER 24

1. NPN, November 15, 1950; *Arabian Oil and the World Oil Shortage* (Arabian American Oil Company, N. D.), p. 16.
2. Denny, p. 31; Fanning, p. 58.
3. Denny, pp. 31-45.
4. Fanning, pp. 24-25; *Mexican Petroleum* (Pan American Petroleum & Transport Company, 1922), p. 56.
5. *World Geography of Petroleum,* pp. 160, 172; Leeston, p. 97; Fanning, pp. 59-61; British Information Services, "Anglo-Iranian Oil Company: Some Background Notes" (May 1951), and "Anglo-Iranian Oil Negotiations" (June 1951).
6. Fischer, pp. 241, 244-245.
7. Denny, p. 16.
8. Denny, pp. 16-17.
9. Denny, pp. 4, 32, 41, 43, 274.

CHAPTER 25

National Petroleum Convention, September 9-18, 1951 (Ministry of Mines and Hydrocarbons, Caracas, 1952) describes the physical and technical aspects of the Venezuelan oil industry. *Petroleum in Venezuela,* by Edwin Lieuwen (University of California Press, 1955) contains useful historical background.
1. *World Geography of Petroleum,* pp. 45, 60; Leeston, p. 191.
2. Denny, p. 110.
3. *Since Spindletop,* by Craig Thompson (Gulf Oil Company, 1951), p. 74.
4. IPC, pp. 163, 167-169.
5. IPC, pp. 171, 175, 177, 179, 180, 184.

6. IPC, 175, 184; *World Geography of Petroleum,* p. 50; *Venezuela Up-to-Date* (Venezuela Embassy, Washington), September 1953.
7. Creole Petroleum Corporation, Annual Report for 1952.
8. *Venezuela Up-to-Date,* January 1953.
9. *Venezuela Up-to-Date,* June 1953.
10. *Venezuela Up-to-Date,* June 1953.
11. *De Una a Otra Venezuela,* by Arturo Uzlar-Pietri (Ediciones Mesa Redonda, Caracas, 1949), p. 36.

CHAPTER 26

1. Denny, p. 18.
2. Denny, pp. 37, 95 ff., 117 ff.; Fanning, pp. 62-63.
3. Fanning, p. 4; Denny, pp. 36, 38.
4. Denny, pp. 32, 169; Fischer, pp. 43, 222; Fanning, p. 89.
5. Denny, pp. 19, 22, 151, 156; IPC, p. 47; Lenczowski, p. 424; Leeston, p. 110; *New Yorker,* September 30, 1950.
6. IPC, pp. 50-51; Denny, pp. 35, 152.
7. IPC, p. 51; Fanning, pp. 5-6; Denny, p. 37; Fischer, p. 216.
8. IPC, p. 53; Denny, p. 43.
9. IPC, pp. 54, 61; Fanning, p. 7.
10. IPC, pp. 57, 65, 72, 84; Fanning, p. 92.
11. Fanning, p. 92.
12. IPC, pp. 76-77.
13. IPC, p. 99.
14. IPC, p. 80.
15. Leeston, p. 110; *New Yorker,* September 30, 1950.
16. IPC, pp. 84-85; *World Geography of Petroleum,* p. 162.
17. IPC, pp. 61, 91-92.
18. *New York Times,* November 9, 1949, January 16, August 12, 1950, June 24, 28, July 11, August 14, 1951; Spingarn, pp. 10, 13; *New Statesman & Nation,* May 31, 1951; *Oil Forum,* October 1951; *Petroleum Outlook,* June 1953; *Oil Daily,* February 22, 1952.
19. IPC, p. 95.
20. IPC, pp. 197-199; Denny, pp. 183, 186, 233, 296.
21. IPC, p. 199.
22. IPC, pp. 199-200.
23. IPC, pp. 201-203, 207, 218, 352.

CHAPTER 27

1. Spingarn, pp. 14-15.
2. *World Geography of Petroleum,* p. 162; *Middle East Oil Developments, 1952,* by Arabian American Oil Company.
3. *World Geography of Petroleum,* p. 224; IPC, pp. 73, 113.
4. Lenczowski, pp. 211, 339, 347, 416; Mikesell and Chenery, p. 72; *World Geography of Petroleum,* p. 222; Fanning, p. 93; *City Club Bulletin,* Chicago, April 5, 1948; IPC, pp. 114, 116; Leeston, p. 77.
5. Additional Report of the Special Committee Investigating the National Defense Program, U. S. Senate, 80th Congress, 1st Session (Brewster

Committee), 1948; Lenczowski, p. 348; Mikesell and Chenery, pp. 132-137; IPC, pp. 118, 359.

6. *Navy Purchases of Middle East Oil,* Special Committee Investigating the National Defense Program, U. S. Senate, 80th Congress, 1st Session (Brewster Committee), 1948; Mikesell and Chenery, pp. 90-95, 133; IPC, p. 359.

7. IPC, p. 359; Mikesell and Chenery, p. 133.

8. *In Fact,* May 24, 1948.

9. *New York Times,* February 2, 4, 19, 1949, March 26, 1953; *New York Herald Tribune,* February 16, 1949; Lenczowski, p. 349.

10. *New York Herald Tribune,* February 16, 1949; *New York Times,* March 26, 1953.

11. IPC, pp. 119, 122; Leeston, p. 84.

12. IPC, pp. 123-124.

13. *Overseas News Agency,* June 17, 1953.

14. *World Geography of Petroleum,* p. 199.

15. IPC, p. 130.

16. IPC, pp. 129, 131, 133.

17. IPC, p. 129.

18. *Chicago Tribune,* December 20, 1953.

19. IPC, pp. 132, 134, 138, 139.

20. IPC, pp. 143, 145.

21. IPC, pp. 145-146.

22. IPC, pp. 150, 157.

23. Leeston, p. 93; *Wall Street Journal,* June 19, 1947; *New York Times,* July 7, 1948.

24. *New York Times,* July 7, 1948, April 2, 1949, March 25, April 30, 1953; *Oil Daily,* April 30, 1953; *Dallas Morning News,* March 7, 1949; Pacific Western Oil Company, Annual Report for 1952; *Oil Forum,* July 1951.

25. *Oil Forum,* February 1955.

CHAPTER 28

1. *New York Times,* January 3, 1951; Leeston, p. 86.

2. *U. S. News & World Report,* November 16, 1951; *Fortune,* October 1952.

3. *New York Times,* April 1, 1949, February 13, May 8, 1952, October 11, 1953; NPN, January 2, 1949.

4. *New York Times,* April 29, 1951, July 31, 1952.

5. Lenczowski, p. 355.

6. *Manchester Guardian,* September 10, 1953.

7. *New York Times,* October 20, 21, 28, 1953.

8. NPN, September 12, 1951.

9. *U. S. News & World Report,* November 16, 1951; *New York Times,* March 21, 1952; *Providence Journal,* August 10, 1952.

10. *New York Times,* December 11, 13, 1953, August 14, 15, 1954; *World Interpreter,* April 16, 1954.

11. *Oil Daily,* February 12, 1954.

12. *New York Times,* June 23, 1954.

13. *New York Times,* June 25, 1954; *Providence Journal,* June 25, 1954.
14. *New York Times,* December 15, 1951.
15. *New York Times,* February 8, November 3, 1952.
16. *New Statesman & Nation,* October 24, 1953; *Manchester Guardian,* September 13, 1951.
17. *Fortune,* October 1952; *New York Times,* December 4, 1951; *Providence Journal,* July 30, September 13, 1953.
18. *U. S. News & World Report,* November 16, 1951.
19. *U. S. News & World Report,* November 16, 1951; *Report of Oil Mission to Middle East, Project NME/6, November-December 1952,* prepared by Loyd A. Haskins, International Representative, Oil Workers International Union, January 6, 1953, reported in *International Oil Worker,* April 6, 1953.
20. *New York Times,* August 16, 1951, September 3, 1952, March 12, 1953; *New Statesman & Nation,* March 14, 1953.

CHAPTER 29

"The Past, Present and Likely Future Price Structure for the International Oil Trade," by Walter J. Levy, in *The Third World Petroleum Congress,* a Report to the Select Committees on Small Business of the Senate and House of Representatives, 82nd Congress, 2nd Session, 1952, pp. 21-37; also, "The Significance of the Marshall Plan for the Petroleum Industry in Europe—Historical Review of the Period 1947-1950," by E. Groen, Secretary, Netherlands Government Office for Petroleum, pp. 37-73; also, "European Petroleum Refining and Marketing," by Elmer Patman, pp. 74-78.

1. IPC, p. 356.
2. IPC, pp. 361-363.
3. IPC, pp. 364-366; NPN, May 13, 1953.
4. IPC, p. 367; NPN, December 6, 1950; *New York Times,* June 10, 1953.
5. Spingarn, p. 3.
6. *New York Journal of Commerce,* July 10, 1953.
7. IPC, pp. 369-370.
8. IPC, p. 377; *Petroleum Outlook,* July 1954.
9. *New York Times,* June 26, 1950.
10. *New York Times,* August 23, 1952; NPN, December 31, 1952.
11. *Chicago Daily News,* August 25, 1952; *Oil Forum,* September 1953.
12. *New York Herald Tribune,* June 28, 1948.
13. *Chicago Tribune,* February 25, December 13, 1948.
14. *New York Times,* March 12, 1949, September 6, 10, 1950, April 25, 1952.
15. *New York Times,* September 10, 1952.
16. *Oil Daily,* February 19, 1953.
17. *Overseas News Agency,* January 24, 1950; *New York Times,* October 23, 1951.
18. Leeston, pp. 124-127; *New York Times,* June 5, 1949; *The Lamp,* September 1953.
19. *New York Times,* June 5, 1949.
20. *New York Times,* June 5, September 18, October 9, 26, 1949; NPN, October 19, 1949.

21. *New York Times,* June 27, September 4, 15, 18, 25, November 5, 1949; NPN, October 19, 1949.
22. *New York Times,* December 20, 22, 25, 28, 1949, January 4, 1950; NPN, December 28, 1950.
23. *New York Times,* January 31, February 1, 2, 1950.
24. *New York Times,* February 9, 11, 12, March 7, 9, 10, 17, April 5, June 9, 1950; NPN, March 8, 1950.
25. *New York Times,* February 13, 1951; *Manchester Guardian,* February 15, 1951.
26. *New Statesman & Nation,* September 15, 1951.
27. *New York Times,* December 22, 1952, June 8, 1953.
28. *New York Times,* June 8, 1953.
29. *The Lamp,* September, November 1953.
30. *The Price of Oil in Western Europe,* published by the United Nations' Economic Commission for Europe (Geneva, 1955).
31. *Oil Daily,* March 14, 1955; *New York Times,* March 19, 1955.
32. *New Statesman & Nation,* February 26, 1955.
33. *Oil Forum,* September 1952.
34. *New Statesman & Nation,* February 26, 1955.
35. *New York Times,* March 19, 1955.
36. *New York Times,* March 18, 1955.
37. *New York Times,* March 18, 1955.
38. *New York Times,* March 18, 1955.
39. *New York Times,* March 18, 1955.
40. *New Statesman & Nation,* March 26, 1955.

CHAPTER 30

The Mexican point of view on nationalization and the controversy with the foreign companies is discussed in *Petróleo: Pasado, Presente y Futuro de Una Industria Mexicana,* by José Domingo Lavín, EDIAPSA (Mexico, 1950); *El Problema Petrolero,* by the same author, Edición de la Camara Nacional de la Industria de Transformación (Mexico, 1951); *Petróleo Mexicano,* by Jesús Silva Herzog, Fondo de Cultura Económica (Mexico, 1941); *Problemas Industriales de México,* by various authors, EDIAPSA (Mexico, 1951); *La Epopeya del Petróleo en México,* by Jesús Silva Herzog, in *Cuadernos Americanos,* January-February 1953.

Contrasting points of view are expressed in *Present Status of Mexican Oil "Expropriations,"* Standard Oil Company (New Jersey), 1940; *The Mexican Oil Seizure,* by Donald Richberg (Arrow Press, 1939); *Shirt Sleeve Diplomacy,* by Josephus Daniels (University of North Carolina Press, 1947); *Mexico at the Bar of Public Opinion,* by Burt M. McConnell (Mail and Express Publishing Company, 1939).

This chapter is condensed from an article which appeared in *Monthly Review,* December 1952.

CHAPTER 31

British Information Services, "Legal Aspects of the Anglo-Iranian Oil Question" (June 1951), "Anglo-Iranian Oil Negotiations" (June 1951), "Anglo-

Iranian Oil Company" (May 1951). International Labour Office, *Labour Conditions in the Oil Industry in Iran* (Geneva, 1950). *The Middle East in World Affairs*, by George Lenczowski (Cornell University Press, 1952), pp. 153-189.

1. Fischer, p. 225; Denny, p. 173.
2. *New York Times*, February 13, 1951.
3. *Oil Forum*, September 1953.
4. *New York Times*, August 26, 1953.
5. Anglo-Iranian Oil Company, Annual Report for 1952.
6. *U. S. News & World Report*, November 9, 1951.
7. *Oil Forum*, March 1952; Denny, p. 103; *New Republic*, December 8, 1951.
8. *Report of Oil Mission to Middle East, Project NME/6, November-December 1952*, prepared by Loyd A. Haskins, International Representative, Oil Workers International Union, January 6, 1953, reported in *International Oil Worker*, April 6, 1953.
9. *Control of World Oil Resources* (Item 36): Proposal for the Creation of a United Nations Petroleum Commission Under the Authority of the Economic and Social Council, Supporting Document No. 2, Presented by the International Cooperative Alliance to the Fifth Session of ECOSOC, Lake Success, N. Y., July 19, 1947.
10. Robert S. Allen in the *New York Post*, November 6, 1951.
11. *The Third World Petroleum Congress*, A Report to the Select Committees on Small Business, U. S. Senate and House of Representatives, 82nd Congress, 2nd Session (1952), pp. 12 ff.
12. *New York Times*, October 11, 12, 22, 1953, February 3, 1954.
13. *New York Times*, December 31, 1953, March 1, 12, 18, April 11, 1954; *Petroleum Outlook*, September 1954.
14. *The Cooperative Consumer*, March 31, 1955; *Petroleum Week*, May 13, 1955.
15. *Oil Forum*, October 1953; *New York Times*, December 30, 1953, February 5, 7, 8, 1954.
16. *New York Times*, February 25, April 4, May 20, July 4, 1954; *Nation*, April 3, 1954; *Oil Forum*, April, July 1954.
17. *New York Journal of Commerce*, August 9, 1954; *New York Times*, October 22, 1954.
18. *Oil Daily*, February 24, 1954.
19. *New York Times*, August 3, 1954.
20. *New York Times*, August 30, 1954.

CHAPTER 32

1. Recorded, p. 202, in *Lobbyist for the People*, the memoirs of Benjamin C. Marsh, published posthumously in 1953 by Public Affairs Press. As director of The People's Lobby, Marsh for years conducted a one-man campaign in Washington for public ownership of natural resources and in his later years was about the only spokesman for the idea there.
2. Same, p. 194.
3. Letter of International Cooperative Alliance to Economic and Social Council, United Nations, March 13, 1947, published March 17, 1947; Mike-

sell and Chenery, pp. 104-105. See also, *Control of World Oil Resources*
(Item 36): Proposal for the Creation of a United Nations Petroleum Com-
mission Under the Authority of the Economic and Social Council, Supporting
Document No. 2, Presented by the International Cooperative Alliance to the
Fifth Session of ECOSOC, Lake Success, N. Y., July 19, 1947.

4. Submitted to ECOSOC, August 8, 1947.

5. *New York Times*, December 7, 12, 1952; *Nation*, December 27, 1952.

6. *Oil Daily*, December 21, 1951.

INDEX

365

368

Humphrey, Sen. Hubert H., 209
Hunt, Haroldson L., 5, 202-204, 211

I. G. Farben, 25
Ickes, Harold L., in crisis of 1933,
  65; code administrator, 66, 185-
  186, 188, 189-190; on offshore oil,
  190-193, 281, 287, 333
Imperial Oil Ltd., 21
Imports, 214-222, 263
Independent Petroleum Assn. of
  America, 217-218, 219, 220, 241
Independent Refiners Assn. of Amer-
  ica, 331
Indiana Independent Petroleum
  Assn., 121
Integrated companies, 19-20
International companies, 19; import
  dilemma, 214-222; assets, etc., of
  the Big Seven, 253, 301; Iranian
  consortium, 329-332, 335
International controls, 327, 333-340
International Cooperative Alliance,
  plan for Middle East controls, 334-
  337, 339-340
International Cooperative Petroleum
  Assn., 161, 327, 330, 337
Interstate Commerce Commission,
  pipe lines, 91, 93, 238
Interstate Oil Compact Commission,
  authorized, 67; activities, 68-70,
  114, 117, 183
Iowa Independent Oil Jobbers Assn.,
  120
Iran, 4, Anglo-Persian concession,
  257, 290, 299, 306; nationalization, 324-332; consortium, 329-
  332, 338
Iraq, 4, concession, 270-273, 275,
  331
Iraq Petroleum Co., 271-275, 280,
  285, 286, 290, 297, 300, 306, 307
Ise, Dr. John, 243-244

James, Marquis, 142
Jennings, B. Brewster, 28
Jester, Beauford, 76
Jobbers, 111-122; complaints, 113
Johnson, Hugh S., 66
Johnson, Walter R., 193
Johnston, Victor A., 203

Joiner, C. M., 9, 16, 17
Jones, Jesse, 189, 201
Jones, W. Alton, 33, 179

Kaltenborn, Hans V., 137
Keck, W. M., 194
Kemnitzer, William J., 96-97
Kentucky Petroleum Marketers Assn.,
  120
Kerr-McGee Oil Co., 20
King, W. L. Mackenzie, 167
Kirby Oil Co., 20
Kirk, Grayson L., 28, 141
Knight, O. A., 170
Krug, J. A., 180, 184, 190
Kuwait, 4, 29; Gulf concession, 284-
  285; cartel agreements, 286-287,
  289-290; social conditions, 295-
  296, 300, 302, 306, 324

Lago Oil & Transport Co., 4, 21
Land Management, U. S. Bureau of,
  60
Lario Oil Co., 287
Leasing, 57-61
Leeston, Dr. Alfred M., 142-143
Levorsen, A. I., 80
Library of Congress, 184
Lignite, 84-85
Lloyd, Henry Demarest, 21
Lobby, 69, 85, 180-181, 183, 187-
  199, 201-208
Lucas, Anthony F., 8-9, 11

MacArthur, Douglas, 201
Magnolia Petroleum Co., 16, 28, 76,
  107, 200
Major companies, 19-37; financial
  statements, 40
Manchester, Harland, 148-149
Marketing, of gasoline, 103-110; exclusive dealing, 103-104; wastes,
  104-105; market leaders, 106-107;
  price control, 106-107; breakdown
  of costs, 109; price-fixing, 109-110;
  jobbers, 111-122; number of enterprises, 111
Marland, E. W., 57
Marsh, Benjamin C., 241, 333
Mattei, A. C., 61
Maverick, Maury, 206